Time to Fly
Exploring Bird Migration

by Jim Flegg

Dedicated to the many thousands of volunteer and professional
ringers, field observers and researchers who over almost a century
have assembled our knowledge and understanding of bird migration.
More particularly, we should also acknowledge with gratitude the
millions of birds that have carried rings, however inadvertently, all
over the world in the cause of science.

Published by The British Trust for Ornithology

The British Trust for Ornithology
The Nunnery
Thetford
Norfolk
IP24 2PU
01842 750050

First published in 2004
© 2004, British Trust for Ornithology, Thetford

Text: Jim Flegg
Design and layout: Cottier & Sidaway, 01767 262858
Printers: Crowes of Norwich, 01603 403349

Front cover: Common Tern by J. Higgins
Title page: Hirundines by Simon Gillings

Time to Fly
Exploring Bird Migration

Contents

Chapter heading illustrations by Simon Gillings

Acknowledgements

First and foremost, my thanks are due to the ringers whose efforts have produced the ring-recoveries on which this (and most other books on the practicalities of migration) are so heavily dependent. Secondly, they are due to the editors and 190 expert authors of the species accounts in *The Migration Atlas: movements of the birds of Britain and Ireland*, published for the BTO by T & AD Poyser in 2002. This is a *magnum opus* in every way: at 884 pages, it is a monumental and unparalleled compilation of data and detailed analyses of immense value.

At the BTO, Graham Appleton developed the concept of *Time to Fly* as a readily-readable distillation of the key information from the inevitably complex wealth of data within *The Migration Atlas*, appealing to birdwatchers of all levels of interest. Throughout *Time to Fly's* production he has been on hand with guidance and suggestions, for which I am most grateful. My thanks are also due to Jacquie Clark, Mike Toms, Rob Robinson, Mark Grantham, Jenny Gill and Chris Cox for checking and providing skilled and helpful comments on the text as it evolved.

Barry Jarvis has transformed my spidery arrows into the elegant maps that enlighten the text pages and also produced the various text diagrams. The maps are based upon figures from *The Migration Atlas*. In some cases all of the foreign or long-distance recoveries of British and Irish birds are shown as blue dots and in others the ringing and finding locations are joined by straight lines. In most cases the migratory journeys have been simplified, with arrows indicating the generalised movements of populations of birds, occasionally with the addition of blue spots for outlying or interesting recoveries. The photographs also embellish and amplify the text and the photographers are individually credited on the appropriate page. Simon Gillings has captured the essence of each habitat in the banner heading at the opening of each chapter and also adapted the 'Swallows come/Swallows gone' vignettes from the Thanksgiving Service for the late Stan Chesson, a Kentish farmer. I am most grateful to the Chesson family for allowing me to use them.

On the production side, Phil Cottier of Cottier and Sidaway has kept a steady and helpful hand on the helm. My wife Caroline has been a tower of strength, not only editing the text while transferring it to electronic mode, but also suggesting numerous ways of simplifying and making more meaningful the presentation: I am eternally grateful for this – and so much else besides.

Jim Flegg

The production of this book was made possible thanks to a bequest from Lorna and Sydney Ireland. The BTO acknowledges this gift with gratitude.

Graham Appleton

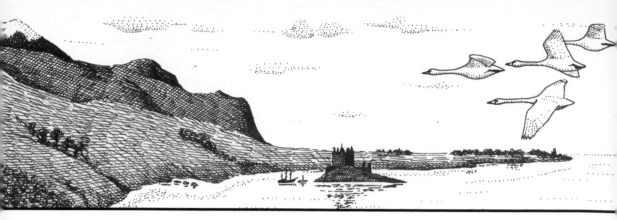

Time to Fly

Exploring Bird Migration

The ideas for this book began to come together on an unprecedentedly hot August afternoon, on a cliff-top on the Gower Peninsula in South Wales. Over a mirror-calm sea, 45 km away, the island of Lundy, one-time bird observatory and still a migration hot spot, floated on its reflection out on the Bristol Channel horizon. Between the Gower cliffs and Lundy, hundreds – maybe thousands – of Manx Shearwaters sat in close-packed rafts. Perhaps they had gathered from their nearby breeding grounds on Skokholm and Skomer in Pembroke (and indeed on Lundy), before their amazing oceanic journey to winter in South Atlantic seas off the coast of Brazil. Half an hour later, the sea was shearwater-free. They were off on their migration, but where to next?

Also offshore, the local Kittiwakes gathered, feeding casually with passing Sandwich Terns bound for West Africa. Migrants both. Seemingly fragile and lightly-built for a gull, the Kittiwakes would shortly head for the storm-tossed open North Atlantic for the winter. They mingled with a fleet of small fishing boats, bristling with rods and lines, indicating the presence beneath the surface of schools of Sea Bass, always here at this time of year. This annual gathering indicates that the Sea Bass, too, are migrants, navigating to precise coordinates in time and space, but in the open sea – a very different medium from the air.

Onshore, the local Wheatears and their offspring fed furiously, putting on the weight necessary to fuel their journey to Africa, now only days away. Migrants again. On the rocks closer to the water rather drabber Rock Pipits, issuing piercing calls to their young nearby, fed with equal enthusiasm on the abundance of beach flies. But they will be here, or hereabouts, right through the winter. Why? How do they survive where Wheatears cannot? Overhead, Swallows and House Martins wheeled and twittered, also feeding up before their usual evening departure south, Africa-bound. Suddenly, the noise ceased, the skies cleared, and these migrants too were off.

Wheatear – Derek Belsey

Above the splash zone on the rocky shore, that afternoon every Golden Samphire plant was in full bloom and held feeding butterflies, sometimes by the score. Painted Ladies, Red Admirals and Small Tortoiseshells were in abundance, with occasional Commas and Clouded Yellows, all in immaculate condition, together with fast flying Silver-Y Moths. The urgency of their feeding prompted a follow-up through binoculars of their approach route to this south-facing shore. As far as the aided eye could see, swarms of butterflies, flying strongly and directly, were heading for the shore, to alight immediately and recoup on the nectar-rich flowers. Migrants again, but this time apparently anomalously heading north in late summer. And apparently so fragile, ephemeral and ill-equipped for long flights, especially over the sea. Again the questions "why, and how do they do it?" come immediately to mind.

What better stimulus could there be than this summer afternoon snapshot of migration on the Gower coast to look further into migration as a whole, and the marvels that it entails. This introduction was actually written as it all happened, sitting on those Gower cliff-top rocks, with nothing but the back page of a daily newspaper for a notepad and making full use of all the blank margins as well as the box provided to work out troublesome crossword clues.

Extending my line of thought; what sort of snapshots would we experience at other seasons during the year, or at other favoured birdwatching sites like gravel pits, woodlands, heathland, estuaries and so on through the habitat spectrum, not forgetting our gardens? I have taken this matrix of birdwatching habitats as the organisational basis of this book on migration, as possibly the best and most useful way of exploring what birds are where, and when, and where they are heading for or have come from. Obviously, it is not perfect, as most birds have the delightful habit of ignoring our attempts to attach them to particular habitats and move freely about our countryside. It was a wise bird observatory pioneer who carved on the wall the practical message "You never know!" You don't, so it is

Painted Lady – Mike Toms

vitally important that birdwatchers' minds are as open as their eyes and ears.

While not ignoring other migrant creatures, a birdwatcher is inevitably going to focus principally on birds, where indeed our knowledge is probably greatest in both scope and depth. Tantalisingly, some of the key questions remain unanswered – but then it would be a very dull world if we knew everything about everything!

What better place to search for relevant information than the vast data banks of the British Trust for Ornithology, the BTO, which, for well over half a century, has been accumulating detailed information on bird biology, habitats, distribution, numbers, and here most relevant of all, movements. The BTO organises and administers the bird ringing scheme for Britain and Ireland and holds the details of all birds ringed in Britain and Ireland, and of these birds recovered anywhere in the world. It also holds details of birds ringed overseas and subsequently recovered in Britain and Ireland. But more of this anon! Without the BTO, and its thousands of birdwatcher members, past and present, volunteer and professional, aided and abetted by the BTO's professional biologist staff, books like this simply could never be written. I am immensely grateful for access to the data banks, and for the help and skilled guidance provided by BTO staff members. So now read on …

What is migration?

Migration must surely have been a recognisable feature of the environment even to the earliest of human populations. Much as day followed night or, more appropriately, season followed season, migratory movements of large birds like the White Stork, north in spring, south in summer, would have been very evident anywhere along their route. Similarly, obvious metronomic calls like those of the Cuckoo or Chiffchaff simply must have been noticed. We can only speculate whether, to those primitive eyes and ears, the birds were regarded as indicators of a change in the season from winter to spring, and of easier times to come in what must have been a pretty hostile environment. At the other end of the season, the likes of the Cuckoo and Chiffchaff simply fade away (in the case of the Cuckoo, almost by midsummer) although Storks, and to an extent Swallows, are as conspicuous in their departure as in arrival, departure indicating that late summer and autumn warmth and fruitfulness has come to an end. Over Britain and Ireland, it may well have been the arrival of the skeins of wild geese and swans that gave those primitive peoples the first sombre warnings that the hard times of winter were close at hand.

Even today, most people, thinking of migration, probably almost automatically bring the Swallow into mind, or alternatively the Cuckoo. In literature, we have known about migration as an annual seasonal event since before Biblical times. In the Bible, the Song of Solomon says: "for lo, the winter is past, the rain is over and gone; the flowers appear on the earth; the time of singing of birds is come; and the voice of the turtle is heard in our land". The 'turtle' being the Turtle Dove with its extended purring song, not the almost voiceless reptile. The inscriptions, roughly translated, on an ancient Greek vase note "Look, there is a Swallow" and "There she goes, spring has come". The Roman naval commander and natural historian Pliny, writing in the first Century AD, also noted the synchrony of the Swallows' arrival in the Mediterranean with the flowering of early spring plants.

Gilbert White, who lived through much of the 18th Century, is justly famous for the detail of his observations on the natural history of the parish of Selborne in Hampshire, whose curacy he held. In *The Natural History and Antiquities of Selborne*, published in 1788, he dwells at length on Swallows and House Martins, recording their arrival dates faithfully year on year. The book is largely founded on numerous letters that Gilbert White wrote to friends and to his wide range of scientific contacts. He obviously had a soft spot for Swallows and House Martins, warmly welcoming their spring arrival and discussing in depth their 'departure' in autumn. At that time there was much earnest scientific debate over whether the birds departed overseas, or hibernated at the bottom of ponds. This theory was based on the still commonplace last sightings of the year being of birds in the reeds around ponds and lakes, or skimming low over the water surface, and the similar nature of many first sightings in spring. After considerable contemplation of the arguments surrounding both possibilities, he settled finally in favour of the hibernation theory – and this not much over 200 years ago.

Interestingly, the popular image of migration is of seasonal journeys along established routes, and essentially a feature of summer. As we shall see, this is only one aspect of the dynamic year-round story, particularly when it comes to the importance of Britain and Ireland to migrants from further north or east, arriving in autumn to seek our more temperate winter climate created by the proximity not just of the Atlantic, but of the Gulf Stream. A quick comparison in midwinter of the temperatures in London or Dublin with those in Paris or Berlin indicates just how much chillier it is on the Continent, even such a short distance away.

House Martin – Derek Belsey

Migration: just how is it defined? The *Concise Oxford English Dictionary* puts it, as its name suggests, concisely: "moving from one place to another; (of birds and fishes) coming and going with the seasons". It adds, not very helpfully, that the derivation is from the Latin *migrare*, to migrate! The ornithological equivalent of the OED is A *Dictionary of Birds*, edited by Bruce Campbell and Elizabeth Lack, which is more helpful. Published in 1985, it notes that "hitherto" migration referred only to bird movements "occurring at predictable times of year, between breeding and one or more non-breeding areas, and

therefore involving flights in predictable directions". It suggests that current usage now embraces all forms of "exploitation of different geographical areas at different stages of the annual cycle", and includes movements that do not necessarily have a return journey. Included under this broader definition are dispersal movements, eruptions and irruptions, emigrations and immigrations, and nomadism. As with human population movements, emigrants and eruptions are departing from where you are (in this case Britain and Ireland), while immigrants and irruptions are coming in. All of these will be discussed in more detail later, and each may be a response to one or more changes; in climate, food availability, environment or population density.

So the concept of come-in-spring, depart-in-autumn or come-in-autumn, depart-in-spring covers only part of the migration story, though probably a very substantial part. At any time of year, but particularly in our winter months, periods of extreme cold weather, either near at hand on the Continent or far away to the east, can cause mass evacuation of the affected area, usually producing a westward stream of migrants, often called a weather movement. Conspicuous birds sensitive to this type of threat include Woodpigeon and Lapwing, but amongst others, ducks, geese and many thrushes may also become involved. Should the weather improve or a thaw set in, back at their point of origin, some or all of these displaced birds may make the return journey before the spring. Studies of radar displays (see Chapter 3) reveal that some birds are migrating in various directions most hours of most days and nights, most of the year.

A failure of the autumn berry, cone or seed crop in some part of Europe, or indeed the aftermath of an unusually productive breeding season when there are simply too many mouths to feed, may also cause mass emigration, often westwards, bringing us exceptional (and welcome) numbers of Bramblings (irregular in numbers at best and heavily influenced by the availability of Beech mast) and Crossbills, and also the much rarer Waxwing and Nutcracker. Dramatic immigrations like this are appropriately called 'irruptions'.

In a sense irruptions are one form of dispersal, an extreme form provoked by food shortage. Other dispersal movements include the more routine (but often almost as spectacular) departure of birds like Starlings and Pied Wagtails from their overnight collective roosts and out to their feeding grounds. Dispersal after the breeding season is a widespread feature, though often lower key. Great Tits and Pied Flycatchers do this, as do Black-headed Gulls. Female and juvenile Great Tits disperse further than adult males, many of which hardly move, and immature Black-headed Gulls disperse almost twice as far as adults. If the dispersing birds do not return to their natal area, a degree of genetic intermixing will occur, commonly regarded as being good for the vigour of the species. Other researchers argue that in some cases such genetic mixing can be disruptive, but this would apply mostly to scarce birds with isolated populations adapted to their local circumstances.

Dipper – George H Higginbotham

Though obviously most easily observed with the naked eye during the day, much (maybe most) migration takes place at night, evidenced amongst other things by the presence of migrant birds in the morning that were not there the evening before, and confirmed by radar observations. The actual numbers of birds migrating at night are naturally difficult to guess at, let alone quantify with any accuracy. Although counting daytime migrants might appear simpler, the height at which small migrants fly is often far above easy binocular range. So

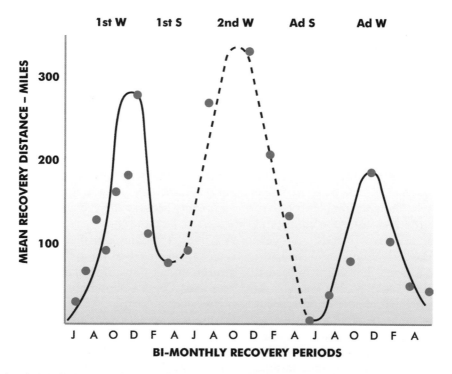

Black-headed Gull dispersal from natal colonies – Jim Flegg

assessing the volume of migration is something of a problem, considered again in Chapter 3.

Arctic Tern – Derek Belsey

Not surprisingly, the distances involved in bird migrations vary substantially, even between individuals or populations of the same species. At the top end of the scale, even the Manx Shearwaters mentioned in the Introduction are surpassed by the Arctic Tern. Breeding from the north of Britain northwards to the Arctic Circle, Arctic Terns migrate to the seas off the Antarctic pack ice for the winter, an each-way journey of at least 12,000 km. With a life-span (revealed by ring-recoveries) sometimes in excess of 20 years, the oldest on record to date being just short of 30 years, their lifetime mileage must be unthinkably high.

At the other extreme, a bird like the Dipper, moving at the onset of freezing winter conditions from its breeding stream in an upland valley, may only fly a few kilometres downstream, and altitudinally only a few hundred metres lower, to reach an ice-free environment. Dippers, and sometimes Kingfishers, perform perhaps the simplest migratory journeys. Theirs is termed 'altitudinal migration', where a bird whose nature it is to be sedentary must move out as its environment becomes uninhabitable.

Nor are migratory patterns in routes and timings necessarily the same from year to year. Not only may early or late springs or mild or harsh winters influence bird movements, but the weather (wind, rain, low cloud and fog) can at any time interrupt the smooth flow of a

journey and cause a hold-up or diversion or, in the worst case scenario, a disaster with massive fatalities. Additionally, some birds – Linnets and Goldfinches are classic examples – are classed as 'partial migrants'. In these, part of the population may migrate in some years but not in others, when they see the winter through in Britain and Ireland.

Linnet   *Goldfinch*

Passage migrants, as their name implies, are birds in transit through a particular location from the breeding grounds to their winter quarters. Knot and Turnstone are classic examples, breeding around the Arctic Circle and some wintering in Africa, as far south as the Cape in the case of Knot. Our estuaries and coasts are vital to the success of these long-haul migrations (Chapters 9 and 10). However, the picture of passage migration can become confused by some populations of these waders that elect every year to remain in Britain and Ireland for the winter, and by birds that freezing weather has forced westwards from the Continent, which may pass swiftly on or stay until conditions improve.

Homing (as in racing pigeons) may not be a migration in the strictest sense, as it is usually a response to artificial displacement from 'home', but it must involve similar navigational capabilities by the birds concerned. Pigeons are the classic example, and their loft keeper plays a part in selective

Pied Wagtail – Tommy Holden

breeding programmes designed to produce champions for speed or endurance, in training the birds over steadily increasing distances, and in maintaining the pigeons race-fit, with suitably enhanced diet, and in fresh plumage for best flight performance. Classically, it is reputed that the Roman army during the series of Punic Wars (between 264 and 146 BC) not only used elephants on Hannibal's epic march through the Alps, but may also have used Swallows to carry messages (attached to their legs) over enemy lines, in much the same way as pigeons were used as messengers in the European wars of the 20th Century.

Much more recently, in the 1960s, unexpected homing abilities were discovered in Pied Wagtails. Carnation and chrysanthemum greenhouses in Hampshire became winter roosting sites for hundreds of Pied Wagtails from miles around. The overnight warmth, maintained to maximise flower production, was an irresistible attraction to the Pied Wagtails, which gathered on the rooftops as evening approached and entered the greenhouses through the automatic vents just before these were closed down for the night! Inside, the Pied Wagtails were out of the wind, warm and dry, and on their perches amongst the beams and struts, safe from predators (although the local Barn Owls soon located an easy meal and took their daily toll of latecomer Pied Wagtails in the gloom!). Overnight, the Pied Wagtail droppings did nothing to enhance the value of the expensive blooms beneath them. The naturally concerned but conservation conscious grower contacted the BTO, then based at Tring in Hertfordshire, for advice on how to eliminate his problem without, if possible, eliminating any Pied Wagtails.

Racing pigeons in their home loft – Dora Biro

The BTO dispatched two expeditions in quick succession, each of two cars with several

bird ringers (see Chapter 3) equipped with large butterfly nets. Once the birds were in for the night, the greenhouse lights were turned off briefly and the ringers, armed with their nets and head torches, to dazzle the wagtails, went into action. Swiftly, the greenhouses were cleared, several hundred Pied Wagtails were captured, placed safely and securely in holding bags, and transported back to Tring, suspended comfortably in the backs of the cars. In the morning, they were ringed and had details of their age and sex recorded before they were released back into the wild.

Not much over a month later, the grower telephoned to report a recurrence of his problems, and the BTO responded as before. Much to everyone's surprise, many of the Pied Wagtails captured on the second expedition already bore rings. A rapid examination of the records from the first expedition revealed that over 60% of the adults captured then had found their way back to Hampshire, a straight-line journey of over 130 km. None of the juveniles returned.

Bird migration is all-embracing, and evidently far from a simple to-ing and fro-ing. As we have seen, birds will be migrating, or at least moving in some mode or another, and in various directions, most days every month through the year. And where do Britain and Ireland stand amongst the multiplicity of flight paths, some local, some national, many international? The simplest answer is 'at the crossroads'. Britain and Ireland provide summer breeding grounds for birds like the Swallow, Swift, Cuckoo and the warbler family, with wintering grounds far away to the south and southeast. Winter shelter is provided by our comparatively mild Gulf Stream-influenced weather for countless wildfowl and thrushes like the Fieldfare and Redwing from distant countries to the north, northeast and east. And in spring and autumn, Britain and Ireland offer a staging post where long-haul travellers (like many of the waders on our estuaries) from just about every quarter of the compass may rest and feed, in effect fuelling-up for the next stages of their prodigious journeys. How lucky we are!

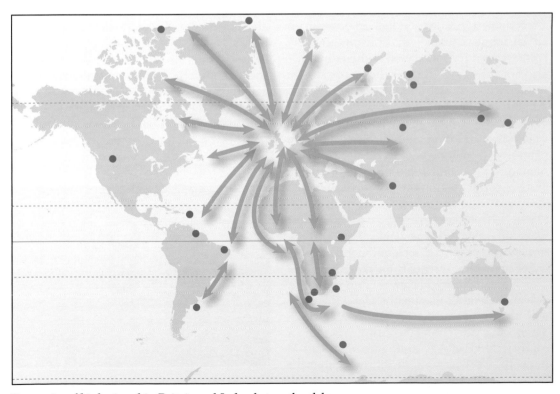

Recoveries of birds ringed in Britain and Ireland span the globe

Why migrate? And what are the risks?

What capabilities must a successful migrant have? Obviously, a good sense of direction – but that simple statement masks a great deal of detail. Perhaps a good way to start is to draw some comparisons with our lives. Today, journeys by plane, if not commonplace (and inevitably tedious), are at least familiar to almost everybody. What are the needs and logistics of medium- or long-haul flight by aircraft? Essentials include an aircraft of effective performance and fuel economy, with an airframe capable of withstanding the buffeting not just of take-off and landing, but also of any adverse conditions such as turbulence or storms encountered at altitude. At cruising height, often well in excess of 30,000 feet, not only are external temperatures way below freezing, but air pressures are painfully (sometimes dangerously) low for humans, so the aircraft must be well insulated and pressurised within the passenger cabin.

For long-haul journeys, advance logistics must make sure that fuel is available at any interim stop, together with a replenishment of food, water and other essentials for passengers and crew – and a change of crew is often necessary. Advance weather information along the route will also be required, and regularly updated. This, and air traffic control, dictate a sophisticated global radio communication network. On board will be all the equipment necessary for the accurate navigation of the aircraft to its destination, including altimeters, air-speed indicators and the means of assessing external wind force and direction. In times past, there would have been a compass, an array of charts covering the journey, perhaps a sextant to measure the angle of elevation of the sun, and certainly an accurate chronometer. Interestingly, an accurate knowledge of the time is the key to precise navigation; the invention of the chronometer back in the days of sailing ships revolutionised global voyaging far more than did accurate charts. Today, the navigational training and abilities of the aircrew are largely a back-up to the extremely bulky but sophisticated computer, absorbing and processing in-flight data from the aircraft instrumentation, from air traffic control and, above all, from a network of satellites or ground-based radio beacons that mark the chosen flight path.

Concorde cockpit instrumentation – courtesy of **British Airways**

On the flight deck, an aircrew several strong monitor progress, amending the automated instructions that keep the aircraft in flight and correcting the course only when necessary. On the ground below, armies of diverse ground staff ensure that navigational beacons function, and that aircraft are moving safely along flight paths, individual in their altitude, speed and direction, until destinations are reached. All-in-all, an extremely complex piece of teamwork, demanding the highest quality logistics and technology to ensure the safe delivery of a few hundred passengers.

Designed for the task

And what is the avian equivalent of all this manpower and technology? Soberingly, just the brain and the airframe provided for the bird by nature through the processes of evolution. A brain, often little bigger than a pea (and sometimes smaller than a pea), with outwardly at least few differences, let alone dramatic differences, between migrants and non-migrants. Nor are huge differences outwardly evident between the brains of migrant birds and relatively sedentary vertebrates of comparable size, like voles. Within a bird species where some individuals or populations migrate while others are sedentary, no anatomical differences can be found. It is tempting to speculate that the ability to navigate is almost another sense, possessed but not always employed. Maybe all or most birds have the latent ability to migrate?

As to the airframe component, birds are anatomically and physiologically geared by evolution to their high performance lives. They have a strong but lightweight skeleton, often with hollow bones (sometimes with internal cross-struts, the layout of which would be familiar to a structural engineer), robust enough to support the comparatively massive flight muscles. The weight balance of this structure is impeccable, with the wings operating from the centre of gravity and head and neck balancing legs and tail. In an aircraft, powerful shock absorbers and pneumatic tyres cushion the landing for

passengers, and in birds the leg muscles perform the same function. However, in many birds, unlike an aircraft, the leg muscles also provide extra propulsion to launch the bird into flight efficiently, getting the beating wings clear of the ground at take-off, and of special value in providing a quick take-off to avoid terrestrial predators.

Robin coming in to land – Dick Jeeves

Feathers are made of keratin, light and tough but flexible. The outer wing feathers (primaries) provide the power for flight, the inner wing feathers (secondaries) give the lift to keep the bird airborne. In cross-section, the inner portion of the wing is broadly akin to the curved cross-section of an aircraft wing, designed to provide lift when in forward motion. Although some modern jet fighters have what is known as 'variable geometry' in their wing configuration (popularly 'swing wing'), birds' wings provide an almost infinitely variable wing geometry to suit all flight conditions, a layout far superior to those devised by human technology. Just consider the Knot, a long-haul migrant wader wintering as far south as southern Africa and breeding on the tundra around the Arctic Circle. The wings that power the purposeful, energy-efficient flight between staging posts on its migratory journeys are so adaptable in their variable geometry that vast flocks of densely packed Knot, tens of thousands strong, can also perform amazing aerobatics over our estuaries, twisting and turning as one, wingtip to wingtip, appearing from a distance as clouds of smoke, changing colour from grey to white as they turn in the sunlight.

Turnstone: a long haul migrant's wing –
Graham Austin

Birds, like mammals, are warm-blooded and in control of their body temperature. Streamlined and well-insulated by their various feather layers, which are sometimes waterproof, they have a four-chambered heart at least comparable to that of mammals, and blood with excellent oxygen-carrying capacity for highly effective muscle function. They have small but highly efficient lungs for oxygen exchange with the surrounding air, augmented by a series of much larger air-sacs, so arranged as to allow a continuous flow of oxygen-rich air to pass through the lungs. Air movement through the system is provided by the squeezing action of the flight and other muscles at work, and thus naturally geared to the oxygen requirement at all times. In this way, birds have avoided the diaphragm-controlled breathe in, extract oxygen, breathe out, carrying waste carbon dioxide regime, and the associated heaving chest of an exercising mammal, efficient only half-time in oxygen extraction.

Bird physiology, like a jet engine, is more efficient in the cold temperatures at high altitude, which assists in the 'fuel economy' of long-haul migrants – but birds do not require pressurisation! There are astonishing records of Whooper Swans seen out of the cockpit window by a civil airliner pilot, flying at over 30,000 feet between Iceland and Scotland, and of climbers spotting Bar-headed Geese overflying the highest peaks in the Himalayas, migrating south to wintering grounds in India.

Why take the risks?

Birds are clearly able to tackle the rigours of migration, but what is it that they seek that makes their (often prodigious) journeys worthwhile? Fundamentally, the reasons for almost all migrations can be traced back, in one form or another, to climate and the advantages (or disadvantages) conferred by changes, be they of the nature of winter/summer or wet/dry, occurring with reasonable regularity year on year. This could, with good reason, be supplemented by the old adage that 'nature abhors a vacuum'. An environment, even a temporary one, capable of sustaining life is extremely unlikely to be ignored by wildlife, plant or animal.

However tough they may be on migration, most birds are not good at withstanding prolonged spells of freezing weather or snow cover. Even in comparatively low-lying Britain and Ireland, where peaks at altitudes exceeding 3,000 feet are sufficiently scarce that climbers list them as 'Munros' and aspire to have conquered the majority in a lifetime, in winter most upland areas become inhospitable and some uninhabitable to all but a specialist like the Ptarmigan. Ptarmigan have particularly good insulation, including feathered toes, and can live grazing on plants beneath the snow if necessary. An isotherm map of Eurasia in midwinter clearly demonstrates the impossibility for most birds of remaining in Siberia, the northern parts of the old USSR, Fennoscandia and the Baltic States. Equally inhospitable in winter away to the west, and with an impact on migrants to or through Britain and Ireland, are Iceland, Greenland, northern Canada and Alaska.

The isotherm map also shows well the beneficial effects of the Gulf Stream, the mild eastern Atlantic current sweeping warmer waters along the western shorelines of Britain and Ireland. Perhaps counter to expectation that climates improve as you head south from the North Pole, the thermal gradient from Siberia and Russia is markedly east-west rather than north-south. This, coupled with the imposing mountain barriers of the Himalayas, Caucasus, Carpathians and Alps strung along the width of Eurasia, serves to channel many migrants (but not all, as some species can and do overfly the highest peaks and others weave their way through mountain passes) westwards in autumn towards Britain and Ireland. For those birds escaping the inhospitable winter across North America and Greenland and heading towards our warmer autumn and winter climate, Iceland may provide a useful 'stepping stone', reducing the oversea legs of the journey east or southeast to around 1,000 km at the most.

Although the number of birds remaining through the harshest winter months at high altitudes or latitudes is small, other animals can survive. Some mammals, like voles and lemmings, retreat beneath the snow and carry on rather as normal. Others hibernate either briefly or for an extended period, and even specialists like the Polar Bear, supremely adapted in many ways to the cold and the topmost predator in arctic food chains, has a long hibernation in snow caves. Arctic plants close down their metabolic processes for the winter, relying on sugar-rich sap to serve as antifreeze as, deep frozen, they await the coming of spring warmth and the resumption of active growth. Their seeds, of course, survive. Insects and other small invertebrate animals use similar strategies, overwintering as frost-resistant eggs, larvae, pupae or, more rarely, adults.

Food is the key factor

Come the thaw and life burgeons. The arctic tundra, with its mosses and pools, supports an unbelievable quantity of individuals of numerous insect species, many of them blood-sucking midges eagerly awaiting the return of the food supply provided by the migrants. All these insects have rapid life-cycles and, as a result, once the brief late spring and short summer are under way, in most years (providing adverse weather conditions do not intervene) insect food is abundant, particularly for waders and wildfowl. This, then, is the migratory 'pull', in contrast to the migratory 'push' exerted as winter closes in.

Much the same is true further south. Through Britain and Ireland and much of western continental Europe, although winter is appreciably milder than further east into Eurasia, temperatures are still too low for much active insect life and certainly too low for their reproduction. In consequence, the insect-eaters – swallows, martins, swifts, flycatchers and warblers in particular – must head south to warmer, more insect-rich environments, some around the Mediterranean, the majority further south still, throughout the African continent.

As February turns to March and April in Africa, to the north a massive and largely untapped source of food is opening up, ripe for exploitation by migrant birds. Thus, across the globe, food availability is a key determinant of migratory patterns – though it, too, is ultimately governed by the climate. I have already talked about seasonal fluctuations in insect numbers, but the picture is broadly similar for the fruits of plants – seeds, berries, nuts and cones – for birds that are predominantly vegetarian. These seasonal fluctuations impact not only on the origins and destinations of migrants, but also on the 'refuelling' opportunities, where migrants must feed *en route*, and it is equally vital that these be in place for migration to be a success.

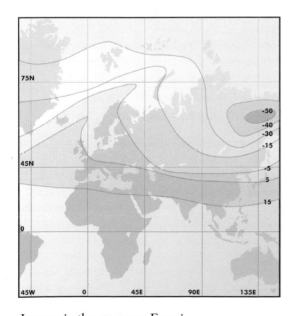

January isotherms across Eurasia

Food availability is also key in sporadic migrations; the irruptions mentioned in Chapter 1 of birds like Waxwings, Crossbills and Nutcrackers usually result from the imbalance between high bird population levels and food supply shortfalls. The story is different in desert country, where nomadic bird populations move in response to a food availability which is ephemeral in both timing and location. The response of hordes of wetland birds to the very sporadic rainfalls across the 'Red Centre' of Australia is typical, seeking out the flooded areas and establishing breeding colonies in an incredibly short space of time, capitalising on sudden food abundance. The movements and breeding seasons of the Budgerigar in the same region are responses to the same stimulus, only in their case to a sudden abundance of plant seeds. For most irruptive birds, a return to the usual breeding area is the norm, but for nomads, as the name implies, the next stage in their journey could be in almost any direction.

Let us paint the food availability picture with broad brushstrokes to see where migrants stand, starting at the Equator and moving toward the North Pole. Within the tropics, seasonality is determined by 'the rains' in Africa, and the monsoon in southern Asia. Sometimes there may be long rains and separate short rains, the pattern varying substantially across Africa. Both plant and insect food in the tropics is reasonably plentiful year-round, obviously with some variations, particularly with the productivity peaks that closely follow the rains. As an example, the *Acacia* trees in many areas can be found in all stages from bud, to flower, to fruit in almost any month, providing a steady enough supply to satisfy nectar- and fruit-feeding birds, with the blossom attracting insects for the insect-eaters.

Further to the north, in the Mediterranean Basin, though winters may not be really harsh, flower and fruit availability is reduced, as is the supply of flying insects. However, herbaceous plant and grass seeds remain in good supply and most terrestrial or underground invertebrates remain accessible.

Altitude, though, does play a part and most mountain areas are pretty barren and inhospitable, other than to specialists. Further north still, around the latitudes spanned by Britain and Ireland, in winter, deciduous trees have shed their leaves and flowers are generally unavailable, although there remains a plentiful supply of fleshy fruits and seeds. Flying insects are scarce but terrestrial invertebrates remain accessible as long as the ground is unfrozen. This is true along our coasts and particularly true of our estuaries, where an abundance of intertidal marine invertebrates, particularly worms and shellfish, remains available in the mud and sandflats throughout all but the most exceptionally severe winters. At the latitude of (say) Aberdeen, the adjacent Continent is far, far colder even than northeastern Scotland, let alone the milder northwest, hence the richness of our winter migrant population. In spring, everything changes; plant life erupts into flower, seed and fruit, and insects again become plentiful – an abundance harvested by some resident species, joined by myriads of migrants from further south. Far north, in the boreal forests and tundra regions, where the winter is extremely harsh (the 'push'), making these regions uninhabitable by birds. The summers, though comparatively short-lived, produce an abundance of insect life (the 'pull') visually typified by dancing columns of midges, whose larval stages sustain those migrant bird populations capable of reaching the area and completing their breeding cycle in the brief summer season.

Identifying the hazards

Clearly, from the huge and highly diverse range of birds migrating and discussed in detail in the following chapters, evolutionary success (based on the survival of individuals *and* species) indicates that migration is worth the risks involved. So what are those risks?

Whereas climate may be the main determinant force behind migration, weather may well be the principal hazard. Weather can either dictate or disrupt food supplies in several ways, some substantial, and interestingly (though on thought not surprisingly) some will be familiar to human gardeners and holidaymakers alike. Included, for example, are unusually severe winters, late springs, wet summers and periods of drought. Such weather abnormalities are relatively unusual, but can have adverse effects on the birds themselves or on their plant or animal

Tundra pools, rich in insect life – Jim Flegg

food supplies. Such problems are as important to the migrant on its journey (for example to the insect-feeding Swift with its almost entirely aerial life style) as on its wintering or breeding grounds (for example waders nesting on the arctic tundra).

Equally, though birds are undeniably extremely competent in both their flight and navigational capabilities, the onset of sudden storms, fog or more prolonged hostile conditions, in the form of headwinds, crosswinds or extended rainfall, can be disastrous. Implicitly, from their overall migratory success, birds must be far better at weather forecasting than ourselves, for all our technological back-up. The timing of their migrations, correlating food, weather and other factors to achieve a successful transit, appears to outstrip our own logistic capabilities.

Birds do sometimes make mistakes. In days past, when lighthouses had a continuously burning lamp and the beams were created by a revolving series of blinds or lenses, the sudden onset of dirty weather at migration times not infrequently resulted in catastrophe, as birds lured by the mesmerising beam flew headlong into the light. At particularly notorious lighthouses, it was not uncommon to record hundreds of fatalities in a single night. Introduced over the last quarter-century, modern on-off flashing lighthouses almost entirely avoid this problem. It is interesting to speculate on the possible effects of our increasingly well-lit cities, towns and roads, to say nothing of floodlit sports arenas and goods yards. Might they be distracting to overnight migrants, or have they become established visual landmarks to assist their journey? We simply do not know, but it seems certain that they do not exert the fatal attraction of old lighthouses. And what of the giant blades of wind turbine power generators – wind farms? These have obvious appeal as providers of 'clean' power, although positioning them prominently to best catch the wind inevitably intrudes on landscape quality. As yet there is little good information of their impact on birds, but presumably not for nothing does their colloquial German name translate to 'crow-mincers'. Wind farms will remain of concern until we have better information on their safety to wildlife. The current vogue is to plan such wind farms out of sight offshore, but in some cases possibly in the paths of migrant geese, ducks, gulls, skuas and terns.

Not quite so disastrous are 'falls' of migrants, occasional autumn features and usually occurring along Britain's eastern coast. After a 'fall', triggered by a sudden adverse change in the weather, coastal dunes and scrub can be almost literally heaving with tired migrants (Pied Flycatchers, Redstarts and Robins feature prominently) grounded during the night. These are nocturnal migrants, but occasionally the unexpected onset of heavy overcast conditions followed by rain along the east and south coasts can result in a startling fall of birds, tumbling (like the rain) out of the sky. Also involved are members of the thrush family, including more exciting species like the Ring Ouzel, forced to seek refuge on the ground. How often such mishaps become disasters when they occur out of sight – over the sea, or in remote or upland areas – again we can only speculate, but the population dynamics of the birds concerned seem to be flexible enough to avoid lasting damage to the species.

In some springs and autumns, Britain and Ireland can be subject to unusually long spells of stable weather with the wind in an unusual quarter, conditions usually associated with established high-pressure areas (anticyclones). In spring, the resulting southeasterly winds may bring unusual numbers of birds to our shores that we associate more with the Mediterranean, including Hoopoes, Red-backed and Woodchat Shrikes and Ortolan Buntings, probably overshooting their target destinations with the assistance of the wind. In autumn, anticyclonic conditions over the Continent result in easterly or northeasterly winds, and the arrival in Britain and Ireland of birds like the Bluethroat, blown or 'drifted' to the west of their normal southbound flightpath. Sometimes these conditions may bring quite exceptional rarities to our shores – for example Pallas's Warbler (the size of a Goldcrest) from eastern Russia and beyond, which normally migrates southwards through Asia (see Chapter 11). Rarity is one thing, the endurance and survival of these mere scraps of birdlife so far off their usual beaten track is quite another, and one at which we can only marvel.

Nor do these oddities originate only from the east. High in the atmosphere over the Atlantic, particularly in the late summer and autumn, weather conditions may be right to generate 'jet stream' winds. When these are northerly, they assist southward-bound migrants from northern America, but any westerly component can cause problems for birds. These westerlies may reach speeds in excess of 200 k.p.h., and sometimes result in the earlier than scheduled arrival of international flights from North America. If jet aircraft can benefit, then the jet stream is also available to birds flying at appropriate altitude, and many larger birds, especially waders and wildfowl, do this. Thus an Atlantic Ocean crossing, unthinkable at a flight speed of 50 k.p.h., becomes possible at a tail-wind-assisted 250 k.p.h., and a journey of, say, 5,000 kilometres from Canada to Britain or Ireland could be accomplished in less than 24 hours, well within the endurance of larger long-haul migrant birds. Ducks and particularly waders – a range of species from the small 'peeps' like the Semipalmated Sandpiper to the larger Pectoral Sandpiper, dowitchers and Lesser Yellowlegs – are now regular, if rare, autumn arrivals on this side of the Atlantic. As perhaps would be expected, Ireland fares rather better, proportionately, for these exciting strays.

Pectoral Sandpiper – Colin Varndell

A hostile planet

The physical geography of the landscape can present migrants with hazards almost as dangerous as those created by the weather. Natural barriers created by mountain ranges do shape migratory routes, but we have no way of measuring any mortality that straying into mountainous regions might cause. Likewise, deserts, with little or no available food or water, baking hot by day and astonishingly cold by night, present a truly formidable obstacle particularly to small birds. But many millions accomplish desert crossings each year, exemplified by the Willow Warblers leaving our shores in autumn to make a spirit-lifting return in spring, having crossed the Sahara Desert twice in the interval. We have no way of assessing with accuracy what the mortality is on the crossing. In the case of the Sahara, the desert of most concern to migrants from Britain and Ireland, there is a further hazard – the southerly Saharan fringes, a dry, shrubby

Sahara Desert, a formidable obstacle – Peter Jones

zone known as the Sahel, are drying and turning into desert under the current series of almost annual droughts. In consequence, and further amplified by overgrazing of shrubs and trees by the ravenous goats and cattle of distraught tribesmen, the Sahara is widening at an appreciable rate and the insect food available to migrants is much reduced. This food supply is key to the migrants' overwinter survival, and to allow them to fatten – essentially to fuel-up – for their northward trans-Saharan journey. The potential impact of this was best seen in the late 1960s, when our populations of Whitethroats, Sand Martins and Sedge Warblers crashed in an extremely dramatic manner. Between departure in autumn 1968 and return in spring 1969, heavy mortality obviously occurred, as less than half (in some places only a quarter) of the Whitethroat population returned to their hedgerow and scrub haunts in Britain and Ireland. This sudden decline was attributed largely to drought conditions in the Sahel, and only over the last decade have Whitethroat numbers begun to return to something like their previous levels. Over timespans far in excess of our 'three score years and ten', such traumas presumably occur irregularly, as must extended periods of favourable conditions, which encourage survival and consequent population increases.

Water, in the form of long sea crossings, can present just as formidable an obstacle as the most barren of deserts. If an unexpected weather change occurs during an over-sea crossing of just a few too many hours' duration, there is no emergency landing ground. True, there are many records of migrants landing on the sea, many of them seen from cross-Channel or North Sea ferries and others by observers on the coast but, though the exhausted birds can float for a while, their feathers soon become waterlogged and increasingly heavy, making take-off very difficult. Few will recover, get airborne again and survive.

Large birds like pelicans, buzzards, eagles and storks have problems with sea crossings of any length. Their long broad wings, often with 'fingered' tips, have evolved for soaring flight with minimal need for flapping. This energy-saving flight depends on the presence of upcurrents of air – the lift provided by cliffs, mountain ridges, or by thermals (upcurrents of air warmed by the ground beneath). They are, for obvious reasons, also enjoyed by glider pilots and, because the Earth takes time to warm after sunrise, neither gliders nor soaring birds, such as raptors and storks, are to be seen in prolonged flight until mid-morning. Nor is overnight flight normally possible. A migrating bird of prey will usually roost overnight until thermals began to stir, then take off with a few flaps into a steadily ascending spiral to a substantial altitude. Once at cruising height, it glides away on its migratory route, slowly losing height until it finds another thermal where it spirals upwards and repeats the process. The problem is that there are no thermals nor ridge-induced upcurrents over the sea. In consequence, to avoid inefficient and laborious flapping flight, a sea crossing needs to be accomplished in one descending glide.

Broad-winged birds seek the shortest practicable sea crossings – examples being the Kattegatt between Sweden and Denmark, the Strait of Gibraltar (essentially the western link between Europe and Africa) and the Bosporus and Dardanelles between European and Asian Turkey (the eastern link between Europe and Asia/Africa). Such crossing points provide a migration spectacular with few equals, lasting for several weeks each autumn. Over the Bosporus, on good days sometimes hundreds of thousands of birds will cross, at amazingly close-range, almost eyeball-to-eyeball, as they glide in low over the hills and then begin to spiral away upwards. To those of us living in Britain and Ireland, birds of prey by the thousand per day might seem unthinkable but the catchment area, the breeding ground of those birds crossing the Bosporus in autumn, is truly vast, stretching from around longitude 30° E (St Petersburg) across the northern hemisphere east to perhaps 120°, equivalent to a quarter of the way around the world.

Natural or semi-natural hazards also play their part. Predators, particularly birds of prey but also shrikes and owls, not forgetting members of the gull and crow families, are ever waiting for the opportunity provided by a less than alert victim. Tired, hungry migrants are inevitably less wary, less able to respond swiftly to danger and may more easily fall victim to attack. And, as the migrants move south, the number and variety of birds of prey increases considerably, especially south of the Sahara, where numerous predators wait for their chance. Two falcons have even evolved a specialist life style to capitalise on the autumn migration south. Because the southbound migrant stream contains both adults and the young of the year, migrants are inevitably more numerous in autumn than in spring. In the Mediterranean and North Africa, Eleonora's Falcon, and further south the Sooty Falcon, have substantially later breeding seasons than most birds, including their predator competitors. Evolution has shaped their breeding so that the young are at the peak of their growth and food demands just before, at and after fledging. This coincides with the autumn southerly migration season, when their small-bird prey is at its most plentiful and, as it contains many relatively inexperienced novice migrants, probably most easily caught by both harassed parents and trainee young.

Bird migration is not a static process, with stable patterns persisting unchanged. It is necessarily dynamic in the short term, to allow for seasonal and weather vagaries, and may also reflect changes that we do not understand; the newly developing migration of our wintering Blackcaps, for example (Chapter 6). In the longer term also, species and their migrations must be able to evolve in step with climate and other changes. The last Ice Age, covering and making uninhabitable almost all of Britain and Ireland ended about 11,000 years ago, in evolutionary terms quite recently. Migrants have clearly adapted to and exploited to good effect the newly-available habitats far into the High Arctic. Since the Ice Age ended, the climate has fluctuated substantially. As one indication of this, about 1,000 years ago, Greenland was far more temperate in climate than today, with woods, meadows, and settled farming communities, hence the name Greenland. As another, and much more recently, Britain and Ireland suffered a series of 'mini ice ages', typified by extremely cold winters (reflected by artists of the times, for example in paintings of the River Thames in London frozen over). This, too, would have necessitated flexibility on migrants' part. Regrettably the meteorological data and historical or pictorial accounts allow us no detailed insight into the impact of these changes on bird populations. Similarly, global climatic changes will have an impact in the future, but these we must await.

The human impact – abroad

The hazards for migrants increase southwards towards the Mediterranean. In France, shooting remains a popular pastime, particularly of waterfowl for sport. In the south, netting is added to the threat, with

Morocco, from Spain, across the Strait of Gibraltar – John Marchant

almost any bird considered fair game, including thrushes and larks destined for domestic consumption or the delicatessen trade. In the Pyrenees in autumn, netting or shooting Turtle Doves on passage is a long-standing Basque tradition.

Throughout southern Europe north of the Mediterranean Sea, from Portugal eastwards to Greece and Turkey, sport shooting is widespread and largely unregulated. At migration times, the hunters are well aware of favoured routes, especially through hills or mountains, and valley floors can be littered with spent cartridges almost like pebbles on a beach. Though shooting for food may play some part, no bird is safe and the 'sportsman' returning home to his village may have Buzzards and Kites dangling from his bandolier, far from edible but maybe slow-moving targets and easier to hit. Not infrequently do visitors to the Mediterranean comment on the often near-continuous fusillade of shots on Sunday mornings, and on the relative scarcity and shyness of birds. No wonder.

The trapping of wild birds by bird-fanciers to maintain and add genetic variety to their cage and aviary stocks was regarded as a way of life for centuries. In Britain and Ireland this activity and subsequent trade is now illegal. Offenders can be heavily penalised, and today this is also the case across much of continental Europe. Back in the 1960s and 1970s, large numbers of ring-recoveries of Goldfinches, Linnets and Redpolls indicated the magnitude of the toll taken by Belgian bird catchers on autumn migrants, from Britain and Ireland, passing through their country on the way south. Thus ringing data provided valuable information for conservationists seeking to ban the trade in these attractive birds.

Ostensibly for food, in some Mediterranean countries netting, trapping, snaring and bird-liming are carried out, again primarily during migration seasons, to catch especially warblers for pickling. Unlike trapping by cage bird fanciers, who need their victims alive, the methods used by those satisfying a delicatessen market are as unpleasantly effective with the victim alive or dead. Liming – the placing of sticky twigs in the bushes to trap unwary birds by their feet or feathers – is an age-old technique but now has a modern touch, as petroleum-based tacky glues have replaced the traditional lime paste. Sadly, though there is some local consumption, it is thought that much of the carnage is to satisfy markets across Europe, including those in what most would hope to be more conservation-minded societies, in northern Europe, including Britain and Ireland.

Over much of Africa, the human threat to migrants is less well documented, not surprisingly, bearing in mind the problems of literacy, poverty and communication. We receive relatively few recoveries of ringed migrants from much of Africa and can only be grateful for the reports of ringed birds that do percolate out. Some African nations would not regard birds as a legitimate food source, and in others the magnitude of hunting pressure is unknown. Many of our terns, particularly Sandwich Terns, winter along the southern coast of the 'bulge' of Africa. In fishing villages, the youngsters have developed techniques for catching terns on the beach – perhaps for fun, perhaps as potential 'pets', and some ringed birds are reported in full from these activities. Other

Stonechat awaits its fate – Guy Shorrock/ RSPB images

reporting letters withhold the ring details, offering to pass them on only when a satisfactory reward (a football amongst other things) has been promised or received – street-wise indeed!

There is mounting pressure to reduce or eliminate these practices, both within the countries concerned and from outside. The results from ringing schemes across Europe, recording the mortality of migrants in the areas of most concern, provide invaluable factual data to conservation bodies attempting to limit or eliminate such damaging activities. However, pan-European bird protection legislation is only slowly being implemented and special derogation seems to be applied by the governments concerned, to minimise the impact on the hunters, not their quarry!

... and at home

It would be comforting to say that in Britain and Ireland, other than legally-permitted and fairly well controlled wildfowling and game-bird shooting, the activities of man, the hunter, were a thing of the past. Ethical considerations apart, and allowing for the fact that wildfowling associations both retain and manage wetland areas appropriately, there can be no doubt that mortality of wild migrants occurs due to wildfowling, and recoveries of ringed birds confirm this hazard. Comparatively speaking, the numbers of ducks and geese shot are small and the impact of wildfowling in Britain and Ireland on population levels overall is difficult to assess, but likely to be small since numbers of most species are increasing.

But in truth the other adverse pressures, egg collecting and live-trapping, still remain in Britain and Ireland, illicitly, and undoubtedly at lower levels than elsewhere in Europe and certainly in Africa. Sadly, for less common species here, like the Tree Pipit and Hobby, egg collectors still take some toll, as do bird fanciers targeting a range of species but primarily finches. Overall, the impact of these depredations may be slight, but it is difficult to avoid the conclusion that for the Red-backed Shrike the activities of egg collectors were probably the final nail in the coffin. Unfortunately for the Shrike, its eggs are variable from clutch to clutch (as are those of the Tree Pipit) and also finely-coloured – both features enhancing their attraction as works of art.

The following chapters explore, habitat by habitat, the substantial – often massive – part that migrants play in our birdwatching. They also reflect the many ongoing changes in those habitats, and in land use, that take place naturally or (perhaps more often) through human agencies. Such changes may impact on migrants whilst in Britain and Ireland, or on their wintering or breeding grounds, or at stop-over sites *en route* between. Here the evidence provided by the results of bird ringing is of particular value to national and international conservation bodies.

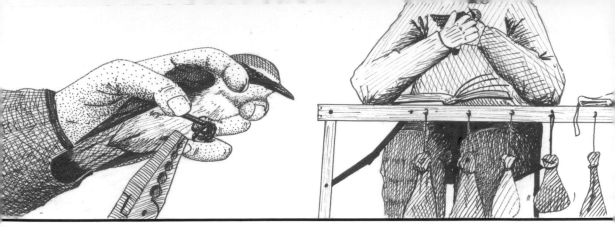

Investigating migration

Migration in action must have been a noticeable feature in peoples' lives for thousands of years. Long ago, perhaps more than today, new arrivals would imply an impending change in the season and thus the oncoming comforts or hardships that the new season would bring. For over 2,000 years, philosophers and naturalists have recorded their sightings, timings and thoughts about migration, but as isolated individuals, not often in contact with others with similar interests. About 200 years ago, like-minded people were more numerous and were able, through books and through developing social, philosophical and scientific societies, to communicate their findings and thoughts to a much wider public. But, though the scientific structure was beginning to be put in place, the observations still lacked cohesion and organised collaboration.

During the 19th Century more and more bird books were published, building up a picture of changes in bird populations and movements. The 20th Century saw the rise of birdwatching, initially very much a hobby for the rich or those whose employment allowed sufficient leisure time for them to pursue their interest. Not until after 1950 did birdwatching really take off. Clubs and societies became established in many places and at all levels, particularly influencing youngsters, and those who participated were no longer regarded as eccentric (if not downright strange) by their contemporaries.

Local clubs and societies, usually organised at a county level, began to publish annual accounts of ornithology within their boundaries, focusing on bird populations, migration and the rarities that occurred from time to time and provided added sparkle. The Royal Society for the Protection of Birds (RSPB) was founded in Victorian times to protect species like the Great Crested Grebe from slaughter, for their feathers to adorn ladies' hats, and the St Kilda Wren from the pressures of trophy-hunting egg collectors. It soon began to develop into a conservation body, lobbying for birds on a broad front and beginning to develop a network of reserves. Over the last half-century, growth in membership and in conservation activities has been enormous, resulting in the internationally influential conservation body that the RSPB is today.

In the 1930s, an embryo British Trust for Ornithology (BTO), founded by interested amateurs and a handful of scientific colleagues, began to establish the pattern of national censuses and population surveys that developed post-war into a highly-effective collaborative operation. The BTO brings volunteers and professionals together to study a wide range of ornithological issues, some on a reactive, immediate-action basis, others as long-term studies designed, for example, to help unravel the mysteries of bird population dynamics – and migration. Post-war, the BTO too has grown, its membership different from that of the RSPB, not in dedication to birds but in its preparedness to commit much time and effort to participating in censuses and surveys, including bird ringing. It is the results of collective efforts in bird ringing, or at least bird marking, that form the major foundation for the habitat-based chapters on migration which follow.

The 'Old Light' at Dungeness – Dawn Balmer

Direct observation

Initial attempts to plot the routes of migrating birds and to understand the processes of migration were based on straightforward observations. In Victorian county avifaunas such observations were collected on an *ad hoc* basis but several decades later a more formal process was adopted by county or regional societies for their annual records. Many of the records came from migration 'hot-spots', sites which quickly became known as excellent places to be during migration times, not just to see the spectacle of migration *en masse* but also because of the chances of encountering 'red-letter-day' birds, spectacular in plumage, in their rarity, or simply because they must have come from so far away. Such hot-spots are often on hilltops or prominent headlands; Dungeness and Beachy Head in southeast England are good examples, offering birds only a short sea crossing to the Continent. For each, there was the added bonus that, besides migrating passerines, the chances are also high of observing wildfowl, waders or terns, migrating through the Channel narrows. Several such sites became the natural locations for bird observatories, many of which are still in operation.

Visual counts on a collaborative basis at a number of known migration observation points are fair enough, so far as they go. They do have problems however. Are the birds counted representative of migrants as a whole? Clearly not, as we know that many migrants travel overnight, thus out of sight. What is the impact of the prevailing weather conditions in making birds visible (or invisible) to observers? Are many (or not many) flying over at a sufficient altitude to be above binocular range? Until the advent of radar studies, answers to these questions were simply unobtainable, but some determined attempts to assess nocturnal migration levels were made by counting migrants crossing the face of a full moon, as observed through a telescope. Arduous, eye-aching and chilly, and demanding some adventurous statistics in scaling up observations to produce some idea of the numbers of birds involved, little real progress was made, other than confirming that nocturnal migration occurred, at least on clear nights!

Enthusiasts at work – Dawn Balmer

Radar revelations

The problems of overnight migration, and of diurnal migration too far away to be seen, were at least partially resolved by serendipity. During the Second World War and afterwards, the scientists who were developing radar to provide information on incoming aircraft movements were puzzled and irritated by slow-moving belts of interference, looking rather like a snowfall crossing the screen. The name 'angels' was coined for these dots of

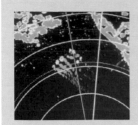

There has been a resurgence in radar studies in the last few years, for instance in North Africa, focusing on migration across the Sahara, and in mainland Europe, to understand the impact of wind turbines sited in migration hot-spots.

In this image, a flock of geese shows as a series of yellow and green echoes, the yellow dots indicating the latest positions. The yellow and orange areas at the top are land. Mark Deshelm/NERI

interference, which were eventually found to be due to flocks of migrating birds. David Lack and George Varley recognised the potential of radar in migration research as early as 1945, but the breakthrough came while Ernst Sutter was watching the radar at Zurich Airport in Switzerland in the mid 1950s. Using time-lapse cine-photography, Sutter made sense of the angels' movements, linking direction with season.

While angels continued to be a problem to military and civil aviation controllers, ornithologists saw in them an ideal method of adding a new dimension to the study of migration. Led by David Lack in Britain, one of the early findings was just how much migration took place across broad fronts. The early concept was that migration routes generally followed quite narrow channels along leading lines such as coasts, rivers or lines of hills. Sometimes this is the case, for example storks and birds of prey, needing lift for migration, use hill-generated upcurrents on the way to the short sea crossing from Gibraltar to Africa. Generally, however, migrant movements recorded from radar observations are on fronts tens, or often hundreds, of kilometres wide.

Interestingly, radar swiftly disposed of the idea that migration was something that took place in spring and again in autumn. At almost any time of year, some birds could be seen migrating somewhere, and the movements, particularly during the winter, could be in almost any direction, presumably motivated by changing weather conditions and food availability. The origin of another fascinating phenomenon, that of 'ring-angels', concentric rings of echoes looking as if a pebble had been dropped in a pond, was quickly positively identified. Ring-angels are characteristic particularly of Starlings, departing from their overnight roost in pulses a few minutes apart and dispersing to feed to all points of the compass.

Although other types of radar were developed, allowing accurate measurement of the heights at which migration was taking place, problems remained. The main one was that the blips, the echoes birds leave on screen, could not be identified to species. Sometimes it was possible to say that they were Buzzard-sized, or Lapwing-sized, and to tie this in with the migration of known species going on at the time. Difficulties arose when a tight pack of small birds produced an echo similar to that of a single larger bird. Sophisticated work by Glen Schaefer and others, on breast-muscle bulk and shape changes in flight and consequent changes in echo-type, gave some identification pointers, but no more than that. Additionally, increasing sophistication for air traffic control purposes almost eliminated angels at source as unwanted and potentially dangerous interference. Military radars were increasingly shrouded in secrecy as they became more and more powerful, and as (at that time) the 'Cold War' became more intense. There, regrettably, radar studies largely rested for some years, hugely promising technology but failing to deliver fully in the brief window of opportunity that occurred before sheer cost, sophistication and confidentiality intervened. The current return to the use of specialist radar equipment in bird movement studies (in Britain, Europe, North Africa and elsewhere) is greatly to be welcomed.

Ringing for results

Bird-ringing, called bird-banding in the USA and elsewhere, may perhaps not be the perfect technique for studying migration, because of the biases that may creep into the picture both at the time of ringing and in the timing and circumstances of the recovery – the finding of a ringed bird. Nevertheless ringing is the mainstay of bird migration studies and underpins our understanding of what is taking place. Ringing is a surprisingly age-old technique; there are Roman records of marked homing or message-carrying birds, while other schemes that attached rings or other marks to birds (for example, notching the beaks of Mute Swans to distinguish 'ownership' between the Sovereign and two City of London Livery Companies) were essentially proprietorial and usually involved larger birds. Lord William Percy, marking Woodcock with rings inscribed with an N, for Northumberland, and the year was one such. Perhaps surprisingly with such a stark 'address', several interesting movements were nevertheless recorded.

Historically, bird ringing, using rings with an address and serial numbers stamped on, was invented in 1899 by a researcher called Hans Mortensen in Denmark, and in Britain and Ireland two schemes started in 1909. One was based at Aberdeen University, the brainchild of Sir Arthur Landsborough Thomson, the other organised in London at the offices of Harry Witherby, publisher of natural history books and the journal *British Birds*. The two schemes merged in 1937 and were transferred to the control of the Ringing Committee of the BTO. Today, many European countries have organised schemes, as do other nations globally. In Europe, the schemes are linked by EURING, which coordinates techniques and the electronic handling of data, unifies standards and formats and stimulates international projects. These common formats hugely assist the analysis of recoveries on a pan-European basis.

To serve their prime function, rings have a number of essential features. For a start, they must be as light in weight as possible, as there is no point in fitting a ring to a bird which then interferes with its behaviour or flight endurance. Over the years, ring sizes have been developed to suit all birds from Goldcrests to Golden Eagles and designs developed to ensure that the ring survives as long as the bird. Specially designed pliers are used to ensure the proper and precise fitting of the ring to the bird's leg.

The choice of metal or metal alloy has developed over the years. Aluminium alloys are extremely light in weight and easily stamped with the necessary details, making these ideal for smaller birds from Goldcrests upwards. Such metals do not last well under abrasive conditions (for example a Guillemot shuffling along its rocky nesting ledge) or if in frequent contact with salt water, when corrosion is focused and accelerated by the stamped indentations of the numbers. This influences all wader, wildfowl and seabird recoveries and explains why, in the 1960s and 70s, tern rings were being sent back from Africa full of holes and illegible, with many of the numbers corroded out. To resolve this problem, some larger rings are made from stainless steel, others from nickel or molybdenum alloys. These prove stronger than aluminium alloys, much more resistant to electrochemical attack and to abrasion, and are now not only the basis of bird rings but also ships' propellers!

Ringing a Curlew – Graham Austin

Most British and Irish rings carry the address of the British Museum. This simple inscription is clear enough to generate letters from all over the world.

The ring must carry a simple, legible address and one that can be readily understood by the finder (even in remote areas) and by the various postal or communication systems through which news of its finding must travel. Obviously too, the ring must carry a unique serial number as traceable as a car registration plate.

Painstaking recording of all details of the bird ringed, longhand and each on a separate card, was replaced half a century ago by pro-forma recording of batches of 50 sequential numbers, handwritten still but with many details (such as age and sex) coded. Today, the majority of ringing information arrives electronically and after checking is entered on the database. Once the details of a recovery have been matched with its ringing data, print-outs inform the ringer and the finder. The details are then registered on the BTO database, where (with permission) they can be accessed, nationally or internationally by interested researchers.

Just as the ring itself must be a correct fit and not hamper the bird wearing it, so too must the actual ringing process give paramount importance to the bird. Birds could easily be damaged by rough or incorrect handling. The fitting of a ring requires a considerable degree of skill and care, and all ringers in Britain and Ireland must have a permit, issued by the BTO, acting on behalf of the governments of Britain and Ireland. The issue of permits is only allowed after thorough and extensive training in all aspects of bird ringing, under

the supervision of an authorised trainer. This process will take one or two years and will usually involve the supervised handling of hundreds of birds. Currently about 750,000 birds are ringed annually by 2,000 ringers, and about 12,000 ring-recoveries are reported from round the world. It is a tremendous privilege to handle birds, not just to participate in ringing and migration studies, but to see plumage details at really close quarters. Our growing knowledge of moult patterns and what they reveal about a bird's age, or of weight changes and what they can tell of a bird's condition or readiness to migrate, almost entirely stem from the bird in the hand. New ringers are always wanted; there is no better way of participating at the cutting edge of ornithological research.

Weighing a Bar-tailed Godwit – Graham Austin

The success of ringing as one of the tools in the study of migration depends very much on ringed birds being found or seen again. Therein lie some problems. For a start, most recoveries involve the finding of a dead bird; clearly the chances of this are near enough zero should a migrant die whilst over the sea, and not much greater should it die on a mountain or desert crossing. Such journeys are familiar to many European migrants. There are other biases; large, colourful or white birds are simply more likely to be found than tiny, drab or well-camouflaged ones, so that about 25% of ringed Mute Swans have been recovered against about 0.25% of Willow Warblers! Edible waterfowl, quarry species to wildfowlers throughout their range, are naturally at high risk of being shot, and thus ringed birds are more likely to be reported (91% of all Pintail recoveries for example). In the case of swans, reports are less likely from areas without power cables, a potential blank on the recovery map. Similarly, the migratory route of the Pintail, as depicted by ring-recoveries, reflects the distribution of wildfowlers (and their shooting seasons) and may not give the full picture of the Pintail's travels from breeding to wintering grounds. Whatever the case, it is important to be aware that various biases may occur, and to interpret ring-recoveries making due allowance for them if necessary. But we would be nowhere in our understanding of migration without them!

Colour marking

Numbered metal rings have the disadvantage that, to be of value, they need to be read again, in the hand on a dead bird or on one that has been recaptured alive and then released. This problem can be helpfully overcome by a variety of colour-marking strategies. One simple way to show that a group of birds has been ringed at a particular location, or on a particular day, is to paint a conspicuous part of the plumage with a dye that does not damage the feathers. The white undertail coverts of Brent Geese in Essex were painted yellow during the studies associated with the proposal to site a new London Airport on Maplin Sands, earning themselves the impolite nickname 'sun-bums' amongst Thames Estuary birdwatchers. The dye, though, only lasted for a few months until the geese moulted.

Swans, geese and waders particularly, but also a range of other birds, are large enough, and have stout enough legs to carry laminated plastic rings or leg flags which can be both colour coded and offer the chance to etch a number and/or letter combination on the ring. The characters are large enough to be read at a distance, sometimes through binoculars, more often with a telescope. Recent dramatic improvements in telescope design allow this sort of marking technique to be used on birds as small as Dunlin. In this way, individuals may be identified without the need for

recapture, often on numerous occasions over the season and from year to year. Geese and swans once again, but also a handful of other species, have long necks much more easily seen than their legs. At the base of these long necks, plastic collars, coded as for the leg rings, can be fitted and read from a distance without the need for recapture. If the legs are not so easily visible, then similarly colour-coded back or wing tags, suitably sized plastic pennants that sit comfortably on the feathers without disrupting flight (or indeed display behaviour) may serve the same purpose.

Turnstone fitted with a leg-flag – Nigel Clark

A great many birds of all shapes and sizes, including small species, have been the subject of colour-ringing studies. Here the metal BTO ring is augmented by the addition of one or more colour or bi-coloured plastic rings on one or both legs, so individuals or classes of birds can be recognised in the field. Waders, with their long legs, are especially amenable to this approach. This approach has been satisfactorily used on birds from Bullfinches to Buzzards, and bigger. It goes without saying, that all colour-marking techniques are tested extensively, often on captive birds in aviaries, before being used in the field. It also goes without saying that colour-marking is an extremely valuable adjunct to standard ringing. Colour-ringing has helped greatly in understanding the movements of Mediterranean Gulls, as they expand their range, and can also have a dramatic impact on reporting rates. For example, before colour-ringing was introduced for Black-tailed Godwits, only 2.5% of metal-ringed birds had been recovered. Resighting rates of colour-ringed birds exceed 80%, with many individuals being repeatedly resighted over several years and in different countries.

Osprey fitted with transmitter – Anglian Water Osprey Project – see page 86

Osprey fitted with transmitter – Anglian Water Osprey Project – see page 86

The most innovative tracking technology is the fitting of a transmitter to the migratory bird. Since this is an extremely expensive approach, only a few individuals can be fitted with transmitters in a single study. High power and low weight are the necessities; obviously the bird must be able to carry the transmitter with minimal additional energy expenditure, as we would our binoculars. Equally obviously, the transmitter must be powerful enough, and the battery must last long enough for the bird to be located, and then tracked, for some distance and over some days, if not weeks. This imposes a size restriction on which birds can be fitted with such transmitters, something that is now changing as smaller transmitters and batteries become available.

Transmitters small enough to be glued to the back feathers of, for example, a Starling (so they detach and are lost with the feathers at moult) allow researchers with hand-held receiver aerials to follow birds over a radius of more than a kilometre. Large birds (the technique has been used on geese, swans, cranes, spoonbills, eagles, Ospreys and vultures, amongst others) can carry transmitters giving signals powerful enough to be tracked from satellites in low Earth orbit. Though yet far from foolproof, satellite-tracking offers an amazing hour-by-hour insight into a migrant's journey and into the impact of prevailing weather conditions. Most importantly, satellite-tracking offers the opportunity to open a totally new window of understanding on the precise pacing of a journey, any variations in direction and any stop-overs *en route*, either on remote landing areas or, in the case of waterbirds, on the sea.

First catch your bird

Many birds are ringed as youngsters still in the nest, or nearby in the case of waders that leave the nest almost immediately after hatching. This is especially valuable, as they are of precisely known age and geographical origin, but carries the perennial problem that, in birds, infant mortality in the nest and shortly after fledging is often extremely high. With the exception of larger birds like geese, it is a small minority of migrant nestlings that embark on their first major journey at the end of the summer.

Ringing a nestling Jackdaw – Dawn Balmer

Investigating migration

The great majority of birds ringed are caught when full grown and normally when free-flying (although in the past, large numbers of geese have been rounded up whilst flightless during their moult period). Most of the techniques and traps used by ringers are closely akin to, or developments of, the equipment used by the bird catchers of times past, trapping birds for the pot or for caging. Simplest, but still effective in the right circumstances, is the 'sieve and stick'. This is little more than an oversize garden sieve, propped up over some bait (ranging from bread crumbs, berries or nuts to mealworms to tempt insect-eaters) by a stick, to which is attached a cord running to the catcher some metres away in concealment. Birds enter the catching area, the cord is tugged, and the birds caught under the sieve can be removed for ringing.

Next up the scale is the 'chardonneret' (French for Goldfinch), a simple box cage with a flap lid held open by a notched perch. Bait is positioned as before, the bird hops in and onto the perch and the lid closes. Chardonnerets can be more effective set in groups, especially in gardens, but have an unexpected disadvantage. Birds like garden Robins and Greenfinches soon realise that a continuous food supply is theirs for the taking. Counter to expectations that, after the first capture they would shy away from traps, many will return immediately, feeding fast while awaiting release, but of course preventing unringed birds from entering the trap.

Chardonneret trap – Dawn Balmer

Funnel traps, netting cages of various sizes depending on the target species (but essentially derived from the gamekeepers' crow trap) have the benefit that several birds can be caught at once. Funnel traps have been adapted to catch migrant waders on muddy lagoons, using low guide-walls to steer feeding birds into the funnel entrance, and also built over water to catch various ducks very successfully.

Bird catchers used a variety of nets; 'springbows', which resemble giant spring-powered mousetraps, triggered as the bird tugs at the bait; and 'clap nets', where a much larger net, up to several metres long and a couple wide, is pulled manually on two hinged poles that swing the net up and over the birds on the ground within the catching area.

A cannon-net catches birds before they take off – Nigel Clark

Ringer-based developments have included elastic-powering of the up-and-over pass, with tensioned elastic (released by a trigger) replacing the often substantial man-powered pull.

More sophisticated still, the elastic was replaced by initially rockets and later 'cannon' (but more properly classified as mortars). Here a much larger net, upwards of 20 metres by 10, can be pulled quickly and safely over feeding or roosting birds by heavy metal projectiles attached to its leading edge, and fired by explosive charge from tubular cannon dug into the ground. The technique is spectacularly successful with birds like geese, ducks, gulls and waders, and has contributed greatly to our understanding of the migrations of such birds. It naturally demands a very high degree of additional training and well-coordinated teamwork, but has been developed to such a high degree that at times, for some populations of these birds, upwards of 1 in 50 of all individuals in the world may be wearing a ring!

Large-scale trapping at places like bird observatories has long depended on huge funnel-shaped wire netting traps, set over a row of bushes or a suitable gully. These are called Heligoland traps, after the anglicised name of the island of Helgoland in the German Bight, site of the first-ever bird observatory, where these traps were designed. Migrants in the bushes are gently ushered by ringers further into the trap, which narrows to a catching box, where the birds are collected and removed for ringing.

In some ways working to the same principle, similarly wide-mouthed, steadily narrowing netting funnels ending in a catching area, were used in old duck decoys, set over an arm of a lake. Resident tame ducks on the lake tempted in their wild cousins, and the decoy-man then set to work. Using a sandy (foxy) coloured dog weaving in and out of wattle hurdles, the ducks were ushered further and further up the decoy funnel until the decoy-man appeared at the entrance, shepherding the ducks into a removable narrow netting tunnel, like a fisherman's keep-net. Thence they were taken in times past to the butcher, but more recently a few decoys have been used to catch wildfowl for ringing.

Removing a male Bullfinch from a mist net – Mark Grantham

For smaller birds, up to wader-size, a huge leap forward in catching took place in the mid 1950s, when the first 'mist nets' arrived in Britain. Mist nets originated from the bird catchers of Japan, and were initially made of silk. These swiftly increased the numbers of birds ringed tremendously as well as the range of species that the average ringer could aim to catch. Mist nets are best likened to giant hairnets, from 6 to 20 metres in length and 1 to 3 metres high. Erected on poles against a background of trees or shrubs, or even rising ground – anything but the sky – they are fine enough to be invisible to most flying birds. So

Heligoland trap – Fair Isle Bird Observatory

33

soft and elastic are they that even a fast-flying bird is brought gently to rest, before sliding down into the pocket of net formed by one of the three or four shelf strings threaded through, there to await, unharmed, swift removal by the ringer.

Unharmed is the key word. To the old (and present-day overseas) birdcatchers, trapping for the pot, the welfare of the caught bird was immaterial. For ringers, the welfare of the bird is absolutely vital. All their time, dedication and training would be wasted unless the ringed bird not only lived to tell the tale, but behaved in exactly the same way as the rest of the population. The migration information in the chapters that follow depends heavily on the results of ringing; much is owed to the birds that have carried and still carry rings, and to the efforts of their ringers. This is where all birders can play their part. A lot of effort goes into ringing birds; to maximise the benefits to our understanding of migration and to international bird and habitat conservation, do please report any ringed or colour-marked birds you may encounter.

To report a ringed bird contact the Ringing Unit via the BTO's website (www.bto.org) or write to Ringing Unit, BTO, The Nunnery, Thetford, Norfolk, IP24 2PU. The key information required is the place and date you found or read the ring and, if possible, the cause of death (for dead birds).

Migrants in towns and gardens

Not in my back yard?

The first thing that many of us look out onto in the morning is our garden. No matter whether it is urban, suburban or rural, looking out of the window, even in winter, the garden seems full of birds. Where have they all come from, or are they here all the time? Although some of the Starlings will have nested under the eaves of our house, or in the hole in next door's old plum tree, they have probably been joined on the lawn by migrants, perhaps from as far away as Russia. And what about the tits on the feeders – where will the Blue and Great Tits be when summer comes? Robins and Dunnocks, Wrens and Long-tailed Tits, Blackbirds and Song Thrushes seem to be with us all year; is this really the case? The Long-tailed Tits will have travelled only from the nearest woodland but the Blackbird may be a winter visitor from Finland. Just what other surprises may our gardens have in store?

Urban areas, be they villages or towns and cities with their suburbs and industrial areas, show by far the most extreme impact of human presence on our landscape and the habitats it contains. Like them or loathe them, most of us live and work in built-up surroundings and wherever possible usually do our best to improve them, both structurally and visually, with the aim of making them better places to live – for us, that is! At the planners' insistence, even factory estates are today landscaped with a variety of lawns, shrubberies and trees, the aim being to minimise maintenance as well as embellishing the surroundings and reducing visual and noise pollution.

However unappealing we may think some of our built-up areas, through birds' eyes they too are a habitat, and habitats are there to be exploited. Even in the heart of the starkest city centre there are some birds, maybe Carrion Crows, Starlings or (still in some places) House Sparrows, with almost everywhere feral pigeons. Perhaps not too exciting on a check list, but they all have fascinating aspects of behaviour.

Our activities in landscaping or gardening add considerably to the basic habitat structure. Though the plants involved may technically be alien or specially bred or developed for garden use, many bear fruits or seeds that birds find perfectly adequate for their food needs. Some fruits may be rather too attractive to birds and result in conflict between the grower and the birds – cherries or plums and Starlings are but one example of this. Gardens and parks, by their nature and to suit our desires, are in habitat terms very varied both in the bird foodstuffs they produce and the insects they support, as well as in their physical structure. All of this is appealing to urban birds.

The results of the BTO's Garden Bird Feeding Survey and BTO/CJ Garden BirdWatch are an amazing testimony to the value of our gardens to birds – and also to the way birds are able to exploit the opportunities they provide. Never has the BTO organised a more popular cooperative study, with results both easily accessed and meaningful to all concerned. They are politically (in conservation terms) as well as scientifically useful, leave aside their fascination and intrinsic interest. In the comparatively affluent latter part of the 20th Century and the beginnings of the 21st, never have householders lavished such attention not only on their gardens but on providing nestboxes, water and foodstuffs for visiting birds.

True, there are negative aspects; though modern gardens provide ample semi-natural nest sites, modern buildings (in comparison with those in the past) certainly do not, and much remains to be done to compensate for this, for example for Swifts. Natural predators like the Sparrowhawk and Magpie readily capitalise on the greater food resource available to them, the Magpie as a nest predator, the Sparrowhawk taking birds in flight. The circumstances reported when a ringed bird is found indicate that the impact of Sparowhawks and other natural predators is very small, hardly registering in comparison with the non-natural circumstances that predominate in built-up areas. These include factors like collisions with cars and windows, being trapped within buildings and being killed by domestic predators such as cats. Dead ringed birds are far more likely to be found and reported in towns and gardens than in the surrounding countryside, particularly if the unfortunate victim is brought in by the cat. Perhaps the best measure of the impact of these urban-related mortality factors is that most garden birds continue to flourish, a tribute to the ability of their population dynamics to soak up punishment.

It is tempting to assume from the artificial nature of built-up areas that those birds that can and do exploit this habitat are well-adapted to urban life, and thus are with us as individuals year-round. Carrion Crows, Magpies, Nuthatches and House Sparrows, with an average distance moved between ringing and recovery of around one kilometre,

certainly fit this bill, as do (at least some of the time) Blackbirds, Song Thrushes, Blue Tits, Coal Tits, Great Tits, Robins and Wrens. To most of us, the Dunnock is the epitome of a homely, and sombrely plumaged bird (their name comes from *dun* – brown, and *ock* – small, the archetypical 'little brown job'). We think of it as a sedentary bird, and indeed the vast majority of ringed Dunnocks move less than one kilometre from where they were ringed. Occasionally though, for some reason things change. There is some evidence from ringed birds, not well defined or understood, indicating occasional eruptions of young birds dispersing over greater distances than is normal. More materially, the continental race of the Dunnock (which is not readily distinguishable from our resident birds) is migratory and almost certainly accounts for the majority of the exchanges with Europe mapped. Many Dunnocks pass down the east coast of Britain in the autumn. So you never know – the bird you see may be a genuine migrant!

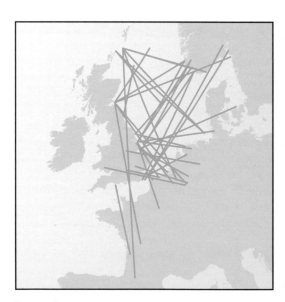

Dunnock

Not as parochial as they seem

The Robin is common and friendly enough to claim the position of our 'most popular bird' and has national emblem status when it comes to Christmas cards, wrapping paper and cake decorations. It also provides us with another example of a garden bird having little or no climatic reason to migrate and thus remaining largely sedentary. Some adults will establish separate breeding and winter territories, perhaps moving between gardens or to nearby woodland, but it seems that no great distances are involved. Even young dispersing after the breeding season are likely to settle down in territories within 20 km of their birthplace. Despite this general conservatism, over the years 20 or so Robins ringed in Britain and Ireland during the breeding season have been recovered outside the breeding season in France and Iberia, traditional wintering grounds for the genuinely migrant continental Robin populations. So perhaps 'occasional partial migrant' would be a better descriptor.

the Low Countries, and migrate southwestwards through France (and occasionally further east) to overwinter closer to the Mediterranean. They return on roughly the reverse course in spring. Robins are night migrants, and varying numbers reach Britain during the autumn, predominantly along the eastern seaboard. If conditions are right (from the birdwatchers' viewpoint, *not* the Robins') these numbers can be substantial, even huge – a 'fall' as described in Chapter 2. So far as the ringing evidence goes, it suggests that most of these migrants are with us just long enough to rest and feed-up for the next leg of their journey, although a relatively small number of continental birds do winter in British and Irish woods and gardens.

Robin

Not all Robins in Britain and Ireland during the autumn, winter and spring share the breeding population's stay-at-home habits. In fact, the overseas recoveries of Robins trapped and ringed in Britain and Ireland in these seasons tell a clear story; these birds breed in Scandinavia, the Baltic States, Germany and

Wren – Tommy Holden

Tiny in stature, but powerful of voice and swift to scold, the Wren is also capable of long distance flights which belie the normal knee-high whirring away into cover so familiar to us in our gardens. Elsewhere, in North America the Winter Wren (the same species, *Troglodytes troglodytes*, as ours) migrates routinely in autumn south from Canada to winter over much of the USA, and many European populations of Wrens are migratory, at least to some degree, moving west or southwest in autumn, returning in spring. A ringed Scandinavian Wren is on record as travelling 2,500 km, and one from the Russian ringing station Rybachy on the Baltic flew just over 1,500 km to be found dead in Sussex! Such spectacular efforts are not to be expected of the vast majority of our garden Wrens. They are best classed as sedentary, although there is some dispersal of both adults and immatures away from breeding sites during the autumn and winter. Some of these birds may simply be moving to more temperate lower altitudes or coastal areas for the winter. The dozen or so exchanges of ringed birds with Europe are most likely to be birds of continental origin trapped in Britain on migration and subsequently recovered back on the Continent.

At the feeders and beyond

In most years and most places, garden Blue Tits are essentially sedentary. Although some young bred in Britain and Ireland may disperse over distances in excess of 50 km in late summer or autumn, most cover far shorter distances. In contrast, continental Blue Tits may be migrants or partial migrants, and very occasionally cross the Channel or North Sea. Rarely, continental Blue Tits become vigorously eruptive, the last major occasion being in 1957 when literally hordes of tits arrived on the south and east coasts of England in autumn. They were clearly starving hungry and behaved in a most bizarre manner, including getting into houses and eating almost anything left exposed, including tearing off strips of wallpaper! A smaller scale eruption, following another overly successful breeding season, took place in 1959.

The rather larger Great Tit is just as familiar in the garden year-round as the Blue Tit. The Great Tit must be a contender for the title of most adaptable bird, widespread (and often common) on local, national and global scales. Great Tits originating on the Continent also featured prominently in the eruptions of 1957 and 1959, but normally British and Irish populations are largely sedentary. The only movements of note are of young birds, although even for these dispersal after fledging distances in excess of 50 km are exceptional. However, there is no telling when the next eruption might occur to boost the handful of ringed bird exchanges with the Continent. That said, the evidence from mainland European ringing schemes indicates that the

once migratory or partial migratory tit populations are showing substantially lesser movements than in previous decades, perhaps because more winter food is available or because winters have become milder.

Great Tit – Tommy Holden

Just as routine a visitor to garden bird feeders as these two tits is the Greenfinch. Those breeding in Britain and Ireland are best described as largely sedentary but with some occasional partial migrants. About three quarters of our birds featuring in ring-recoveries remain within 20 km of their place of ringing, the remainder showing movements apparently random in both distance and direction. Birds on the feeders during the winter day may gather to roost communally, often 5 km or more from their feeding sites. Ringing provides evidence of regular cross-Channel exchanges between the south and southeast of England and the immediately adjacent Continent, but so far no Irish-ringed bird has travelled overseas other than to Britain. The pattern is different in east and northeast Britain, where each autumn and winter longer-haul exchanges take place as Greenfinches leave Norway to overwinter in Britain.

The Chaffinch may not be so agile on feeders as the Greenfinch but is just as familiar as a regular garden bird, winter and summer alike. British and Irish breeding birds are sedentary year-round, with around 90% of ring-recoveries within 5 km of the place of ringing and the remainder (mostly young birds) almost all within 20 km. However, it is estimated that our Chaffinch population doubles in winter with the autumn arrival of immigrants, mostly from Norway and Sweden, but with some from Finland and as far away as Russia. Chaffinches migrate by day and can be seen doing so almost anywhere, but most noticeably along the east and particularly southeast coast. A sufficient number have been ringed for the recoveries to reveal that they have an unusual 'hooked' migration route. Looking for the shortest practicable sea crossing to ease their journey, they head south or even south-southeast out of southern Scandinavia, then veer southwest to cross the Channel from The Netherlands, Belgium and France. Once across the water, migrating parties disperse north and west to Scotland, Wales and Ireland. There is evidence that some – maybe many – adult migrants return to the same locality in successive winters.

Chaffinch

Interestingly, the recoveries indicate that females travel further than males, as they do in a wide range of birds. The theory is that males stay closer to 'home' as they need to be there earlier in spring than the females to set up their territory for the oncoming season. It may also be that by doing this they get better clues about weather patterns that could influence the start of the season. The specific name for the Chaffinch, *coelebs*, is derived from the Latin for bachelor, as in 'celibate',

and reflects the apparent winter abundance of males compared with females in Sweden, as noted by Linnaeus when he named the Chaffinch in 1758.

The Brambling is certainly not such a routine garden bird as the Chaffinch, its near relative. On its Scandinavian breeding grounds the male Brambling, in orange and black, is a striking and memorable sight but, even in winter camouflage plumage, close inspection through binoculars reveals a most attractive bird. Only a small handful of Bramblings have ever attempted to breed in Britain, so our sightings are almost entirely of migrant winter visitors. Numbers vary greatly from year to year, and several years may pass in many places during which Bramblings are something of a rarity. The reason for this is that their favoured winter food is beechmast, the nutritious nut-like seeds of the Beech tree. With its liking for chalk or limestone soils, the Beech is one of the less widespread of our native trees, and it is notoriously variable in the quantity of seed it sets, so the seed food provided in gardens performs a valuable service. We can only envy those birdwatchers in Scandinavia who see Bramblings in their breeding plumage, or those elsewhere in Europe who may encounter huge Brambling flocks in winter, containing it is estimated, hundreds of thousands of birds. An amazing spectacle it must be, and amongst the largest gatherings of finches on record.

The migration pattern of the Brambling is very different from that of the Chaffinch. At first sight the picture that ring-recoveries give is a confused one, but examined more closely it becomes clearer. Bramblings arriving in Britain in autumn come from breeding grounds to the northeast in Scandinavia and Finland. Unlike the day-migrating Chaffinch, they travel by night and, rather than heading for the narrows of the Channel, cross the North Sea on a broad front stretching from the Shetlands to Kent. The confused picture arises in subsequent winters, when ringed birds may return to Britain and Ireland, even to the same locality, or alternatively may winter somewhere else in Europe entirely. The suggestion is that some get caught up in mass movements in other directions, possibly triggered by a regional abundance of beechmast. As beechmast normally falls early in autumn, any snowfalls can disrupt feeding and it is then that we see sudden arrivals of Brambling in our gardens.

Brambling

On the grass

As a breeding bird, the Pied Wagtail is more or less confined to Britain and Ireland. In our subspecies *yarrellii*, the male is distinctively black and white, whereas the Continental subspecies *alba* (the White Wagtail) is white and pale grey, with fewer black markings. Many Pied Wagtails are genuine migrants on a medium-haul scale, with over 3,000 ring-recoveries providing a comprehensive picture. Young birds disperse widely after fledging, those from northern Britain and Ireland being quicker off the mark than those in the more leisured south. Dispersal seems to be in all directions during the first few months, but as winter approaches a marked southerly trend emerges. 'Northern' birds move southwards, many remaining in southern Britain, others passing on to the nearby Continent, while 'southern' birds move off south through eastern France to wintering grounds in the south of France, Spain and Portugal, and there are even three recoveries from north Africa. Adults are easily recognisable, and overall travel less far to their wintering grounds than their young. Most adults return to the same

breeding area in the following spring, and about two thirds of ringed nestlings are recovered in subsequent breeding seasons within 20 km of their birthplace. So the Pied Wagtails scampering about on the grass in your garden, or in the nearby park or playing fields are worth much more than just a passing glance; they may be seasoned travellers.

This White Wagtail, wearing a Belgian ring, was recaught in Lincolnshire. It is in active wing moult, with new feathers in the middle of the wing. You can see why birds need to moult; just look at the worn outer flight feather! – Dawn Balmer

Continental White Wagtails are long-haul migrants. Many pass through Britain and Ireland early each spring and in the autumn, on migration to and from their wintering grounds in southern Europe and northern Africa. White Wagtails are easily identified from Pied in spring, but in autumn separating the two can be a problem, more easily resolved when the wagtails are in ringers' hands. It is thought that these migrants are, almost exclusively, the breeding populations from Greenland, Iceland and the Faeroes. Ring-recoveries support this view, in that not only are there numerous reports of Icelandic-ringed birds in Britain and Ireland, but results from the Swedish ringing scheme indicate that their birds take a southeasterly track in autumn, with no evidence of any crossing the North Sea.

Blackbird

*Blackbird –
Tommy Holden*

Not only one of our most widespread and probably most numerous birds, the Blackbird must be one of the most familiar in our gardens. Many of those breeding in Britain and Ireland are sedentary, moving little from the gardens in which they have established territories. Particularly in the north, some may be short-haul migrants moving south, or more often west or southwest – to Ireland – as winter approaches and food becomes scarce. For Blackbirds overall, though, the position is far more dynamic. Visual observations, backed up by ring-recoveries (there are over 50,000 to draw on) show that vast numbers of Blackbirds on the Continent are long-haul migrants, moving southwestwards in autumn towards Britain and Ireland. Over 40% of these recoveries originate in Scandinavia and another 30% plus in Denmark and Germany. The remainder are short-haul migrants from the adjacent Continent. Some of these migrants remain with us through the winter, augmenting our resident populations in gardens, woods and on farmland. Others, after varying lengths of stay, move on southwards to overwinter in southern France and the Iberian Peninsula.

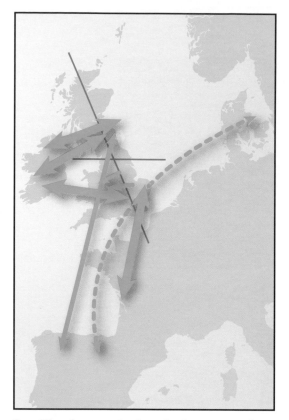

Song Thrush recoveries from the four sectors of Britain and Ireland

In most years, distant recoveries are not numerous, but the west and south exodus (and the difference between birds from northern and western districts and those from the southeast) is dramatically increased during severe freezing weather. The Song Thrush and its similar-sized relative the Redwing are the smallest in body size of all the thrushes, and the least able to survive prolonged cold spells. It is some years since the last really hard winter affected most of Britain, but the memories of Song Thrushes exiting in droves west and south from Britain remain, as do images of those eventually too weak to escape becoming tamer and more ravenous in gardens, all too frequently succumbing to the cold, starvation or predators.

The mobsters

Familiar to us all, the Starlings in our gardens are iridescent favourites for some, anathema to others as the 'bully boys' of the bird table. The Starlings breeding under our eaves or in any suitable holes nearby are with us year-round, and their offspring disperse only over very short distances, gathering in noisy mobs sometimes to wreak havoc on any available fruit crops. From late summer onwards, in gardens, parks, playing fields and meadows, our birds are augmented by migrants from overseas, all of them spending a great deal of time usefully probing for and consuming Crane-fly larvae (gardeners' leatherjackets) that would otherwise be damaging plant roots, sometimes severely. These winter visitors often come in huge numbers, originating from much of northern Europe including

Two species of thrush can be seen feeding on lawns and in parks. The larger Mistle Thrush is mainly sedentary, although some northern British birds do move south in the autumn. Most Song Thrushes are sedentary but recoveries show winter movements away from breeding areas in Wales, Scotland and western and northern England, mostly towards the west or southwest with only a few movements into France and Iberia. In contrast, from southeast England, the large movement is south into France and Iberia, with rather fewer movements west into the Cornish peninsula, Wales and southernmost Ireland. There is also recovery evidence, though nowhere near as much as for the Blackbird (or the Redwing and Fieldfare, Chapter 5), that we receive some winter migrants from Scandinavia, the Baltic States and the Low Countries. As for the Blackbird, some of these may pass through Britain on their way south into France and beyond.

Starling – Richard Vaughan

Collared Dove

Collared Dove – Tommy Holden

Like it or loathe it, the Collared Dove has an astonishing record of success and is evidently here to stay. It is also difficult to categorise in the context of this book, as those that colonised Britain in the early 1950s, and Ireland a few years later, were certainly westwardly mobile – probably most aptly described as eruptive.

The first colonists arrived in Lincolnshire in 1952, following a population spread (almost a tidal wave!) across Europe from the Balkans at an unprecedented pace of almost 50 km per year. Breeding took place in Norfolk in 1955 and in Kent in 1956, and by 1959 a couple of pairs had bred in Ireland, one as far west as Galway City. Rapid

infilling and successful consolidation followed, to reach today's almost universal levels of abundance. Recoveries of ringed birds tell us that the average movement in the 1960s and 1970s was around 6 km, compared with less than 1 km in the 1980s and 1990s, although there are a handful of longer-distance journeys, including exchanges in both directions with the near Continent. Such as it is, dispersal is in all directions but with a slight northwesterly preponderance.

The Collared Dove enigma is threefold; the first, what triggered and then maintained the original and unusually vigorous range extension westward? The second, what caused the 'settlers' to settle and switch to the sedentary lifestyle? The third, if 'nature abhors a vacuum' why have no other birds capitalised on the rich pickings favoured by the Collared Doves. With hindsight, Collared Doves do appear well suited to a variety of situations; they associate effectively with humans, even damagingly if you would rather feed your chickens in their run than the local Collared Doves, they are adaptable in their choice of habitat and they are recorded as breeding in every month of the year.

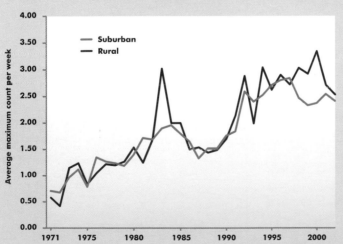

Increasing counts of Collared Doves – BTO Garden Bird Feeding Survey

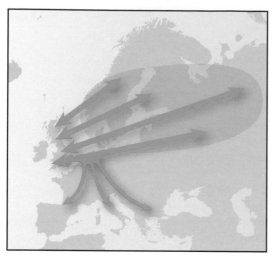

Starling

Scandinavia, the Baltic States, the Low Countries, Germany, Poland and Russia, east to Moscow and beyond.

Though the flocks we see today may seem large, and spectacular to watch as they twist and turn in flight in perfect synchrony, the last half century has seen very substantial but unexplained declines in both breeding and wintering numbers. Time was when the skies over town and city centres would literally darken as tens, or often hundreds of thousands of Starlings wheeled in dense flocks in aerobatic displays before plunging noisily to roost on building ledges and windowsills. The collective noun for Starlings is a 'murmuration' – entirely appropriate (if a little low key) for these gigantic gatherings. Lucky are they who have had, or in some places still have, this dusk experience to relish.

Summer comes

Late arrivals on the urban spring scene they may be, but somehow the season is not properly under way until the Swifts have arrived. In the past, they were known as Devil Birds in many parts of Britain and Ireland, though it is difficult to find a good explanation of why; perhaps it was because of the way gangs of these all-black birds hurtle around homesteads at breakneck pace, screaming as they go. Whatever, Swifts for

most of us do have a compelling attraction because undeniably they *are* rather special.

Of all our birds, Swifts have by far the most aerial life style. Familiar for their long slender sickle-shaped wings and flickering flight, at close range through binoculars the superb streamlining of the torpedo-shaped body can be seen, with large eyes inset within contour feathers as effectively as a modern sports car headlights. For much of the year, most Swifts are on the wing almost all the time, feeding, drinking, even mating and roosting, only coming to earth (in fact swooping into their nesting cavity) during the breeding season. Ancestrally, Swifts would have nested in tree cavities and crevices in cliffs. Their legs and feet, though powerful and with extremely sharp claws, are tiny in comparison to their body size and of little assistance at take-off, other than to pull the Swift to its nest entrance, from which it must be able to drop in free-fall until flight speed is reached. Returning, the nest hole must allow an

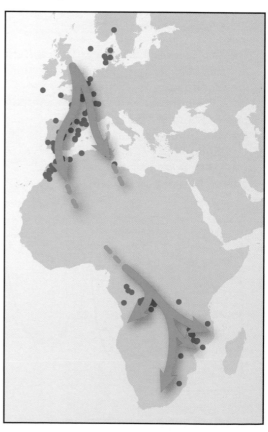

Swift

upward swooping approach and, once inside, the Swifts can scrabble across to their nest.

The outwardly tiny beak is all that is visible of a huge mouth. Much as basking sharks have huge mouths to sweep in vast quantities of minute marine plankton, so the gape of the Swift collects small flying insects like aphids, accumulating a compressed food ball the size of a marble to take back to the nestlings. In the early days of studies of bird movements using radar, a stunning account of the evening movements of London's Swifts was filmed using time-lapse photography. In late afternoon, the radar echoes showed low-key movements of Swifts apparently at random over Greater London. As dusk approached, echoes increased in quantity as more Swifts left their nests. Soon, the entire mass headed off northeastward out over the North Sea off Lincolnshire and Norfolk, gathering at a clearly visible line marking the approach of a cold weather front from the north. That cold front was sweeping before it masses of small flying insects, concentrating them as a broom concentrates dust. In some way the Swifts had sensed and interpreted what was going on and moved in rapidly to benefit from the food bonanza. Having fed to the full, the radar echoes recorded the Swifts returning later in the evening to London, and the echoes diminished as birds took food to their nest holes. Not all the echoes vanished however, as those birds roosting on the wing high over the city remained on screen.

With their dependence on flying insect food, Swifts are influenced by the weather more than any other of our birds, and both adults and young have evolved strategies to minimise the impact of bad weather reducing food supplies. Visual and radar observations, and some ring-recoveries, indicate that adult Swifts move away as bad weather threatens. The suggestion is that they head into wind, as by doing so they skirt round the depression causing the bad weather, and reach fine conditions and good feeding quickly. The evidence is that they may travel as much as 2,000 km from their nests in doing this, and that their absences may be brief or be as long several days. It is easy to understand this

survival strategy for adults, but what of their young, left with no food supply and without the essential warmth provided by a brooding parent? A few hours without food and parental care would be lethal for some small bird nestlings but young Swifts slip into a torpor, a mini-hibernation, when their temperature, heart beat and respiratory rate drop, minimising energy consumption. In this way they can survive days without food, rapidly resuming active life and growth with the return of warmer weather, their parents and the food they bring.

Ring-recoveries show that our Swifts winter in the southern half of Africa from the Congo River southeast to around the Tropic of Capricorn in Mozambique, Zimbabwe and the Republic of South Africa. The indications are that the route is through France and Iberia and into northwest Africa.

Like the Swift, the House Martin is today normally associated with buildings, although in the past nest sites must have included cliff and cave overhangs and perhaps also large tree hollows with overhangs for the attachment of their characteristic mud nests. House Martins have a wide popularity, not least as urban harbingers of spring but also because they are a delight to watch, as they gather mud pellets for their nests, standing on tiptoes beside muddy puddles exposing (but keeping brilliantly white) their feathered legs and toes. As autumn approaches they are the surest indicators that winter is almost upon us, as they gather on wires or rooftops, soaking up the last bit of warm sun before departing southward.

Over 170,000 Swifts have been ringed, producing 3,000 or more recoveries and a fair picture of their route and wintering grounds. So it is more than a little surprising that, of around 300,000 ringed House Martins, only just over 1,000 have been recovered. Of these, 90% of these are within Britain and Ireland and of little help in indicating possible migratory routes, with just one single recovery in Nigeria in the wintering area. Maybe our concept is wrong, of Swifts as the birds with an aura of mystery about them and of House

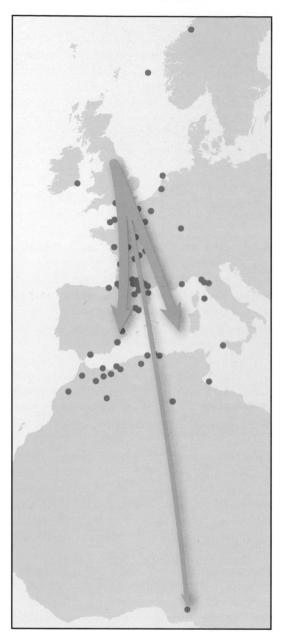

British and Irish House Martins

House Martins crossed the great desert every autumn, yet sub-Saharan *observations* were very scanty. Certainly there was no evidence of the massive roosts typical of Swallow and Sand Martin during the winter months. Today there are many more birdwatchers than prior to 1972, penetrating far further into the African hinterland, but 'scanty' remains the descriptor for House Martin observations. Intriguingly, gathering together all the recoveries available from other European ringing schemes does produce a better indication of where some House Martins are, but fails to resolve the puzzle of how so conspicuous a bird could 'disappear' into its winter quarters.

Interestingly, of the three trans-Saharan migrants most closely associated with built-up areas, parks and gardens, two often vie to be

Martins as the familiar, even friendly, nester under our eaves. It is the House Martins that are the enigma.

Birdwatchers in sub-Saharan Africa see House Martins only rarely, so are unable to throw much light on the House Martin wintering areas. Reg Moreau, writing about trans-Saharan migrants in 1972 after a lifetime in Africa, calculated from estimates of breeding numbers in Eurasia that some 90 million

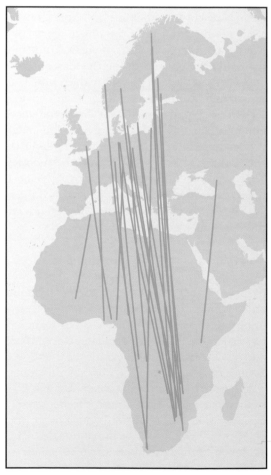

Trans-Saharan ring recoveries of House Martins (Source Hill 1997, by permission of Safring News)

the latest arrivals – Swift and Spotted Flycatcher, both often not appearing until mid-May. Despite their habit of using a favourite perch to sally forth and audibly snap up an insect, Spotted Flycatchers do not advertise their presence. Drab in plumage, brown above and lightly streaked fawn below, they do not attract attention either in plumage or their song, a brief pianissimo squeaky rattle. However, once your ear is attuned, the soft shrill 'zeet' or 'zee-chuck' makes location of the hunting bird much easier.

Though there are not large numbers of recoveries (about 400), they are quite revealing. Spotted Flycatchers are night migrants; in autumn a leisurely passage south starts in late July, with recoveries in southern France and widely scattered through Spain and Portugal. Visual observations in Africa suggest that some Spotted Flycatchers winter in the coastal west, while others pass on eastwards through Cameroon and Angola to winter in the south. The handful of recoveries from Britain and Ireland to Africa confirm trans-Saharan journeys. There is just a suggestion that in spring the route may be more directly north than in autumn. Our Spotted Flycatcher population has declined steeply in recent decades, although the causes are unclear. BTO population data suggest that the population in the 1970s was six times that of today; sad news about an attractive and confiding garden favourite.

... add a dash of excitement

So our gardens are far from dull so far as migration is concerned. True, there are some totally stay-at-home residents like the House Sparrow, and others that only occasionally migrate in a poorly-understood pattern like the Dunnock and Greenfinch. In several other garden species, our breeding birds are augmented, often substantially, by winter migrants from the Continent; one of the Starlings on the bird table could next summer be breeding somewhere near Moscow. But when it comes to summer visitors, our built-up areas and our homes and gardens support impressively long-haul travellers like the

Spotted Flycatcher – Tommy Holden

Swift and Spotted Flycatcher, and for lucky Londoners even a Black Redstart.

Everyday garden birds and their movements are fascinating enough, but if you add others like the Siskin, a conifer and birch-wood specialist that first 'discovered' gardens and peanut feeders in 1963, to that fascination you can add a touch of excitement as well as greater diversity. Small, elegant black, green and gold finches, they are just as agile on the feeders as tits. Siskins are now regular in many gardens in the second half of the winter and are almost better classed as garden birds than woodland ones. Their story is fascinating, if complex. Siskins feed basically on tree seeds, and the annual production of seed by trees is notoriously unpredictable. In consequence, Siskins are both adaptable and mobile (on a European scale). In addition, British and Irish (and some European) Siskin breeding populations have increased substantially in recent decades, perhaps due in part to the maturing of forests planted extensively to replenish timber stocks after the Second World War.

In Britain and Ireland, most Siskins breed in conifer forests and plantations, and some remain to winter in conifers and birch woodland, although their traditional winter

Siskin

chance sighting of a Peregrine or a Hobby as they migrate over. After dark, in spring and autumn many of us may hear all manner of waders, recognised by the contact calls they make as they fly over. Given a crisp, still, starlit autumn night, the thin 'tseep' of the first Redwings arriving for the winter is an annual landmark experience for many of us. Later in the winter, should the weather turn dramatically colder, some of these Redwings together with Fieldfares will leave the fields and seek shelter and food in urban areas, giving wonderful opportunities for close-up viewing of two of the most elegant members of the thrush family. Birdwatchers, especially in the East of Scotland, may even be lucky enough to receive visits from Scandinavian Waxwings, quick to strip the berries from Rowan trees, before moving onto other berrying shrubs.

location is feeding amongst the seed cones of riverside alders. Thus breeding birds may be sedentary or short-haul migrants, depending on food supplies and weather conditions, any movements being generally on a north-south axis and producing a handful of recoveries in the Low Countries, France and Iberia.

In winter, our resident population is augmented by Siskins which ring-recoveries indicate are Fennoscandian breeding birds. Numbers vary from year to year (depending on seed availability) but arrivals can be expected along our eastern coast from Shetland to Kent from mid-September. It seems that some Scandinavian birds move south to the Low Countries before crossing to England, boosting numbers arriving from East Anglia southwards. Some of these continental immigrants will move on towards Iberia, others on a more southeasterly or even easterly track towards the Mediterranean or Central Europe.

Even in town, never forget to look up at the sky overhead, or listen up after dark. What may be overflying could be as straightforward as a Cormorant commuting from one water to another (an almost unprecedented sight only 20 or 30 years ago) or a flock of Woodpigeons, moving west as cold weather approaches. Or you could be lucky enough to achieve a

In an increasing number of gardens a less-expected migrant is visiting feeding stations and enjoying the garden berry crop. Traditionally, Blackcaps are summer visitors to mature woodlands (Chapter 6) moving south in autumn to overwinter in southern Europe and northern Africa. Doubtless for many years the occasional Blackcap has spent the winter in Britain and Ireland, but over the last half-century overwintering numbers have increased steadily, and the vast majority of these spend their time in gardens. Ring-recovery evidence pinpoints the arrival of these overwintering birds shortly after the summer breeding population has departed southwards, and increasingly clearly demonstrates that they are migrants from breeding populations in west-central Europe which stay with us through the winter. Most will have departed for their breeding territories before our migrants return. Quite how or why the medium-haul east-west migratory route has developed almost at right angles to the traditional trend remains to be fully understood, but it may be that it allows an earlier establishment of better breeding territories and thus a more successful breeding season.

We may wonder with eager enthusiasm what the next development will be.

Farmland

Creating a monster?

The origins and development of farming

The urban landscape may demonstrate the most strident evidence of habitat modification due to human presence, but the farmland that surrounds those urban areas comes a close second. The negative visual impact of bricks, mortar and concrete sprawl may be greater than farmland scenery, but such are the consumer pressures driving modern farming that the pace of change in crops, cropping and land management may have a far greater impact on bird populations. It is tempting to assume, from a 21st Century viewpoint, that not only the dramatic nature of the changes but also the pace of change are features predominantly of the last half century. This is far from true. If we turned the clock back 2,000 years or more, we would have found much of Britain and Ireland forest-clad, but already some areas would have been cleared for grazing, and on lighter, more easily worked soils, rudimentary tillage and crop production would have become established. The precise timing and extent of these early clearances is very much a matter of debate.

The process of clearance produced, almost as an accidental consequence, a much more varied landscape than the original forests. Initially, the clearances would have been small and widely scattered, but by mediaeval times they had coalesced and produced, over much of Britain and Ireland, a network of copses and woodlands linked by a hedgerow system. The woodland/hedgerow/field matrix provides food and shelter, a communications network and a 'population reservoir' for all wildlife, plants and other animals, as well as birds, enabling them to exploit farmland to the full. In many ways, clearances of woodland for agriculture (and the subsequent planting of enclosure hedges) would have enhanced the status of many birds, by substantially increasing the equivalent of forest edges, providing more space for nesting territories and more extensive and diverse feeding and roosting habitats.

There can be no doubt about the efficiency of the technology available to the farmer today. Early agriculturalists would have used crude ploughs to produce a poor soil tilth, itself not an encouraging environment for a seed to germinate, establish and flourish. Pest, disease and weed control would have been rudimentary, and pest insects and weed seeds would themselves have augmented the food available to farmland birds. If more of a crop was needed to feed an expanding population, then more acres had to come under the plough to produce it. Ploughs themselves improved and draught oxen or heavy horses were used to pull them, allowing rather heavier (but more moisture-retentive) soils to come into cultivation. An interesting calculation has been made with regard to these draught horses; when horse-power was in its heyday in Victorian England, an estimated five million horses were working the land, pulling carts and carriages or carrying their riders about their business. On average, each horse needed five acres through the year as grazing and to produce hay and oats – a startling total of 25 million acres (10 million hectares) just to keep horsepower on the hoof.

The advent of power and pesticides

In a series of agricultural revolutions from the 18th Century on, better crop and fodder plants were introduced, agronomic practices improved immeasurably with crop rotation, the use of dung as fertiliser, and ultimately a better understanding of crop needs and the development of synthetic fertilisers. Pest and disease control lagged behind until the late 19th and early 20th Centuries, when both organic and inorganic chemicals were developed as insecticides. Some of these were far from benign; lead arsenate for example was an effective insecticide but eliminated both beneficial and pest species. Many pesticides were hazardous to wildlife in general, as well as toxic to the farm workers applying them, and weed control was still the province of farm workers using hoes.

At the end of the 19th Century steam power was increasingly developed, although too cumbersome for many farm tasks, other than powering threshing machines. With the advent of internal combustion engines, a major transformation took place. Lightweight, powerful and relatively agile tractors were swiftly adapted to almost every farm task that could be mechanised and a huge range of implements appeared, tractor-mounted and soon to be power-driven. The range extended from ploughs and harrows, through cultivators and rotavators, to planting and above all harvesting machines. After the Second World War came the combine harvester, and that particular agricultural revolution continues to this day, involving an ever-widening range of seeds from combinable crops of many types. So efficient are combines in collecting the vast majority of seeds harvested, particularly in comparison with earlier reaping and threshing machines, that little spillage remains to benefit wildlife.

... and pollution

Several generations of pesticides arose as 'by-products' of the war. DDT seemed the most benign of these, showing little toxicity other than to its target pests. Only after more than a decade did its sinister aspects become evident. Slowly but inexorably, residues of DDT and its breakdown products had been accumulating in fatty tissues. These residues caused some reproductive problems in their own right, but also altered both physiological and behavioural processes, particularly in predators at the top of food chains. In consuming numerous prey items, each with its own residue content, the top predators by accumulating these chemicals suffered severely, the classic examples in Britain and Ireland being the Peregrine and Sparrowhawk. Elegant research work by Derek Ratcliffe and Ian Newton, respectively, linked with precision both behavioural problems and a marked thinning of the eggshells (with subsequent clutch failure) to the use of DDT and related organochlorine pesticides. The long-running Nest Record Scheme, together with special surveys organised by the BTO, added more weight to the argument and resulted in these pesticides being removed from the Approved List.

The speed with which pests develop resistance to pesticides is surprising, with some products having a working life span of only a few years. Coupled with the high costs of novel active ingredients, far stricter operator and environmental safety assessments before approval, the development of pest and disease

Sparrowhawk – Tommy Holden

resistant varieties, and the adoption of spray only when and where absolutely necessary regimes (in contrast to the old spray routinely as a precautionary measure) have greatly reduced the hazards to farmland birds. Most importantly, these factors have combined to accelerate the introduction of biological control strategies, in a range of crops, where naturally-occurring predators or diseases are encouraged and do the work of the pesticides effectively and with no pollution.

One major feature remains; the control of weeds, those wildflowers growing in the wrong place! Through most of the history of farming, weed control has been back-breaking manual labour, but the last half century has seen the development of a series of herbicides, which without doubt have enhanced productivity and helped keep food prices low. But this is only one side of the story; environmental problems do not simply remain, they are increasing. The weeds produced food for other wildlife, in the form of leaves, shoots, flowers (and nectar) and seeds. Over three or four decades, the reduction in this weed-based food supply has been substantial, possibly enormous. Many farmland birds have suffered, and continue to suffer but, as with pesticides, more rational approaches to herbicide chemistry and use are increasingly apparent, driven by the joint concerns of cost, efficacy and environmental protection.

The role of the consumer

Throughout the history of farming, the consumer has inevitably played a major role. Over 2,000 years or more, there has been a steady increase in the human populations of Britain and Ireland, most marked perhaps over the last two centuries, but that steady increase masks substantial fluctuations over the millennia, due primarily to disease or to war. The first half of the 20th Century saw two World Wars, each with massive loss of life. Consumer-led recovery from the low point immediately after the 1939-45 conflict was the trigger for agricultural intensification on a scale not seen before, and today we see the results of a booming farm economy that has outstripped demand.

Today's consumers are far more sophisticated than those in the past and, because of the globalisation of trade and food supply, have access to a wider variety of foods than ever before. On the one hand, sophistication has brought with it environmental awareness, consumer pressures against pollution and the growth of the organic movement, all very positive. But on the other, global trading and widening consumer tastes and desires have brought under cultivation (with consequent heavy demands on water supplies) huge areas of largely unspoilt land in countries where labour is cheap and where environmental concern is minimal. This includes detrimental impacts on parts of Africa which are the winter destination of some of our migrant birds. Accompanying this overseas agricultural intensification are air-miles of a less desirable sort, popularly known as 'food miles', a term which better embraces the energy consumption of the various types of transport that are used to bring these imported food products, and even luxury flowers, to our shores but leaves ill-defined the additional atmospheric pollution caused.

Farmland is one of the most complex and dynamic of our habitats. Recently, the BTO's Common Birds Census has revealed a great deal about which birds (sedentary and seasonal migrants) are in decline (or not) and tells us much about the magnitude of those declines. The range of birds involved is broad, and some of the declines are disturbing, even worryingly severe, a few dangerously so. Despite this, and alert to the problems, today's farmed countryside continues to provide for us a rich array of birds, including some fascinating migrants, generally readily accessible, easily seen and there to enjoy.

Farmland birds

As in urban areas, farmland has a basic cast of characters present year-round. This includes those that are also urban stalwarts, like Carrion Crow, Magpie and House Sparrow, all sedentary, with an average movement between place of ringing and recovery of 10 km or less. More characteristic farmland birds like the Stock Dove, Barn Owl, Little Owl,

Buzzard and Jackdaw show similarly tiny average movements as adults, although dispersing young after the breeding season may be recovered up to 10 or 20 km from their place of birth. Similarly, smaller farmland species like Yellowhammer, Corn Bunting, Bullfinch and Tree Sparrow, together with game birds (partridges and Pheasant), move only very short distances, if at all.

Three species, absolutely typical of farmland walks, are more difficult to position as sedentary or migratory. The gregarious Woodpigeon is often a problem to farmers because of its appetite for newly-emerged oil-seed rape seedlings, and is sometimes so numerous that in severe weather its attacks on fields of brassica crops can be devastating. British and Irish breeding Woodpigeons are generally sedentary, although the young may disperse on average 30 km in late summer. As winter approaches, the ring-recovery information is strangely at odds with visual observations, especially along the east coast of England. Here, regular autumn sightings of Woodpigeons on the move southwards or westwards may involve tens of thousands of birds. Ring-recovery data provide only a handful of birds of Continental origin, and of more than 2,500 recoveries of British-ringed birds, only 29 have been reported from overseas, all but one in France and the other in Germany. Maybe the Woodpigeons seen on the move are from the Continent, where the Woodpigeon is a medium- to long-haul migrant, but ring-recoveries are lacking to back this up.

Second, the Skylark. Although almost 50,000 have been ringed, only just over 200 Skylarks have been recovered. This may in part be because around one third have been ringed as nestlings (with a high pre- and post-fledging mortality) and in part because dead Skylarks are well-camouflaged and thus inconspicuous. The Skylarks we see overhead in bouncy hovering flight seem similarly fluttery when on the move. Southward movements can be seen during autumn in many areas, involving daily counts of sometimes hundreds, occasionally thousands. It may well be that these are northerly British and Irish populations behaving as partial migrants, augmented particularly in eastern Britain by continental birds passing through from Scandinavia and the Low Countries, on their way to wintering grounds in France, Spain and Portugal. Albeit small in number, recoveries of Skylarks ringed overseas and recovered in Britain and Ireland support this. Such British recoveries as there are, largely come from birds ringed in England and Wales, and two-thirds of them fall within 10 km of the place of ringing, so the more southerly English and Welsh Skylarks may be sedentary ones.

Third, the Rook. Rooks are widespread and familiar as feeding groups striding across fields and meadows, probing for insect food, and for their noisy aerobatic displays over nesting colonies. Ringed British and Irish breeding birds are recovered on average around 6 km from where they were ringed, most moving far shorter distances. As is so often the case, young birds disperse rather more widely, with an average recovery distance more than double that of adults. Northern birds, both adult and young, tend to move slightly further than southern ones. Even this is less than the observed distances travelled each day by some colour-marked Rooks from their communal roosts to favoured feeding areas. So most of the Rooks we see while birdwatching in farmland are probably going about their daily business, primarily getting enough to eat. But maybe not all; two British-ringed Rooks have ventured abroad, one from Scotland to Norway, the other from southern England to France. In addition, there are over 60 recoveries in Britain in winter of Rooks ringed in the Low Countries, Germany and the Baltic States. So, some migration may take place, although the indications from Continental ringing schemes are that this may be on a diminishing scale.

Winter geese

Like Rooks, Pink-footed Geese are noisy and gregarious, and their largest flocks are most typical of lowland Scotland, northern England and East Anglia. There can be no doubting their status; autumn arrivals, flying high in serried ranks of staggered (and often ragged)

V-formations are amongst the most visible and audible manifestations of migration in action. And wonderfully evocative of wildness it all is.

Pinkfeet are characteristic of both inland and coastal open farmland, favouring stubble fields on arrival and later supplementing spilt grain with carrots, potatoes and turnips as well as close-cropped grass. In Norfolk, the major mid-winter food source is the remains of the sugar beet harvest, a crop not available to them elsewhere. Usually there will be large freshwaters nearby – lochs, lakes and the like – where the geese gather to roost overnight in safety on the water, or they may flight out to the security offered by the local estuary. There are few more exciting sights in all birdwatching than, dawn or dusk, geese flighting between field and roost. The first arrivals reach north Scotland early in September and numbers continue to build up until mid-October. Flocks may move around, due to vagaries in food supply or weather, and any tendency to drift southwards is accentuated as they escape from snow-covered fields.

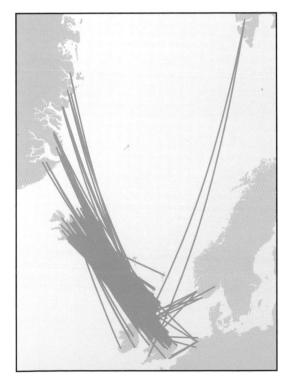

Pink-footed Goose

Pioneering work by Sir Peter Scott and Hugh Boyd of the (then) Wildfowl Trust established that there were two populations of Pinkfeet; one (with about three quarters of the world population) breeds in Iceland and Greenland, the other in Svalbard. Our wintering migrants come mainly from the former, with predominantly Icelandic birds involved, dramatically illustrated by ring-recoveries, of which there are plenty, as the Pinkfoot is a popular quarry species for wildfowlers. The much smaller Svalbard population migrates through Norway to winter in the Netherlands, and the handful of ring-recoveries demonstrates the small chance of Svalbard birds occurring in Britain and Ireland. We must rest content with hosting the great majority of the world population.

Though not perhaps enjoying the same popular appreciation as the geese, the Common Gull also favours good grazing land for its migratory and winter feeding grounds, although their food is the grassland invertebrate population (worms and the like) not the grass itself. Common Gulls breed in Scotland, from Shetland southwards, and in northern and western Ireland, selecting offshore islands or upland lochs or bogs for their nesting colonies. Ring-recoveries indicate that our breeding birds vacate the high ground as winter approaches. Most adults do not disperse far to their winter feeding fields, although a couple have migrated as far as southwestern Europe. Immatures, as is often the case, disperse more widely but most still remain in Britain and Ireland, with a handful of recoveries in France and Iberia.

The winter distribution of the Common Gull (not aptly named as most birdwatchers would consider it noteworthy rather than ubiquitous) covers Britain and Ireland, with absences only from upland areas in Scotland and Wales. So where do these graceful gulls that we see in autumn, winter and spring come from? Ring-recoveries provide a picture of their origins from colonies across much of northern Europe, stretching from northern Scandinavia as far east as marshland beyond Moscow. Their route is west or southwest in autumn, and most of these migrants have

Greylag Goose

Greylag Geese, awaiting release, having been ringed – Mark Collier

The winter distribution of the Greylag Goose, with its familiar farmyard honking calls shows a concentration in the Hebrides and eastern and southern Scotland, and then a broad band at lower density through eastern England to the south coast. Ring-recoveries provide a clear indication of both the origins and the destinations of the majority of genuinely wild migrant Greylags. The vast majority of these breed in Iceland and arrive on their Scottish farmland wintering grounds in early autumn. Though not as numerous as Pinkfeet, they often share the same stubble or root-crop fields early in the winter, turning to good grazing grassland later in the season. Half a century ago this would have come as a surprise, as Greylags then favoured the roots of fresh-marsh or estuary plants, as they still do on the Continent. There is an increasing wild British breeding population of Greylag Geese, mostly in northern Scotland and the Hebrides, and these seem, perhaps strangely, to be sedentary. The same race of Greylags also breeds in Scandinavia and around the Baltic but these are migratory, and a handful of recoveries confirm that some

occasionally migrate to Britain to overwinter. The situation over much of England is further confused due to the increasing numbers of introduced birds, released by wildfowlers, and escapees from wildfowl collections. Most of the Greylags to be seen in the south are likely to be part of this largely sedentary feral population rather than migrants from elsewhere, though tantalisingly there are a few Scandinavian ring-recoveries to indicate that some may be migrants from further afield.

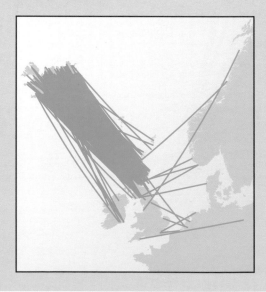

Britain and Ireland as their target wintering area, rather than as a staging post, as there are few indications of any onward passage to France or Iberia.

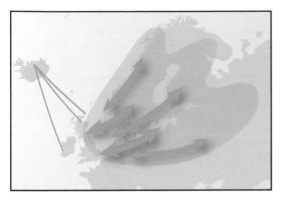

Common Gull

Lapwings enjoy a wide popularity among birdwatchers. They are the most widespread wader in Britain and Ireland, winter and summer, not least because they favour open farmland and moorland. In the air, strikingly visible because of their black and white flopping flight, Lapwing are equally familiar because of their plaintive 'pee-wit' calls. Against plough or muddy grassland, a landing flock seems simply to vanish, melting into the background. Breeding Lapwings are at greatest densities in the north and northeast, lowest in the west, from Scotland, through Ireland and Wales to the Cornish peninsular. In winter the situation changes, with greater numbers in Ireland and southwest, southern and eastern England, and a lack of birds on high ground in Scotland and Wales.

Lapwing movements revealed by ring-recoveries are complex. British and Irish breeding Lapwing are partial migrants, with many remaining through the winter on suitable (and often traditional) fields close to their breeding grounds. Others migrate, sometimes for considerable distances. From the north and northwest of Britain, the autumn trend is for movement westward to Ireland, with some recoveries in France and Iberia. From the southeastern sector, roughly south of a line from the Humber to the Severn, those Lapwing that do migrate head south, primarily to the coasts of France and Iberia, where numbers build up from October to peak in January.

Most youngsters seem to return to their natal area to breed, but interestingly not all. Others have been recorded nesting in subsequent years in countries as geographically diverse as Iceland, the Faeroes, Portugal, Denmark, Norway, Sweden and Russia, as far east as 68°E, the same longitude as Pakistan! This is called 'abmigration' and in the case of the Lapwing, with its varied migratory patterns, may simply be a case of getting mixed up with, and attached to, the 'wrong' flock. It has been argued that abmigration increases gene-flow within a species, and in the case of the Lapwing may help explain the absence of subspecies in so widely distributed a bird.

Those Lapwing that remain in Britain and Ireland are joined from June onwards by migrants from the Continent, originating (recoveries show) in Fennoscandia, Denmark, Germany and the Low Countries. Peak immigration is not until October/November, but it is thought that the flocks we see are a mixture of our breeders and immigrants. Lapwings, feeding on soil invertebrates, are naturally sensitive to cold weather and frozen ground, and are swift to react and move west or south in freezing conditions. Lapwings are a delightful component of our landscape, sadly diminishing as breeding birds as mixed farming is replaced by intensively-managed grassland and winter cereals.

Farmland thrushes

Staying with fields (and adding orchards) in winter, what about our winter-visitor thrushes, smaller but no less attractive and interesting to most birdwatchers? Without doubt, some farmland Blackbirds are migrants from northern Europe, many here to stay for the winter, others onward bound. But just as the calls of the Pinkfeet and Greylags typify the onset of autumn in the north, so too do the slender *tseep* of Redwings overhead on a clear cold night, or the harsh *chack-chack* of Fieldfares in fields, hedges or orchards signify the change of season. Despite the implicit onset of colder weather, welcome they both are, for few would argue that they are amongst the most subtly beautiful of our birds.

Fieldfare

Fieldfare – Tommy Holden

Globally, Fieldfares have a huge distribution, breeding from Iceland and Britain in the west (although in very small numbers) across northern Europe to Siberia and Lake Baikal at around 120° E, with no defined subspecies. Also globally, they are amongst the topmost east-west passerine migrants, those from furthest east performing a round-trip migration to Europe each winter estimated at around 12,000 km! Our widespread, familiar and often numerous winter Fieldfares may not be quite in this league; ring-recoveries show clearly their origins in Scandinavia and Finland, with the majority coming from Norway.

During the early winter, some arrivals in eastern Britain will push on westwards to Ireland, others may continue southwards into France and Iberia, having used us as a staging post. What is particularly fascinating about Fieldfares is that while some (around 20%) return to the same area in Britain and Ireland in following winters, the remainder of those ringed in Britain and Ireland migrate to pastures new in subsequent winters. Evidence suggests that Norwegan birds are more likely to be more site-faithful within Britain and Ireland but that Swedish and Finnish birds are less so.

Recoveries come from across France and Iberia, but also (in some numbers) from the broad river valleys of northern Italy. Presumably the reverse is also true, that Fieldfares in southern Europe in one winter may well come to us in a subsequent one, though concrete ring-recovery evidence is lacking. An interesting winter migration strategy for a bird with such a huge breeding range.

Almost inevitably coupled with the Fieldfare as the thrush family heralds of oncoming winter, Redwings share much the same recovery pattern. Ring-recoveries give a clear indication of the breeding area of most of our winter migrant Redwings, lying in a broad belt across Fennoscandia and Russia almost to the Ural Mountains, a long way east in Russia for a passerine visitor. More than half of the ring-recoveries from the breeding season are from Finland and only 5% from Norway, so winter visitor Redwings originate further east than Fieldfares. We know nothing about the movements of the tiny (about 50 pairs) British and Irish breeding population.

Unlike the Fieldfare, which lacks races or subspecies, there is a distinct population of Redwings breeding in Iceland and the Faeroes, *coburni*, which could be seen on migration almost anywhere in Britain and Ireland. Experts with their 'eye in' can identify *coburni* in the field; it is darker, rather larger, and above all more boldly streaked on the breast than its Fennoscandian relatives, but ring-recoveries make the task a little easier. Icelandic-ringed Redwings pass through northwest Scotland and Ireland, where some winter alongside Fennoscandian birds and where the best chance of positive sightings lies, while others pass through Ireland *en route* to France and Spain, where many of the Fennoscandian population will also be. Considering this mixing, it is remarkable that Icelandic Redwings have

remained recognisably independent and have maintained their own migratory path despite sharing winter quarters – and migratory pathways – with the Fennoscandian stock. As with the Fieldfare, there is no saying where a Redwing in Britain and Ireland this winter will be next winter. Ring-recoveries show that Redwings ringed in Britain and Ireland may revisit next winter, or may be found almost anywhere in southern Europe from Greece and Cyprus and across to the east as far as the Caspian Sea.

Seed-eaters

The widespread and familiar migratory farmland finches, the Goldfinch, Linnet and Redpoll, are no less intriguing. Goldfinch and Linnet are classic examples of 'partial migrants', birds in which a variable proportion migrate each year, the remainder staying put in Britain and Ireland through the winter. There must be driving forces which encourage both migration and residency within species such as Linnet and Goldfinch, but working out how they operate is difficult. A popular suggestion is that the migratory tendency is in the genetic make-up of individual birds, but there is counter evidence that individuals may migrate south in one autumn but not in another. Whatever, it seems that when they do migrate, Goldfinches head generally south to southwest onto the Continent, not to any specific wintering area but halting when they find suitable feeding areas (Map: page 11).

Much the same can be said for Linnets. They too move south to southwest if and when they do migrate, but the ring-recoveries fall in a much narrower band than for Goldfinches. Puzzlingly, in most winters many Linnets remain in Scotland despite the weather, while the evidence points to most Irish Linnets choosing to escape from the milder Irish winter by migrating to France and Spain every year. There is also some evidence that we may see Scandinavian Linnets on the move, either to overwinter in Britain or, possibly more likely, as passage migrants drifted west by the wind from their normal southbound track (Map: page 11).

Redwing

Linnet – Tommy Holden

To suggest that the Redpoll is a complex bird is something of an understatement, as it has long been the subject of earnest debate amongst bird taxonomists. Our breeding Redpolls, the smallest of the group, are Lesser Redpolls *Carduelis cabaret*, recently made a species in their own right. Not easily distinguished by birdwatchers in the field, the slightly larger Common Redpoll from the adjacent Continent is *Carduelis flammea*, which has a race *rostrata* in Iceland and Greenland. More northerly still, and circumpolar in distribution, is the Arctic Redpoll *Carduelis hornemanni*, which is slightly larger and appreciably paler than our Lesser Redpoll and which occasionally occurs as a rare migrant or vagrant to Britain and Ireland, especially in the north. The Lesser Redpoll is a substantially scarcer bird than it was 30 years ago, when the breeding population was at a conspicuous peak. Quite what caused this slump is difficult to be sure of but without doubt increasing herbicide use and agricultural intensification will have played some part. One suggestion from ringing and visual records was that the migrants that left Britain and Ireland in autumn 1977, heading for the Continent, largely failed to return to breed in 1978, but the reason why remains uncertain. It has also been suggested that changes in the population structure of woodland trees, especially a reduction in the production of Birch seed, might also be involved. Running counter to this is the continuing scarcity of Redpolls where Birch still predominates and also where another

favoured food tree, Alder, has been widely planted as a windbreak. Sadly, the decline in numbers continues.

Ring-recoveries for Redpolls (Lesser and Common combined) show a far more southeasterly track than for Linnet and Goldfinch recoveries, with a heavy concentration in the Low Countries (particularly Belgium), with others across central and western France and on into north Italy. The apparent concentration in Belgium may be biased by recoveries from the 1960s and 1970s, when Redpolls were a popular and easily trapped target for local cage bird fanciers; this trade has mercifully largely ceased. Lesser Redpolls are best classed as eruptive, in that more of the population migrates, and also migrates further afield, in years of high population and low food supply. To cloud a confused picture still further, there is evidence that migrant Common Redpolls from Scandinavia may either winter in Britain or pass through on their migration south, and most winters there are sight records of the Greenland/Iceland form *rostrata* in north Scotland. In the light of the ongoing decline in Lesser Redpolls, there is an urgent need to find out a lot more about this intriguing bird and the factors influencing its breeding success and migratory habits.

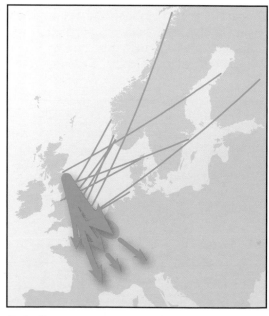

Redpoll

Summer migrants

Rather than start a look at farmland summer visitors with the audibly conspicuous Cuckoo, harbinger of spring and focus of a great deal of popular and media attention, a much smaller, less conspicuous bird, the Whitethroat, shows parallels with and extends the intriguing migration story of the Redpoll. For the first 70 years of the 20th Century, the Whitethroat was one of the most numerous of our summer visitors, and *the* bird of farmland hedgerows in summer over most of Britain and Ireland, the male conspicuous by fluttering up a few metres above the hedge, to parachute down producing its distinctive scratchy song. Suddenly in 1969, they were overtaken by a calamity. The BTO Common Birds Census results showed that a flourishing population, for some years on the increase, left as normal in autumn 1968 for wintering grounds in West Africa. Ring-recoveries show a southerly route through France and Spain into northwest Africa, then onwards (judged on a handful of recoveries and coupled with visual observations) over the Sahara to coastal west Africa.

The Whitethroat's winter habitat is a region of dry scrubland called the Sahel, which extends in a belt along the southern Sahara fringe most of the way across west Africa. Although the vegetation of the Sahel is drought-adapted, 1968 was several years into an annual series of droughts in the region, and by 1968/69 not only was the vegetation suffering, but so were local wildlife and domestic cattle, goats and donkeys, and of course the human population. Ravenous stock and distraught herdsmen eventually impoverished the vegetation to such a degree, it was reasoned, that the Whitethroat simply could not find enough food. The Sahel itself was steadily widening as arid scrub gave way to real desert. The northward journey of Whitethroats back to Britain and Ireland begins with a non-stop Saharan crossing. Unable to fatten – in effect to fuel-up for that journey – substantial numbers (in some areas 60-80%) of Whitethroats failed to make it back in spring 1969, the remainder presumably perishing in the desert.

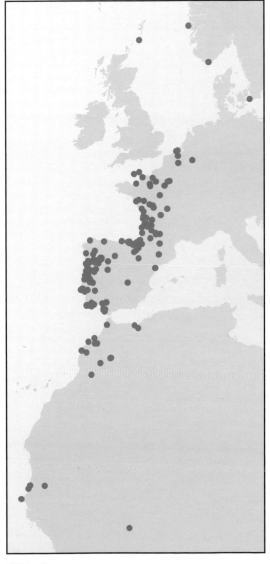

Whitethroat

Whitethroat – Tommy Holden

Today, Whitethroat numbers have recovered somewhat, but nowhere have they attained pre-crash levels. Conditions in the Sahel have not improved markedly and droughts are still commonplace. True, there are fewer mouths to feed amongst local populations and their stock – thus perhaps more for wildlife in general – but humans and domestic stock may recover more rapidly with overseas aid and technical assistance. So how have Whitethroats accomplished this recovery? At this stage we simply do not know.

Turtle Dove song pervades a hot summer afternoon in woodland clearings and along woodland margins like the scent of blossoms. Of all our farmland migrants, Turtle Doves have the most restricted breeding range, largely concentrated in the southeast quadrant of Britain. They also have perhaps even more problems to face on the journey than the others, as they are a popular quarry species with hunters (both trapping and shooting) along much of their migration route, even if protected in Britain and Ireland. The breeding population in Britain (and elsewhere in western Europe) has fallen substantially in recent years, most probably largely as a result of the increased use and effectiveness of weedkillers in arable crops. Turtle Doves love the seeds of short-lived weeds such as Fumitory, which happen also to be relatively easily controlled by herbicides. Other factors involved include hedgerow removal in their breeding areas and problems in their winter quarters in west Africa, due to frequent drought conditions and the cutting of the *Acacia* woodland, in which they roost, for fodder and fuel.

As a saddening by-product, the hunting pressures along the migrating journey of the Turtle Dove provide ring-recovery information which gives a reasonably accurate outline of their route and destination. As, outside Britain and Ireland, they are so widely hunted, it is unlikely that hunting pressure biases this perceived route materially, which can sometimes be the case. Most Turtle Doves leave Britain in August or September, having begun their moult once breeding is over, and suspended the process, mid-moult, to fly south. Their route takes them through France, across the west end of the Pyrenees and through Spain and Portugal to Morocco. It is thought that, although Turtle Doves migrate mostly by night, they are also often on the move by day. It has been suggested that day-flying Turtle Doves are most often juveniles and that these also tend to take coastal routes, sometimes in spectacular flocks both in Iberia and west Africa. From Morocco they head for winter quarters in Senegal and The Gambia, arriving in late September. Return migration begins in February and runs on into March, sometimes again involving spectacular flocks. Our birds pass back through Morocco in March to reach England in late April and early May. As with a number of long-haul

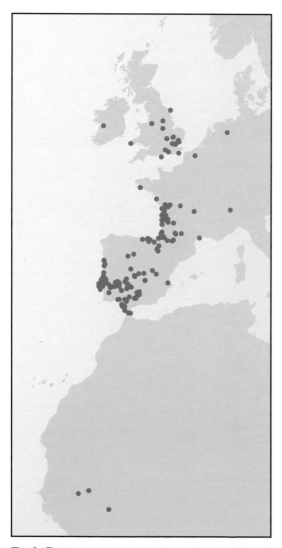

Turtle Dove

Lesser Whitethroat

Lesser Whitethroat – Tommy Holden

summer visitors), their first leg taking them to northern Italy. Ring-recoveries and calculations of flight range based on fat levels at departure points in UK agree; the Lesser Whitethroat fattens up less prior to departure than many autumn migrants. It is thought that birds refuel in northern Italy prior to a Mediterranean crossing from Italy or Greece into northeast Africa.

In spring, the picture becomes even more fascinating, with plenty of visual evidence of migration northwards up the Levant coast at the extreme east of the Mediterranean. Here Lesser Whitethroats are plentiful as spring migrants but relatively rare in autumn. Once beyond the Levant, a northwest course is set for Britain to complete what is known as a loop migration.

The Lesser Whitethroat has a dramatically different migration to other warblers, heading for a much less arid range of winter habitats in Egypt, Sudan, Chad and Ethiopia, where damp thorny scrub is favoured. Sadly there are no ring-recoveries to amplify visual observations, and reveal the precise wintering grounds of our birds, but the route there and back is becoming increasingly well defined. Current indications are that, in autumn, our Lesser Whitethroats depart southeast (not a direction taken by many of our

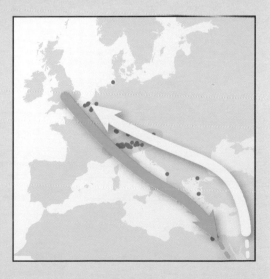

migrants, most adults return to within a kilometre or so of their last nesting area, and most yearlings seem to take up territories within 20-30 km of their birthplace.

Now to the Cuckoo, one bird that needs no introduction, and indeed even tells you its name. In habitat terms, Cuckoos might equally well feature in chapters on freshwaters (reed beds and Reed Warblers), woodland (Dunnocks) or moorland (Meadow Pipits) to name some of their major host species. On farmland it is primarily the Dunnock and to a lesser extent the Robin that play host to Cuckoo eggs. The Cuckoo is a nest parasite – a statement of the obvious maybe but a point of major relevance when it comes to migration. To cut a complex and fascinating story brutally short, adult female Cuckoos patrol their territories after their arrival in Britain and Ireland in April or early May, rather late in the spring to merit the 'harbinger of spring' accolade. Having located several host nests, the Cuckoo adds an egg to the complete or near complete clutch of each host, and removes one of the host eggs. In the majority of cases, the eggs she lays are excellent mimics in colour and markings of those of the host, with the Dunnock (which

lays unmarked bright blue eggs) as a striking and intriguing exception, perhaps indicating that this may be a comparatively recent addition to the host list. No matter, as many host Dunnocks accept the slightly larger usurper egg. The story continues with the precocious Cuckoo chick at a day or two old ejecting the remaining host eggs, or chicks if they have hatched, by the simple expedient of wriggling beneath them, arching its back and using its muscular legs and wings to tip them out over the nest rim. Having gained solo occupation of the nest, the young Cuckoo grows speedily and soon dwarfs its foster parents, who nevertheless feed it at a frantic pace, and will continue to do so for two weeks or more after fledging.

Meanwhile, what of the adults? Compared with most summer migrants, adult Cuckoos depart very early, while most of their young are still in their foster nests. By late June in some years, early July in others, they have started their return migration heading out on a southeasterly path similar to the Lesser Whitethroat. The first leg of their migration takes them to north Italy, where they may stay for some time, feeding up to fuel the next leg of their journey. At this point, ringing ceases to be of much assistance in locating just where our Cuckoos spend the winter, as ring-recoveries are (perhaps surprisingly) conspicuously absent from north Africa. It could be that Cuckoos in Italy put on sufficient fat to fuel the much longer-haul journey well into eastern Africa, maybe south of the Sahara. This is where African migration expert Reg Moreau considered the likely wintering area to be.

Cuckoo: note staging post in northern Italy

Back to the young. Leave aside the marvel that when they leave they already have, genetically, the knowledge of what hosts to seek when they return as adults next year (so that their eggs match their hosts', but how do they gain the knowledge of how to *find* their hosts' nests?), they set off on migration with no adult guidance, again simply on inherited 'information'. Tantalisingly, we do not know whether some or most make it all the way to winter quarters without encountering any adults who have previous experience of the journey. It may be that some adults tarry long enough feeding-up in northern Italy for at least some of the young to catch up, after which they might journey on together. Bird migration as a whole contains many amazing stories, but none so comprehensively wonder-making as this. Dwell on it next time you hear that familiar call.

Not quite so fascinating as the Cuckoo, the Yellow Wagtail is certainly more colourful in spring and differs in that ring-recoveries give a good indication of its entire migratory journey. Yellow Wagtails are largely confined to England and Wales as breeding birds, and are scarce in Scotland and Ireland. They are the westernmost race (*flavissima*) of a tight-knit group of races whose breeding range extends well east across Russia. All races feature a bright sulphur-yellow breast and belly, particularly conspicuous on males freshly arrived in spring, an olive-yellow back, and inevitably all have a constantly wagging, long white-edged black tail. Our birds have a yellowish green crown and yellow eyestripe, while those breeding on the west coast of the Continent have grey heads and cheeks, and a white eyestripe and chin. This is the Blue-headed Wagtail, which regularly occurs in eastern England during spring migration. In autumn, after moulting into winter plumage, the races are much more difficult to separate in the field.

Yellow Wagtails are birds of pastures, damp meadows and marshes, often associating with stock both here and in Africa in winter, where wild herbivores like antelope may also have Yellow Wagtails running around their feet catching the insects they disturb. They are among the earlier summer migrant arrivals, often in March, but surprisingly for such a conspicuous bird, often first draw attention by their distinctive tsweep calls. At the end of the breeding season some dispersal may take place but, by August, communal roosts, often in reedbeds, begin to gather before southward departure. Ring-recovery data suggest a south or southwesterly heading, and a migration in easy stages through France and Iberia, crossing into Morocco during September and reaching winter quarters around Senegal and The Gambia a few weeks later. The return trip is along a similar track, with departure from west Africa in February.

Wet pastures are particularly important habitats for many other migrant species, from the flag-fringed hay-fields of the Outer Hebrides, so vital to Corncrakes, to the wash-lands of East Anglia. Here, providing breeding habitat for Black-tailed Godwits and Ruff can benefit other spring arrivals from Africa, such as the rare Spotted Crake and Yellow Wagtails, as well as many resident birds.

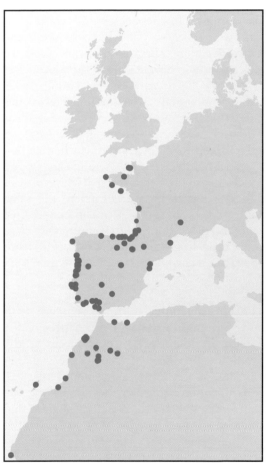

Yellow Wagtail

Last but certainly not least among the farmland migrants is the Swallow, a familiar bird in many urban and suburban settings as well as around farmsteads. Comparatively speaking, the Swallow is an easy-to-ring bird (well over the million mark ringed in Britain and Ireland) as its nests are usually accessible and communal roosts are frequent. Usefully, and unlike many other migrants, Swallows also winter in an area where bird ringers are active, and where again the habit of roosting communally in reedbeds allows big catches and good chances of recaptures of ringed birds. About half of Swallow ring-recoveries are of birds recaught by ringers, rather than being found dead.

With this comparative wealth of ring-recovery data, the route of this homely bird to its winter quarters in the Republic of South Africa can be plotted in some detail. Their route runs broadly south through France and Spain, occasionally further east, and then into northwest Africa. Though there are some recoveries along the west African coast, we pick up more recoveries along the south coast of Africa's 'bulge', the Gulf of Guinea, with visual observations as well as a few recoveries indicating that Swallows overfly the Sahara as a routine. Other recoveries follow from an evidently broad migration path heading towards South Africa, where Swallows are widely distributed in winter. Ring-recoveries indicate that many are faithful to the same winter roosts in South Africa in consecutive years and that adult Swallows return very close to their nesting sites, while most young fetch up within a few kilometres of where they were born.

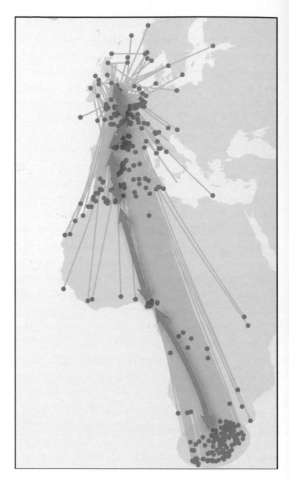

Swallow

The return journey starts in February, with birds arriving on the southern fringes of the Sahara in March. The next stage in the Swallow's prodigious journey, the Saharan crossing, is the most taxing and dangerous, with prevailing northerly winds making the going incredibly tough, even for a migrant that can feed on the wing. The survivors reach the north African coast, cross the Mediterranean on a broad front, and advance northwards across Europe almost like an incoming tide, reaching southern England mid-April, Scotland in early May, Finland mid-May and north of Norway by early June. The record of progress of Swallows and other migrants is now electronically available and can be logged daily. Your active participation, entering details of migrant arrivals and departures, is also both welcome and valuable. You can join in via the BTO website www.bto.org

This staggered northward progress, with almost two months spanning arrivals on territory in the south of France and towards the North Cape in Norway, opens an interesting debate on migration. French birds have ample time to raise three broods, while Scandinavian pairs probably manage only one, and that after the extra wear and tear of an additional 3,000 km or so on the migratory journey. It is tempting to ask if this can possibly be efficient. Why not stop and breed further south? What, if any, are the genetic differences between northern and southern breeders? Is this an evolutionary flexibility on the part of the Swallows that could, for example, be invaluable if global warming accelerates? As is so often the case with migration, a little knowledge simply opens the door for more questions to flood in!

Farmland birdwatching is within easy reach of most of us. The range of resident, partial migrant and migrant birds is wide, and there is plenty to see summer and winter alike. Over recent decades farmland birds have encountered many challenges; there has been a drastic decline in mixed farming and extensive acreages of major crops now dominate the landscape, together with set-aside fields. Oilseed rape has made a stridently colourful and smelly come-back, the gentler blue of flax has returned, but as linseed, grown for oil. Regimented lines of maize, great places for Swallows to roost, appear more and more frequently, and grazing land is now an uninterrupted 'improved' deep green sward. Cereal growing has largely shifted from spring to autumn sowing, so in many areas stubble fields over winter are a thing of the past.

Adaptations to farmland life are fascinating to observe and there is, in this diversity of birds and behaviour, ample demonstration both of the damage caused and of the resilience of bird populations in the face of striking changes in the patterns and practices of agriculture over the years. There is evidence from the BTO/CJ Garden BirdWatch scheme that farmland birds of more species are turning to our gardens, not least because of the amount of artificial food we provide, and are doing so earlier and earlier in the winter. And what of the future? How are changes in world trading agreements going to influence our farms? What is going to be the impact of the current and future rounds of discussions on Common Agricultural Policy reforms? If, as predicted, grants and subsidies are removed from supporting the production of major crops and livestock and redirected towards environmental targets and landscape improvements, are we about to see the start of a restoration of the fortunes of farmland birds? Will resident birds and the millions which join them from Africa each spring and from Scandinavia and Europe each autumn find life somewhat easier?

Woodland

Travellers among the trees

Even two thousand years ago (a very short time in bird population and evolution terms) much of our landscape would have been covered in extensive tracts of hardwood trees, with our only native conifer, the Scots Pine, similarly widespread on sandy or upland soils. Some historians argue that in Roman times those living in southern and eastern England would have looked out on a landscape not dramatically different from today in terms of the amount of land cleared for farming. Others feel that it may have been a millennium later before the need to feed a slowly increasing population and, later still, to provide exports and become a trading nation, made really significant inroads into the forest cover. Forest clearances were not, of course, solely to make space for farming. They provided the timber for domestic fuel, for furniture and housing, for ships and carts, and to fuel the first stages of the industrial revolution.

Today, this forest cover (variously estimated originally at 60-80% of the land surface) has been reduced to a very piecemeal 10% or less, despite recent deliberate emphasis on re-afforestation schemes. In addition, particularly in the case of conifers, much of the new planting is of alien species, introduced for their productivity and timber qualities from other parts of the world. Often these conifers are sited in areas that would once have supported deciduous trees. In Chapter 5 we

have seen how farmland birds in general have adapted to and exploited this forest clearance successfully, despite the fact that most seem originally to have been forest birds. So what of the forest birds themselves; how have they fared? What are their origins or destinations if they are with us for only part of the year?

Some areas of ancestral coniferous forest remain, notably the Caledonian pinewoods of the Spey Valley and other localities in the Highlands of Scotland. Within this living antique of a forest, under serious threat of extinction by the pressures to introduce commercially viable conifer plantations to replace it, widely-distributed woodland birds such as the Chaffinch flourish, as do conifer-preferring species such as the Coal Tit. Two species, however, make this their home – the Crested Tit and the Scottish Crossbill.

Nowhere are Crested Tits numerous, but with its stuttering trill of a call, conspicuous crest and bold black-and-white face pattern, the Crested Tit is not easily overlooked where it is present. Of all the tits, it seems the best adapted to life in coniferous woods, even being capable (as a normal routine) of excavating its own nest hole. In continental Europe it is widely distributed in a variety of conifer types stretching from the Mediterranean coasts north to Fennoscandia. Throughout their range, Crested Tits are extremely sedentary, which explains why the species is still restricted to its ancestral Scottish forests, to which it has become closely adapted over the ages. The general lack of mobility also explains its failure to colonise the 'new' conifer forests of England from sites across the Channel.

The Scottish Crossbill is another example of close adaptation to a particular tree species, not just habitat type. In the Northern Hemisphere, the woody cones of the various native conifers – larch, spruce and pine – are exploited by a very specialised family of birds capable of extracting the seeds from between the rigid wooden 'flakes' of the cones. In Scandinavia and to the east, it is the Two-barred Crossbill that specialises in the small, relatively flexible cones of the larch and the Common Crossbill that tackles the cones of spruce, which are rather larger and tougher. In keeping with the job they have to do, the beaks of these two birds differ in size and thus strength, though retaining the same flattened, cross-tipped profile that allows them to snip out the seeds from the cones with ease and which gives the family its name. Largest of all is the Parrot Crossbill, capable of dealing with the massive cones of European pines, but only slightly smaller is the Scottish Crossbill, adapted by long isolation to feeding from the cones of the Scots Pine.

Interestingly, the Scottish Crossbill, like the Crested Tit, is sedentary and rarely seen outside the Caledonian forest but we see the Common Crossbill of mainland Europe regularly in Britain, and it often breeds in conifer plantations, occasionally in considerable numbers. The Common Crossbill is heavily dependent on Norway Spruce seeds, which mature and are available between November and March, and they actually nest and rear their young during these winter months. They have evolved an eruptive migration stratagem that assists survival when food periodically becomes scarce on the Continent. After the continental breeding season, many birds move away west, sometimes not travelling far before adequate food is found but at other times moving in numbers and over great distances, including crossing the Channel and settling in the 'new' forests of southern and eastern England.

Conifer concerns

Until a few years ago it was fashionable to condemn mature alien conifer plantations as being virtually birdless, either because of their foreign origin or because of their structure. The trees were planted so close that even the rides between plantation blocks seemed like grey/green canyons, muffling all sounds save the sighing of the wind. It seemed that Woodpigeons, Coal Tits, Chaffinches and maybe Goldcrests were the major avian inhabitants, and these only in low numbers. As more and more of these plantations are explored, attitudes are changing. There is now plenty of evidence that, even when mature, conifer plantations may be a perfectly reasonable habitat, carrying fair numbers of a diversity of species, including thrushes, warblers, tits, hawks and owls. There are, too, some special attractions such as the Crossbill, which has been joined in recent years by the migrant Firecrest as a breeding bird worthy of special pilgrimage.

Sharing the title of Britain and Ireland's smallest bird with its relative the Goldcrest, the Firecrest is readily identified by its striking facial pattern of black and white stripes topped by a black-edged gold to flame-coloured crown stripe, raised when the bird is excited. Firecrests are essentially southern European breeding birds, their range extending north to the Baltic and southern England, where varying numbers breed in about 40 localities. In contrast, the Goldcrest has a substantially northern European breeding distribution, covering the whole of Britain and Ireland and stretching on the Continent well north into Scandinavia and Russia.

Firecrest – Tommy Holden

The Firecrest is a special bird, attractive to just about all of us. That attraction centres partly on its diminutive size, partly on its scarcity (a real red-letter-day bird), but surely for most of us largely and simply because of its stunningly beautiful plumage. Though some Firecrests may overwinter in Britain, usually in scrubby areas along the east coast, breeding birds arrive in early March, presumably from wintering areas to the south. They seem to favour, understandably for so small a bird, the shortest possible sea-crossings, which makes the bird observatory at Dungeness in Kent a favourite spot for Firecrest seekers. Others occur elsewhere along the southeast coast, but not in the same numbers or so predictably. Autumn migration along the east coast of Britain begins in September and continues into November, possibly as birds from the Continent pass through.

One great benefit of modern conifer forestry to bird populations is that it is a managed enterprise, with the trees being regarded as a crop, and thus a rotation ensues, normally on a time scale of 40-80 years. Thus, in any sizeable forestry area there will be plantation blocks of widely varying ages, each suiting different types of birds. Those felled within the past year may, if a few deciduous trees remain (as is often the case, especially in the south), be suitable for attractive migrants like the scarce Nightjar, otherwise largely confined to sandy heaths (Chapter 8), and the Tree Pipit, together with the resident or short-haul migrant Woodlark.

The trilling song of the Tree Pipit, descending the scale and increasing in volume to end with a characteristic flourish, is a sure sign that woodland summer is securely in place. Produced sometimes in a parachuting song-flight, sometimes from a perch, it indicates that a pair of these long-haul migrants are in residence in the clearing for the breeding season. On migration, our incoming or outgoing birds are often in company with, and probably outnumbered by, continental birds travelling with them, particularly in eastern coastal areas. Ring-recoveries are few indeed (just over 30 in total) and yield little information on their migration, save that

after leaving Britain and Ireland in the autumn, Tree Pipits make landfall in Portugal, apparently having flown there non-stop, and thereafter depart into Africa. Within Africa, visual observations indicate that Tree Pipits are widespread south of the Sahara from Senegal across to Ethiopia; a sole ring-recovery on the West African coast points to British Tree Pipits wintering towards the western end of that belt.

The value of young plantations in their first decade or so cannot be underestimated, nor can their potential as birdwatching sites. Several species owe both their numerical strength and their wide distribution today largely to the existence of such areas. One good example would be the Hen Harrier, which succeeds well in such areas mostly in the northwest and west, another is the Whinchat. Whinchats are among those birds that have a degree of familiarity as summer migrants, always attractive to see but seeming to be getting scarcer. Following reductions in range during the 1970s and 1980s, Whinchats are restricted as regular breeding birds to the west and north of Britain, scarcer in Ireland. We know comparatively little about Whinchat migrations, not least because out of more than 30,000 ringed birds only about 100 have been recovered.

Whinchat – George H Higginbotham

Without doubt, Whinchats are long-haul migrants, late to arrive in spring and early to depart in autumn, when they follow the south to southwest track of many Africa-bound migrants down through western France and into Iberia. Thereafter, ringing tells us little but field studies and a single ring-recovery suggest that their winter quarters probably lie towards the western end of the grasslands north of the Congo River, probably reached by a non-stop trans-Saharan flight. Based on visual evidence, the northbound trip in spring is also made in one hop, and on a more easterly track than in autumn. Supporting this idea, we know that Whinchats depart from the grasslands after the seasonal rains early in the year, having fed with enthusiasm and to good effect on the termite and other insect abundance generated by the rains, and thus are well fuelled-up for the amazing journey ahead of them over the Sahara and then over the Mediterranean.

Joint holder of the smallest British and Irish bird title, the Goldcrest shows amazing staying power for something so tiny, weighing in at 5-7 g, or four or five birds to the old-fashioned ounce! So far as we can judge, the Goldcrests that breed throughout Britain and Ireland (*not* just mature coniferous woodland – conifers in parks and gardens will do) are sedentary, more numerous in the west and particularly in Ireland. But the migrants that join them for the winter have a very different story to tell.

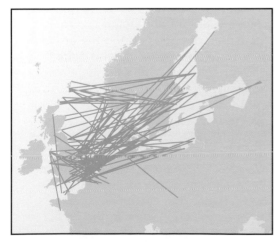

Goldcrest

Fluffy and well-insulated, Goldcrests are astonishingly robust and can overwinter even in coastal northern Norway, coping with sub-zero temperatures and with only a six-hour day in which to feed and generate the energy needed for an 18-hour night. Many migrate from forests further east where winter weather is even more severe. As a matter of routine, many of their migratory journeys are over the sea; winter visitors to Britain and Ireland arrive along the east coast in September and in greater numbers in October, with a few in November.

Their journey from the Baltic States and Fennoscandia involves a North Sea and English Channel crossing on a broad front; a prodigious, almost unbelievable journey for such a tiny scrap of birdlife, in weather that is unpredictable at best, awful at worst. Once into Britain, they press on west on the same broad front but few seem to cross to Ireland. Increasing evidence is accruing from ring-recoveries, indicating that the males take the longest oversea journeys along the Baltic and over the North Sea, while females move along the coast of the southern Baltic and head for the shorter sea crossing over the Channel. The return journey begins in March and runs on into April, on the same broad front but in the reverse direction.

Broad-leaved bounty

In deciduous woodland, too, the physical structure of the wood plays a significant part in determining the sorts of birds that are likely to be seen. This physical structure may be a direct result of management policy but there are still many areas of semi-natural woodland. Here, nature plays the major role in determining where there are clearings, perhaps because an aged tree has fallen, or where there is dense undergrowth. Although making generalisations is inevitably dangerous where birds are concerned, because of the high mobility that flight allows them and because of their opportunist outlook so far as diet is concerned, there is merit in looking at the birds of deciduous woodland on the basis of three broad habitat categories.

Woodcock

Woodcock – George H Higginbotham

The Woodcock, more than any other bird except the Nightjar, seems to relish the bare woodland floor, bare that is except for the leaf litter. This is an unusual bird. For a start, it is a member of the wader family, which we tend to associate with coasts, estuaries, moorland or tundra – but not trees. Woodcocks are intensely secretive but widely distributed as breeding birds in Britain and Ireland, favouring damp woodland (including young conifer plantations) with relatively little undergrowth. They reveal their presence most often by dawn and dusk patrol flights of their territory (roding) but lucky indeed is the birdwatcher who stumbles across a nest. Near-perfect camouflage against the leaf litter conceals the nest (a depression in the litter), eggs, chicks and adults. Chicks and adults will crouch motionless until any approaching danger is literally within inches before fleeing.

Some Woodcock are sedentary residents, as well over half of the ring-recoveries of birds marked during the breeding season are within 30 km of the place of ringing. However others of the breeding population do migrate, the majority of those from northern Britain moving southwest into Ireland, the remainder to France and Iberia. Of the substantially fewer birds ringed in the south and recovered overseas, some show movement westwards to Ireland, others south into France. Around 10% of the Woodcock ringed as chicks in Britain and Ireland were recovered overseas during the breeding season to an interesting and quite different pattern, with four in Scandinavia and one in Russia. Woodcocks are also widespread, if thin on the ground, as winter visitors throughout Britain and Ireland. Almost 300 recoveries of foreign-ringed Woodcock give an excellent picture of the origins of winter visitors to Britain and Ireland, the 'catchment area' embracing Fennoscandia, the Baltic States and Russia.

The first of these habitats is coppice. Coppicing entails clear-felling a whole tract of woodland at regular intervals of between 15 and 40 years, a practice used extensively in past centuries when much wood was used for fuel and by artisans. Thus few trees have substantial trunks, instead forming 'stools' from which a number of straight, slender, erect stems rise. Stools are rarely more than a few feet apart and the slender trunks rise to form a canopy with few perforations. Because of their closeness, side branches are few and poorly developed. The surface area of the almost-flat canopy (viewed from above) is obviously smaller and with reduced feeding areas than when large trees billow (almost like cumulus clouds) through it. With a continuous canopy, too, the light exclusion results in sparse ground vegetation and the shrub layer bushes such as Elder are few and far between.

The second category contains so-called 'standards' – mature, relatively close-spaced trees – so that, as in the coppice, the canopy is complete. However, viewed from above it has a much more irregular appearance, as adjacent trees have canopies that are dome-shaped rather than flat, increasing the surface area (and thus the food-carrying capacity) considerably. As the canopy only becomes complete when the trees are full-grown, the supporting branches are both more numerous and much more robust than in coppice. Major trunks are many yards apart but, once the canopy nears completion overhead, sufficient light is excluded to limit the undergrowth to a few spindly Elder bushes and the occasional patch of Bluebells or Dog's Mercury.

The third and last woodland category can best be called 'gladed'. Here most of the trees will be majestically isolated or in groups of two or three. The patchwork of open areas between them will be filled with various shrubs, colourful drifts of Bluebells and herbaceous plants and grasses. It is easy to imagine the substantial increase in both feeding and nesting sites that tempts so many more individuals of more species to woodland of this type.

What the woodlands offer

We have seen some special examples, but what sorts of birds are generally to be expected in these three deciduous woodland habitat types? How many are resident, how many are migrants? Where do these migrants come from? In coppice, because of the lack of branches and poor development of undergrowth for both food and nest sites, numbers of species and of individuals breeding within such areas are small. There is, however, a flush of life in five to ten year-old coppice, when birds such as Nightingale and Blackcap move in for a few years.

The winter picture is little better, with fewer berries and seeds. Although tit flocks will search the bark, the rather uniform leaf litter apparently contains less in the way of small invertebrate animals to interest the various members of the thrush family, than other woodland types, and the whole structure of coppice does not offer adequate shelter for roosting birds.

The scanty and ephemeral nature of the ground vegetation, and the scarcity of Ivy, greatly restrict the nesting possibilities for the 'generalists' – adaptable resident birds like Wren, Robin and Blackbird – but there is usually a reasonably high proportion of decaying timber. This provides good feeding and abundant nesting opportunities for Great and sometimes Lesser-spotted Woodpeckers, and also the diminutive Treecreeper. Birds of these three species may be attracted to feed with flocks of tits, as they roam through woodland, but only whilst they are in 'their patch'. Marsh and Willow Tits, often difficult to separate other than by call or song, may also join in briefly and are alike in leading sedentary lives, falling amongst the least migratory of our birds so far as ring-recoveries can confirm.

Generally speaking, there are increases both in species richness and in the numbers of individual birds to be seen in areas of 'standard' woodland compared with coppice. The proportion of decaying timber is probably little different from coppice, but the size of the branches which fall or split makes for considerably larger cavities, which are exploited by birds like the Stock Dove (towards the woodland edge) and Tawny Owl, both of them generally sedentary. The greater number and better structure of branches beneath the expanded canopy provides nest sites for large birds like the Jay and Carrion Crow, as sedentary here as in urban surroundings. In some mature woods the Grey Heron, the largest regularly tree-nesting species in Britain and Ireland, builds heronries in which individual nests may be more than a metre across and almost 30 cm deep, with Jackdaws and Tree Sparrows as squatters nesting in the 'basement' of the bulky twig foundations. The last two are sedentary but Herons come to the woods only to breed, afterwards dispersing widely.

In most years, Herons are very early nesters, with nest re-furbishing and courtship in February if the weather is kind. Frenzied and extraordinarily noisy activity continues until June, when the young fledge. Dispersal is immediate, initially in all directions. Over the next few months, average distances away from 'home' increase and begin to show a southerly trend. As winter approaches, many immature birds will be over 50 km away, some as far as 150 km. Longer movements are often associated with freezing weather, as Herons, particularly inexpert young birds, find feeding difficult if ice covers all but coastal waters. Then they must undergo weather-induced movements, often south or westwards.

Although less than 50 Heron nestlings ringed in British and Irish woods have been recovered overseas (a small percentage of about 2,500 recoveries in total) they are spectacular exceptions to the general short-haul dispersal pattern. They are also startling in their diversity, with the majority (as might be expected) moving to the adjacent continental European countries such as Norway, Denmark and the Low Countries, France and Spain, while individuals have travelled to Morocco, as far south as The Gambia and, astonishingly, as far north as Iceland!

Grey Heron

The movements of young Herons ringed in colonies overseas and coming to Britain and Ireland, usually in the autumn, is in stark contrast to the rather hotch-potch dispersal or migration of our native birds. For a start these winter visitors (normally, it must be said to wetland, not woodland) are numerous; there are about 350 ring-recoveries, widespread through Britain and Ireland, over half of them from coastal heronries in Norway, others from Sweden, Denmark, the Low Countries and France. Their migration is on a broad front, the length of Britain, with an emphatic westerly or southwesterly track in autumn and the reverse in spring, as migrants head back towards their natal areas.

Grey Heron – Simon Gillings

Summer comes

The woodland warblers are all migrants, arriving from winter quarters in or near the tropics to exploit the summer flush of insects, and later of fruit, in temperate habitats. On the basis of their slender beaks, all could be classed as insectivorous but, especially towards the end of summer when 'fuel' (in the form of stored body fat) is needed for the southward migration, all will turn to the sugar-rich, easily-processed berry crop, with little indication of any difficulty in accomplishing this violent dietary change.

Chiffchaffs and Willow Warblers are visually often difficult to separate, but have vastly differing songs. Both of these 'leaf warblers' are canopy feeders, mostly in deciduous woodland, picking insects off the undersides of leaves. Chiffchaffs prefer taller timber, Willow Warblers scrub or undergrowth, but these differences are hard to detect where both are common, as in parts of England. Elsewhere, Willow Warblers may tend to favour gladed areas, and penetrate much further north into birch and willow scrub where the climate prohibits the growth of tall trees.

The Chiffchaff is one of a handful of birds aptly named after their song, a simple disyllabic monotony, though the metronomic repetition does sometimes go astray in the excitement of the moment! Chiffchaffs are amongst the earliest of summer migrants, and the woodland birdwatcher's ear is alert for that first unmistakeable sound of spring, even early in March in the south. Ring-recoveries give a good picture of their autumn migration south, which usually starts in mid to late September, the Chiffchaffs moving steadily through France and Spain to reach Morocco during October. Current thinking, supported by ring-recoveries and African studies, suggests that (counter to long-held beliefs) only a small proportion of British and Irish Chiffchaffs stay to winter around the Mediterranean. The majority of these tiny birds overfly the western Sahara to winter quarters in the general region from Mauritania to Guinea-Bissau, but particularly in Senegal. Early February in Africa sees the start of their return migration.

As is so often the case with migrant birds, an enigma remains. Chiffchaffs are overwintering in increasing numbers in Britain and Ireland, perhaps as a result of what is now a longish sequence of mild winters, but we know little of the origins of these overwintering birds except that many seem not to be part of our breeding population. We must await some illuminating ring-recoveries.

Chiffchaff

Willow Warbler safe and secure in a mist net – Dawn Balmer

When the Chiffchaff marks the oncoming spring, it does so with emphasis, not with subtlety. In contrast, for most birdwatchers, the silvery descending trill of the Willow Warbler is a song, and is as much a harbinger of spring as are the Bluebells that carpet the woodland floor. Slightly larger than its near relative, and longer in the wing, the Willow Warbler has an even more impressive migration, astonishing perhaps for a bird averaging 10g.

Willow Warbler

Ring-recoveries indicate that both adults and immatures return to their point of origin – precisely in the case of the adults, nearby for the young. The Willow Warbler is a relatively well-studied bird, with over one million ringed and 2,500 ring-recoveries to work on. These studies show that young birds begin to move south as early as late July in northern Britain, not long after for those reared further south. They are rounder in wing profile than the adults and thus less efficient in long-distance flight than the more pointed-winged adults. The young also depart a gramme or two lighter than adults, travelling south initially in short stages but on a similar south to southeast heading, before turning southwest to cross from Iberia to northwest Africa. Adults will have moulted in Britain and Ireland before departure (from late August onwards), so leave with brand-new, maximum efficiency, flight feathers to speed their journey. As the journey progresses, so the young gain in experience in feeding and flight, very necessary when it comes to the final lengthy stages crossing the western Sahara to their wintering grounds in the Gulf of Guinea, ring-recoveries placing these around the Ivory Coast and Ghana.

The return journey in spring, starting in February after yet another moult, is on a similar track. The journey is quicker and probably taken in even longer stages than in autumn. Males are here a couple of weeks before females, arriving across south and southwest Britain and Ireland in late March and early April, swiftly moving on to establish territories ready for the returning females.

If Willow Warbler and Chiffchaff are alike in plumage but vastly different in song, then the Blackcap/Garden Warbler species pair are the reverse. The Garden Warbler is in plumage one of our least distinguished birds, clad in shades of nondescript greenish buff, whereas the Blackcap has a striking patch on the crown, black in the male, chestnut in the female and young. The seasoned ear, in practice, will often find little difficulty in separating the songs of the two, but there will be numerous occasions when a sight of the singer would help greatly. Both are well worthy of the name 'warbler' (unlike the Chiffchaff) and it is the Garden Warbler which is held by many birdwatchers to be one of the most melodious of our summer visitors.

Wood Warbler

Noticeably larger than its relatives, the Wood Warbler, with its yellow breast and strikingly white belly is readily identifiable, a task made easier if it is in trilling song. It is a summer visitor to woodland in the west and north, but uncommon in Ireland. It has a strange claim to fame as the British and Irish bird with the lowest ring-recovery rate of all, at one in every 400 birds ringed. This is a pity, as what we do know about its movements is fascinating.

Departing migrants in autumn take an unusual southeasterly course to southern Europe, primarily Italy. Few Wood Warblers are seen at coastal ringing stations and observatories in autumn, so their journey may often be in one hop to the Mediterranean. Here they feed avidly, putting on weight for a long journey south. The absence of autumn north African ring-recoveries or sightings, coupled with observations elsewhere in Africa, suggests a direct crossing of the central Sahara to winter quarters yet to be located, but the possibilities are countries round the Gulf of Guinea. It is thought likely that Wood Warblers are loop migrants, returning north on a course substantially west of their outward journey. Again they must overfly the Sahara, to land and recoup

in North Africa, where there are plenty of spring sightings. From there, they depart swiftly to their breeding grounds, where some arrive in late April, and all are well-established on their territories in May. One bird, caught and ringed at the Calf of Man Bird Observatory, had by the end of the next day flown to Glasgow, set up territory, attracted a mate and started nest-building!

Blackcap ring-recoveries give a pretty clear picture of the way these summer woodland residents handle their migrations. They depart after their post-breeding moult, having fattened well on the autumn woodland berry crop, some in September, most in October, and a few as late as November. Their route takes them through western France, into Iberia and on into western north Africa. The great majority overwinter in Iberia and north Africa, but ring-recoveries suggest that some may push further south, perhaps even south of the Sahara, perhaps travelling with continental populations that do winter further

south. There are also indications that their return in spring may be across a broader front in north Africa, with birds moving northwestwards through France. Early birds may return in March, with the majority of arrivals in April, all swiftly establishing their breeding territories.

For some years now, garden birdwatchers have been seeing more and more Blackcaps at their winter bird tables. Tempting as it is to assume that these are British and Irish breeding birds staying on during milder winters, this seems certainly not to be the case. Ring-recoveries

Blackcap

Garden Warblers further dispel any thoughts that woodland summer visitors all do much the same sort of thing on roughly the same track. Visual observations at the coast and ringing stations suggest that British and Irish breeders depart largely through southeastern England in autumn, and more precisely, mainly through Sussex. Unlike Blackcaps, they delay their moult until winter quarters are reached, and so may be off south much earlier in August or early September. The journey south through France and Iberia is made in short-haul stages, and it is not until the migrants reach Morocco that they fatten up prior to their Saharan crossing. Debate still surrounds the issue of whether they put down at oases *en route* to recuperate, but the current view is that most probably cross the desert in a single flight, reaching their winter quarters (from Ghana to Nigeria) from late September. The return journey probably begins in late March and many are still in Africa during April, but they are still back in Britain (and a few pairs in Ireland) to nest during May.

and DNA fingerprinting indicate that our wintering Blackcaps come from Germany and neighbouring countries and that we are observing the establishment of a 'new' migration; an unusual event in itself, made more so by the roughly east/west path it follows, almost at right angles to our north/south expectations. Perhaps this trend has long been present but rarely accomplished, and the recent provision of winter food at bird tables and increasingly mild winters have allowed it to become established.

Garden Warbler – Tommy Holden

Garden Warbler

Blackcaps prefer tall standard trees of mature deciduous woods, where they choose song posts high up in the canopy, whereas the Garden Warbler is far more a songster in dense undergrowth or scrub, thus favouring gladed woodland. Also a bird of dense scrub, the Nightingale is inconspicuous in browns and chestnuts unless seen well, but unmistakeable and incomparable as a songster. British Nightingales (around 5,000 pairs) breed mostly southeast of a line from the Severn to the Humber. They are comparatively late migrants, arriving at the end of April or during May. After raising a single brood and moulting, return migration may start in late July, so their stay as summer visitors is a brief one. Elusive remains the word when it comes to Nightingale migration; about 10,000 have been ringed and less than 70 recovered, half of those re-trapped or re-sighted (when colour marked) by ringers in England. Before their departure in autumn, the weights of trapped birds show substantial increases (in the order of 50%) due to pre-migratory fat deposition. The eight overseas recoveries can give only a hint of their likely migration routes, in autumn south to southwest through France and Iberia, with a single recovery in Morocco indicating a crossing to Africa at the Strait of Gibraltar. Once in Africa, we can only surmise that our Nightingales winter where others have been observed, south of the Sahara, and probably towards the western end of that distribution. The return journey in spring may be the reverse of their autumn track. Single recoveries in Shetland and on Helgoland lend support to the suggestion that some European birds may pass through Britain on migration.

There is a common but inaccurate view that species that come to inland Britain and Ireland to breed in summer have their stronghold in the south and east, closest to the continental centres of bird populations. The Nightingale is one example of a summer visitor which does have a southeasterly bias, the Turtle Dove of woodland/farmland margins another. In interesting and marked contrast to these are two other summer migrants to our woodlands, the Redstart and the Pied Flycatcher. The Redstart breeds in a variety of habitats, ranging from open woodland and parkland to fields fringing moorland, with dry-stone walling and the occasional gnarled tree. It is very much a bird of the north and west of Britain, but intriguingly almost absent from Ireland.

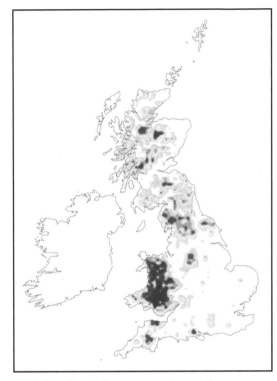

BTO Breeding Atlas map: northwesterly distribution of Redstarts

Redstart – Tommy Holden

With its flicking chestnut-red tail and elegant breeding plumage, the male Redstart may be conspicuous on its westerly breeding grounds but we know very little indeed about where our summer visitors spend their winter. Ring-recoveries mark Redstarts as long-haul migrants and indicate an autumn route departing in August/September on a south/southwest heading through France, Spain and Portugal to Morocco and Algeria. An intriguing but small minority of ring-recoveries indicate that some birds head off on a southeasterly bearing. In north Africa we know that they fatten up for their onward journey. We know too that they take much the same route northwards from north Africa in spring.

Redstart

Visual observations within Africa indicate that most Redstarts (but of unknown origins) winter in the sub-Saharan dry scrub belt, stretching from west Africa across to the Congo and Uganda, and that first autumn arrivals may be as early as September. Two recoveries from The Gambia and Senegal hint

that our birds may winter towards the western end of this extensive belt of habitat. Pre-migratory fattening begins in March, prior to the northward Saharan crossing, and our returning migrants arrive towards the end of April. Ring-recoveries also show that continental birds pass through Britain and Ireland in both spring and autumn, particularly along the British east coast, but sadly they too throw little light on the African component of Redstart migration.

The second bird of the west is the Pied Flycatcher, penetrating also into northern England but scarce in Scotland and, like the Redstart, almost absent from Ireland. Pied Flycatchers are far more pure forest birds than Redstarts, and could quite well be chosen as the bird symbolic of the sessile oak woods of steep-sided valleys that typify much of Wales. Simply but elegantly plumaged, the males in black and white, and briefly tuneful rather than extensively melodious, they get down to the business of breeding after only a short period of song. Pied Flycatchers also differ from Redstarts in that far more have been ringed (almost 450,000 against 85,000) and particularly recovered (nearly 3,500 against less than 350). Most have been ringed in their nesting woods, many as nestlings, so the picture produced by ring-recoveries is, at least for the early stages of the journey, an unusually accurate one for birds of British origin. Autumn migration starts in August and September, and their south/southwestward track through France into western Iberia and on into Morocco is well-defined. Beyond that, the small handful of recoveries south of the Sahara gives only a tantalising indication of where they may winter. There is much less observational evidence of Pied Flycatchers in winter quarters than for the Redstart, but it does seem likely that most winter in the southwest of the 'bulge' of Africa.

The indications are that, on return passage in spring, their route loops to the east before birds head north or northwest, depending on which part of the substantial stretch of north African coastline they set out from. They arrive in Britain in late April or early May, a delight for winter-tired eyes, amazingly fresh-looking in plumage. Again, our birds in spring (and in autumn) may be augmented by some passage migrants from Fennoscandia.

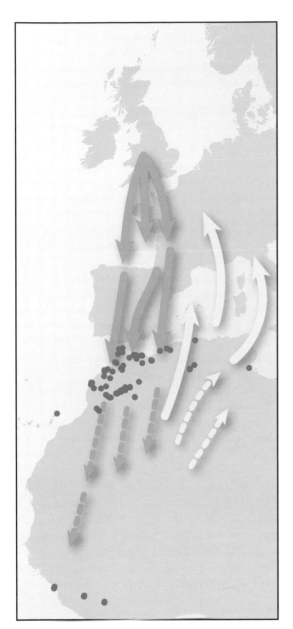

Pied Flycatcher

Bluebells, brambles and birds

In gladed woodland areas, increases in the sheer numbers of birds to be seen are usually most apparent among the thrushes, warblers and finches. Such increases are probably attributable in the main to two features; the greatly increased structural (physical) diversity of the habitat and the increase in both animal and vegetable food materials, consequent on an increased diversity of plant species and on an increase in vegetational surface area. This is where the Bluebells show best and, later in the summer, the Brambles provide territory and food for birds and butterflies. Here is found the maximum nest site and food availability within deciduous woodland, an indication of the benefits of both the 'edge-effect' and of 'scrub' (in the form of undergrowth) to bird populations.

Not unnaturally, the situation in winter is similar to that in summer, with more birds getting benefit from the varied habitat of woodland glades. These are the places to catch a glimpse of the resident Sparrowhawks on the hunt, as not only is there plenty of prey but there is good cover, allowing small birds to be taken by surprise. This may also be the place to find a Long-eared Owl, secretive, superbly camouflaged and hard to find, hunting mammals and birds in the open glades. Long-eared Owls breed thinly but widely scattered through woodland of Britain and Ireland and, so far as can be judged, are sedentary or disperse only over short distances. The picture changes in autumn, when migrants arrive and take up winter quarters in woodland, scrub

Long-eared Owl – David Garner

and orchards, sometimes roosting communally in gatherings of a dozen or more birds. Their timing is variable, probably depending on the availability of small mammals in their breeding areas. Often the first indications are arrivals seen at northern and eastern bird observatories and other regular observation points. Ring-recoveries indicate that their breeding grounds lie in Scandinavia, Finland and elsewhere in northern Europe. The return migration in spring is as leisurely as their arrival, with departures in February in some years and as late as May in others.

Redwings – Tommy Holden

The cutting edge of winter

The dual use of this well-structured gladed woodland (and indeed all woodland) in winter is important, sometimes vitally so. Besides the winter food, numerous and well-sheltered roosting sites are available in the lower vegetation layers. Temperatures in the middle of the night in these sheltered spots may be several degrees higher than out in the open, and woods in general are usually warmer than surrounding fields and even hedges. Research has indicated that for a bird like the Blackbird the midwinter overnight weight loss (usually of body fat metabolised to keep warm) can be reduced by up to 80% by selecting a prime roost site during bad weather, literally a matter of life or death. For many species these roosts may be used throughout the winter, but for others the period of peak use may be quite short, perhaps less than one month. This does not detract at all from their usefulness; indeed they may be the more vital for such birds as an 'ultimate refuge' in times of severest stress.

Speaking of woodland in general rather than any particular type, there is sometimes a tendency to rate 'quality' on the basis of the breeding birds present. Although breeding bird populations are probably more easily surveyed and assessed than winter flocks, the importance of woodlands in winter may often be under-rated if not forgotten. Midwinter, with long cold nights to survive and only short day lengths in which to gather food for survival, may be the most critical or dangerous time of the year for many birds, migrants included, as indicated when Redwings turn to foraging in woodland leaf-litter when fields are snow-covered.

Wetlands

The freshwater system

Wetlands, for the practical purposes of this chapter, includes all types of fresh waterways and their surrounds, from source pretty well to the sea. Where river mouths become estuaries, these fall into Chapter 9. Included in this assemblage are streams and rivers, the ponds, pools and lakes into which they may run, and the bogs, marshes, reedbeds and watermeadows that may form part of any watercourse wherever drainage is impeded. These usually appear as long-established components of our countryside, and many of them actually are natural features, although man has influenced the course of numerous rivers and streams and created (usually many years ago) many of the ponds and lakes that today have such a natural, rather than artificial, appearance. More recent, man-made additions to our landscape have quickly been adopted by bird populations, as part of the broad spectrum of exploitable habitats, and some are now of considerable importance. These newcomers to the scenery include reservoirs and, most recent and maybe most important, accidentally or deliberately flooded or semi-flooded mineral workings. These may be sand or marl pits and chalk quarries, sometimes a fair distance from other water, or clay and ballast workings, usually to be found on the flood plains of river valleys. They may be used as fishing, powerboating or sailing waters, set out as nature reserves, or combinations of any of these.

It seems appropriate to take streams and rivers first, as this is where the freshwater wetland system begins. Immediately, vast differences are apparent between the various regions of Britain and Ireland. As a generalisation, streams in the west and north often flow over rocky beds on an incline and are fast-flowing and clear, particularly on higher ground. In contrast, in the east and south, streams (which may be few and far between in some areas, notably on the chalk) and the rivers which they feed are often cloudy, with suspended silt particles, and meander sluggishly through low-lying countryside. These slow-moving waters often have extensive adjacent marshes, reedbeds or wet meadow systems, whereas the fast-flowing westerly streams have rocky banks and numerous rapids or cascades, and such marshy areas as there are normally form part of the moorland system. Because the rainfall is much higher in the west, the differences between normal summer and winter flow is considerable, and in summer most such streams may occupy only a small part of the 'spate bed' of pebbly banks that will be totally submerged during winter rains. Not surprisingly, there are considerable differences in the waterway birds of the two types.

Sparkling waters

The fast-flowing streams and rivers of the west and north are characterised by a number of birds. Perhaps the most typical of these is the Dipper. With its unique aquatic habits it must be one of the easiest birds to identify. Perhaps best described as a thrush-sized Wren, the Dipper has a jaunty, tail-cocked posture and bobs up and down frequently. The upper parts are a rich, plain-chocolate brown, and both wings and tail look short in proportion to the undeniably plump body; but by far the most conspicuous feature is the large strikingly white 'bib' extending down onto the belly. As soon as it steps off its midstream boulder and disappears under water, to pop up nearby a moment later, its identity is beyond doubt. Dippers are sedentary birds, except that on the higher reaches of upland rivers, they drop to lower altitudes if winter tightens its grip and a freeze occurs, when they become altitudinal migrants. Even post-fledging dispersal is minimal; young females move further from their place of birth than young males, but 10 km would be at the upper end of their travels, and the odd recovery at 40 km is quite exceptional.

Grey Wagtails show a variety of migratory patterns; some in southern Britain and Ireland are sedentary, remaining on or near their breeding grounds, others from high ground may (like Dippers) be altitudinal migrants and drop to lower levels, while yet others, particularly from the north, are short- to medium-haul migrants, both within Britain and Ireland and to the adjacent Continent. With this mixture of migratory behaviours, it is difficult to know what is migrating and what is not, especially as unless they are actually flying along the coast or out to sea, migrants and residents favour the same habitats. It is thought that those that migrate do so by day, and in short stages, eventually reaching France and Spain. Grey Wagtails from further east on the Continent seem to migrate south, and it is thought cross the Mediterranean on a broad front into northern Africa, some reaching as far south as The Gambia. These long-haul migrants presumably move in longer stages, with appreciable pre-migratory fattening. Clearly we still have much to learn and understand about the migrations of this elegant bird.

Grey Wagtail – Colin Varndell

The Grey Wagtail is not so strictly a bird of the north and west, as it seems just as much at home in the lowlands so long as the water is broken. Checking the Ordnance Survey maps for watermills, weirs, sluices and fords will frequently reveal Grey Wagtail territories on the clearer, better oxygenated waters below these man-made features. Handsome, with grey back, prominent white eyestripe and lemon-yellow belly, set-off by a long, perpetually wagging white-edged black tail, this is a favourite amongst birdwatchers.

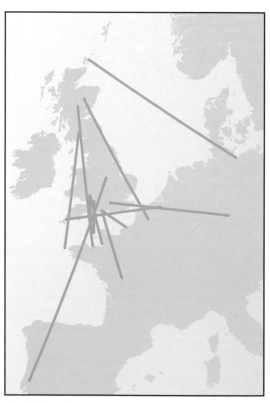

Grey Wagtail

The Common Sandpiper is a wader which, although occurring on many wetland areas in the east while on migration, favours the banks and pebble beds of the clear waters of the north and west of Britain and Ireland when it comes to breeding. Strangely, in the light of their unrelatedness, the Common Sandpiper shares with the Dipper and the wagtail family the habit of bobbing up and down incessantly all day long. Quite what the purpose of this habit is has yet to be discovered, but the fact that it occurs so widely among waterside birds may have something to do with the camouflage effect it creates against a rippling and sparkling background of moving water. Trilling calls and a habit of flying away low across the water on down-curved wings are characteristic of Common Sandpipers, the wingbeats being so shallow that the wings seem just to vibrate in bursts rather than to flap. On the face of it, not the flight pattern of a long-haul migrant.

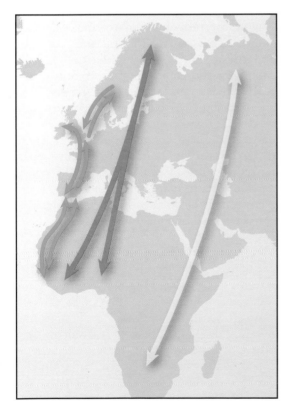

Common Sandpiper migration routes: green – Britain and Ireland, orange – northern Scandinavia, yellow – Russia

Common Sandpipers breed in a broad belt extending latitudinally from the Arctic Circle south to the Mediterranean and longitudinally from Britain and Ireland in the west to Japan in the east, and all winter in tropical latitudes. The breeding season even in the south of their range is unusually but characteristically short. British and Irish birds are back on territory in late April or early May and by mid-July the breeding season is over and 'autumn' migration south about to begin. British and Irish birds migrate swiftly south through France and Iberia and into northwestern Africa, and are presumed to winter in the west of sub-Saharan Africa. Finding details of returning birds through Morocco, Iberia and France indicate an even swifter northbound passage.

Southern Scandinavian breeding birds pass through southeast England in spring, after British and Irish birds are established on territories, and back in autumn a couple of weeks or more after most of our birds have departed. Ring-recoveries from continental schemes indicate that birds from northern Scandinavia take a slightly southwesterly track to the Gulf of Guinea, while Russian-breeding birds head roughly due south to winter in east-central Africa and substantially further beyond into South Africa.

Slow movers

In the lowlands in general, but the southeast in particular, the waterways are much murkier and the water moves much more sluggishly. As a result of this, there is copious growth of a wide variety of water plants, both on the river margins and in midstream, which produces far more cover. These habitats support considerably more food items to suit a wider spectrum of diets than fast-flowing clear streams. In such dense vegetation, the slim body of the Moorhen is well suited to slipping between the plants, while its long spidery toes support it as it crosses mud or floating vegetation just as well as do the similar feet of the tropical lily trotters. These long toes serve almost as well as webbed feet when it comes to swimming, and the Moorhen is one of the most widespread of water birds, as much at home on a tiny pond in the corner of a field as it is in the vegetation beside a large lake.

Another waterbird typical of these sluggish waterways (and other still freshwaters) is the Little Grebe. Regular visits to your local birding spot will have indicated that Little Grebes do not necessarily remain through the winter. Although only just over 1,200 have been ringed and only 40 or so recovered, it seems that while some do remain on breeding waters many others disperse to sheltered coastal waters nearby, the longest distance so far being 215 km but most much less. There is some evidence that in winter our Little Grebes are joined by others of continental origin, with a handful of recoveries of birds ringed in France and the Low Countries and two longer-haul visitors from Denmark and Latvia. Much remains to be understood as, unlike most birds which can be ringed when young and easy to catch, the legs and feet of grebes are slow to develop and ringing has to wait until almost adulthood.

For the familiar Moorhen the picture is slightly different. Breeding birds across Britain and Ireland are almost entirely sedentary, even extremely so, with only a handful moving more than 10 km, including dispersing juveniles. In winter, ring-recovery details indicate a regular immigration, particularly from Denmark and the Low Countries. Most of these visitors seem to arrive into southeastern England – perhaps because Moorhens are normally not the strongest of fliers and this represents the shortest sea-crossing for birds escaping from the colder continental winter.

Kingfishers, too, are birds of placid, reed-fringed rivers or lakes, with plenty of overhanging vegetation and with stretches of low earthen cliffs suitable for nesting. According to the ancients, the Kingfisher (called 'Halcyon') made a nest of fish bones and launched it on the sea. While she was brooding, the gods ordered that the oceans be calmed, the origin of the term 'halcyon days'. Actually, the nest could hardly differ more from the peace and beauty associated with the word halcyon. At the end of a tunnel

Measuring the wing of a Kingfisher – Dawn Balmer

excavated by the birds in a suitable bank lies the nest, made of fishbones, but dark, slimy, noisy and above all smelling powerfully of aged fish and the droppings of the young. So revolting is it that the parents often dunk themselves in the water immediately after leaving the tunnel to remove the scales and slime. The migratory picture for the Kingfisher has some similarities to the Moorhen; the great majority of British and Irish breeders are sedentary or disperse over short distances, but periods of freezing weather provoke movements over greater distances, usually to the nearest coast where frozen water is much less likely. Such movements are more common in the north, and are more regular on the Continent, where many Kingfishers are medium-haul migrants, the occasional one reaching Britain.

Much of the transport of agrochemical pollutants such as pesticide residues and nitrates takes place through lowland fresh waterways, joined as the rivers pass through built-up areas by industrial pollutants and sewerage discharge, some more insidious than others. On the credit side, so far as industry is concerned, measures over the last couple of decades to counter pollution and improve the state of some major rivers have often been strikingly successful. It is usually news of a salmon in the upper reaches of the Thames that makes the headlines, but there have been dramatic improvements too in waterfowl numbers and variety on the London reaches of the river. These now feed in the apparently grotesquely atypical surroundings of busy wharves and river traffic. Hearteningly, the same is true of many other waterways.

Clear, clean waters

Upland rivers are generally less polluted than lowland ones; being faster moving and over a rocky bed, they are better oxygenated, and most are distant from industrial pollution sources and travel through low-intensity farmland. The principle hazard seems to be insecticide residues seeping into the watercourse from sheep dips, but the problem is known and fines await offenders traced after pollution incidents. Typically the slim and supremely elegant Goosander is a bird of these broad clear upland rivers, but perfectly at home also, winter and summer, on slower-moving lowland waters and freshwater lochs, lakes and reservoirs of all sizes.

From first proved breeding in Scotland in 1871, the Goosander has increased steadily in numbers as a breeding bird, perhaps to around 3,000 pairs today. This has been accompanied by an equally steady spread, widely over Scotland but particularly so over northern England and Wales. First breeding has now been recorded in Ireland. As numbers increase, so too does conflict between Goosanders and commercial game fishery interests. Goosanders are one of three 'sawbill' ducks in Britain and Ireland, with slim, sharply-hooked beaks with serrated edges giving a clear indication of their fish diet, including expensive ones like trout. As a consequence, Goosanders are comparatively well studied, and we have not only ring-recoveries but sighting of birds with individual colour-coded wing tags to draw on when attempting to interpret their movements.

British breeding Goosanders disperse after the breeding season, often initially downstream. Some then move in a generally southerly direction for varying distances, but only rarely exceeding 150 km and only

infrequently penetrating further south than the Midlands. Others may move to nearby coasts, or remain close to their breeding grounds. But this applies only to females and young. It had long been a mystery as to where the drakes disappeared as soon as the ducks were settled on the nest. As in many wildfowl, they have no further paternal involvement. They, and the year-old males, had been seen gathering on larger lochs and lakes, but from mid-summer until October nothing was seen of them.

Goosander

Coming as a complete surprise, ringing revealed in the mid-1980s the remarkable behaviour of the drakes, which migrate to the fjords of Norway's North Cape, there to moult, in company with tens of thousands of other drakes from all over northwestern Europe. Moulting completed, they return to Britain, joining the females (which moult here once the young are independent) and young of the year. Ring-recoveries indicate that winter-visitor Goosanders on lakes and reservoirs, and occasionally sheltered waters, in lowland England are from northern Fennoscandia and northwestern Russia, as birds from the Baltic appear to winter locally to their breeding sites. These winter visitors are often late arriving, more in early winter than in autumn, and by late March most have departed.

Rather more bristly-crested, but no less elegant than its slightly larger relative, the Red-breasted Merganser is substantially more coastal in distribution, nesting on coastal islands and besides lochs and rivers. Its summer strongholds are in northwestern Scotland and the Isles, northwest Wales and western Ireland. Like the Goosander, it is a fish-eater and without doubt game fish feature in Mergansers' diets. Unlike the Goosander, there is a suggestion that, after more than half a century of expansion, Merganser numbers are showing a decline, attributed to both legal and illegal killing by fisheries' interests. Why Goosander are able to tolerate much the same levels of persecution and continue to increase in numbers is difficult to explain.

The information available from ring-recoveries and wing-tagged birds is less than for the Goosander, but nevertheless we can build a reasonable picture of movements through the year. After the breeding season, Mergansers disperse to nearby coastal waters. Males leave early to moult in June and July at a number of traditional sites off the Scottish coast (Sound of Gigha, Tentsmuir, Kincardine). They winter in small groups mostly offshore, no matter how rough, and much less frequently on inland fresh waters. Return movements to freshwater rivers begin in late February and continue into April. A small handful of recoveries indicate that some of our birds may winter on the eastern side of the North Sea.

Offshore, our breeding population is joined during the winter by migrants from overseas. It seems likely, from a number of ring-recoveries, that many birds from the more substantial Icelandic breeding population winter off the northern and western coasts of Scotland and Ireland, arriving in October and departing in March. Similarly, Fennoscandian breeding birds winter in substantial numbers off particularly northern and eastern coasts, arriving from October to December and departing on the return migration from February onwards.

In summer, the lochs of the Highlands of Scotland (which on the map often seem to be as much water as land) are often disappointingly barren. True, many will have Common Sandpipers breeding close to their

Osprey

Osprey – Jez Blackburn

One of the most exciting of river birds, also happy on fresh, brackish and saline waters of all sizes from an (admittedly large) well-stocked garden pond up to a major reservoir, is the Osprey. This specialist bird of prey is also a conservation success story. About 50 years ago, defended by round-the-clock watches and sophisticated electronics from the depredations of egg-collectors, the first pair since 1908 settled and eventually bred successfully in Speyside.

Their natural slow spread through Scotland has been augmented by moves to encourage their range expansion through the provision of nesting platforms and the release of captive-bred young. The RSPB and other bodies have much to be proud of. The famous RSPB initial site (though not the original birds) at Loch Garten in Speyside has attracted over a million and a half visitors, birdwatchers and ordinary tourists, an amazing figure but one starkly offset by the appalling figure that about 10% of Osprey nests are still robbed each year by egg collectors, despite protection. There may now be 100 or more pairs in Britain, with encouraging signs that not only the English Lake District but central England may be colonised.

Ospreys are amongst the world's most widely distributed birds, and all populations are migratory. They are also amongst the world's most spectacular birds to watch as they hunt, plunging feet first with a huge splash to emerge carrying a sizeable fish, head foremost like a torpedo, clutched in their highly-adapted rough-soled sharp-taloned feet. Although few British Ospreys have been ringed (just over 1,250), over 50 ring-recoveries are usefully augmented by sightings of wing-tagged birds and by satellite tracking a few fitted with radio transmitters.

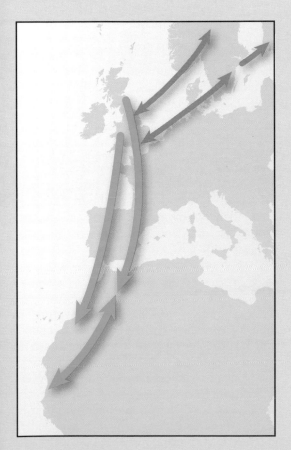

Departure south is in late August and September, adults and their young each travelling independently. Their route takes them on a broad front through France and Iberia and across the Mediterranean into northern Africa between Morocco and Tunisia. Ospreys are powerful fliers, and unlike most birds of prey rely little on the assistance of thermals and other upcurrents, routinely making long sea crossings. Thence they head (still it seems on a broad front) to their wintering grounds in west Africa, from Mauritania south to Guinea. Some immatures may remain in the Mediterranean basin, while others stay south of the Sahara. From sightings of wing-tagged birds, adults seem to be faithful to both their breeding and wintering areas, and may also visit the same areas each year on migration. Return departures of adults and two-year-olds begin during February, with birds arriving back on territory in late March and April.

Radio tracking under the Anglian Water Osprey Project details some pretty direct flights:

• A juvenile female leaving Rutland Water on 30th August reached Senegal, almost 5,000 km south, in 20 days;

• A Scottish juvenile headed south through Ireland to Portugal before its signal was lost;

• Another Scottish adult female caught at Nairn on 21st August reached its winter quarters in Guinea on 29th September, crossing the Sahara well inland from the Atlantic and taking 13 days from Gibraltar.

see: www.ospreys.org.uk

shores, and a few will have the much rarer Wood Sandpiper breeding nearby. Very unusually for waders, some Wood Sandpipers will nest in trees, using the old nests of other species, usually thrushes. In the extreme west of Scotland, shallow lochs (especially in Shetland and on the sandy 'machair' of the Outer Hebrides) still hold a few pairs of Red-necked Phalarope. This is another exception to the avian rule, in that it is the female which plays the dominant role in family life. It is she who is the brighter of plumage and larger in size, and who takes the lead in courtship displays. Having laid the eggs she leaves her drabber partner to incubate them and shoulder most of the burdens of feeding and caring for the growing brood, and frequently will find herself another partner and produce a second clutch, again incubated by the male. This polyandrous mating system effectively almost doubles the number produced each year. Phalaropes disperse to winter, it is thought, pelagically, the open ocean appearing an unbelievable habitat for so fragile-seeming a bird.

Lakes, pools and ponds

Over much of England, but particularly in the south, the majority of pools and lakes are man-made, from tiny ponds in field corners created to water sheep and cattle, through to huge reservoirs. The distinctive Coot, an everyday conspicuous and noisy feature of larger ponds, lakes and reservoirs, seems an unlikely candidate for migration. Bulky of body, with what look like ineffectual wings, and usually seen flying low with legs and long lobed toes trailing, Coot appear far more at home on the water, raising their wings in threat display to neighbours in seemingly endless bouts of aggression. But beneath that black exterior lurks a potential migrant, although (as is quite often the case) British and Irish birds seem mainly to be sedentary. Only 38 of more than 1,000 ring-recoveries are from distances greater than 20 km, while most are within a few kilometres of the place of ringing. Too few young juveniles have been ringed to discover anything about post-fledging dispersal, but distances involved are unlikely to be great. Of birds present in

Britain and Ireland during the breeding season (May to August) there are 9 recoveries overseas including one from East Anglia to Ireland. The others were in the Low Countries, France and Spain, the furthest some 1,100 km from the place of ringing.

Large concentrations of Coot, sometimes of over 1,000 birds, occur in the autumn, as what are presumed to be British and Irish birds gather to moult. As winter bites in continental Europe, more birds arrive and there are over 20 recoveries of Coot ringed as breeding birds overseas and recovered in Britain and Ireland during the winter. These originated in Finland, Denmark, the Baltic States and (most distant) Russia, with a few from the Low Countries and Germany. Recoveries of Coot ringed in winter in Britain and Ireland indicate a return in the breeding season to Denmark, the Baltic States, the Low Countries, France and Italy. So the sombre Coot can be a long-haul migrant, and yes, it could have been the metallic 'kowk' call of a Coot flying over that you heard on that cold, clear autumn night!

Several introduced species have benefited from the provision of man-made ponds. These include the Ruddy Duck, which has dispersed widely, and Mandarin Ducks frequently encountered in the southeast and appearing in other areas, especially in late spring. Of most interest is the Canada Goose, which has "relearned" the migratory tendencies of its ancestors. Non-breeding birds caught moulting on the Beauly Firth, in Scotland, have their origins in the parks and country estates of areas such as Yorkshire and the English Midlands.

Dabblers ...

The ubiquitous Mallard could feature in almost any of these habitat chapters, but ponds and lakes seems as good a location as any in which to position it. Familiar and widespread, the Mallard is as popular today as wildfowlers' quarry as it was as the principal catch in the duck decoys of Victorian times and earlier. 'Converted' duck decoys have been used to catch Mallard for ringing, which are also easily attracted into baited funnel traps. Over

Mallard

150,000 Mallard have been ringed and almost 25,000 recovered, shooting being the recovery cause for the great majority (96%). The breeding population in Britain and Ireland is estimated at about 150,000 pairs, and the BTO's *Atlas of Wintering Birds* suggests a conservative half million for the midwinter peak population, indicating that winter immigration is taking place. Estimates of numbers are difficult enough for such a widespread bird, but the picture is additionally clouded by the release (mostly during the shooting season) of captive reared stock.

As is not infrequently the case, British and Irish breeding birds are relatively sedentary, with over 80% recovered within these islands, over 50% moving less than 20 km and median recovery distances of 22 km for males, 12 km for females. Unusually, adults show a slightly greater trend than juveniles to head off generally southwards in autumn. Upwards of 150 recoveries overseas range from Fennoscandia in the north to Central Europe in the east, but the great majority are from Denmark, the Low Countries and France. Most of these recoveries occurred in subsequent winters but a surprisingly high proportion, about 60 (75% of them males) were reported during the breeding season from over much the same range, probably another example of abmigration, in which birds change breeding location in a dramatic way, perhaps because of the mix of birds which takes place in wintering areas. The map shows the catchment area of winter visitors to Britain and Ireland, which begin to arrive in late summer and build up to a peak, normally in January, with return departures from February onwards largely dictated by the severity or otherwise of the winter.

... and divers

The Tufted Duck, dumpy on the water and neat in a dive, is a delight to watch and almost as familiar to birdwatchers as the Mallard, and certainly is the widest spread of British and Irish diving ducks. As a breeding bird, it is widespread on lakes of all sorts, and on some rivers (except in northern Scotland and southeastern Ireland). The same is true, with the addition of reservoirs, for its winter distribution. Drakes are easily recognised, black with conspicuous white flanks, a drooping crest and yellow eyes; the ducks more subdued in browns with just a vestige of a crest. Breeding numbers continue to increase steadily and spread in Britain (which was first colonised as recently as 1849) reaching currently about 10,000 pairs, but the much smaller Irish population has suffered a fall in numbers in recent years. Winter numbers are reputedly amongst the most stable year-to-year of all wildfowl, at about 100,000 birds.

Tufted Duck – John Harding

Many of the breeding population stay within Britain and Ireland but, unlike our resident Mallard, behave more as short-haul migrants, with males generally moving substantially further than females. Birds ringed in the southeast disperse in all directions, to East Anglia, the Midlands, Ireland and central southern England, while those ringed in southeastern Scotland tend to head southwest into Ireland for the winter. Some travel overseas, but not many, reaching France, the Low Countries and Germany, with two recoveries from Russia. A few ringed as ducklings show abmigration, several to northern Fennoscandia and arctic Russia, others to the Baltic States and Low Countries.

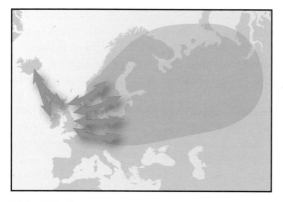

Tufted Duck

The origins of our winter visitor Tufted Duck are plain, a few coming from northwest and north-central Europe, several from Iceland, but the great majority from Fennoscandia, the Baltic States and northern Russia, as far east as 70°E in western Siberia. Earliest arrivals, from late June, are males having departed first from the breeding grounds to moult in Britain and Ireland. Females move later, arriving to moult from August and tend to winter in more southerly locations than males. Both immigrants and residents move about frequently during the winter but not over great distances, generally remaining faithful to their chosen region.

Like the Tufted Duck, the Pochard colonised Britain in early Victorian times but, unlike the Tufted Duck, numbers have increased only very slowly. Subtly plumaged, the drake grey-bodied, black on the breast and beneath the tail, with a chestnut head, the female a mixture of browns, paler on the back and flanks. Their most distinctive feature is a characteristic wedge-shaped head and beak profile. Tufted Duck dive to 3 metres or more, largely for animal food, while Pochard are shallow divers, to about one metre, largely in search of plant material, especially *Potamogeton* seeds and aquatic plant roots and stolons. Current breeding population estimates are about 400 pairs in Britain (concentrated in the east and southeast) and 20 in Ireland, together an insignificant part of the northwest European population. Pochard favour gravel pits, reservoirs, lowland lakes and wider marsh fleets, ditches and drains in the breeding season. They are in much the same habitats in winter, when they are both more widespread (though not in northwestern Scotland) and far more numerous, with estimates of midwinter peak numbers of about 50,000 in Britain and another 30,000 in Ireland.

Again similar to the Tufted Duck, our breeding Pochard are probably mostly short- to medium-haul migrants. Although ring-recoveries are not numerous, and almost all were ringed in southeast England, dispersal in winter is to all points of the compass, with about half of the longer-distance recoveries on the Continent, from Germany and the Low Countries, through France and Spain and in northern Italy, with also several in Ireland. Pochard, particularly drakes, perform moult migrations and gatherings thousands strong can occur at larger freshwaters like Abberton Reservoir in Essex and Rutland Water in the Midlands and on some loughs in northern Ireland. These flocks must be largely of continental birds, which start to arrive in July. Females and immatures move westward later than males, from September onwards, and females show a more southerly winter distribution.

The catchment area of our winter Pochard visitors, though with some overlap, is distinctly further to the south than that of the Tufted Duck, running through France, the Low Countries, Denmark, the Baltic

States (and Finland) and further to the south to the Black Sea in central Europe, extending east across central Russia to around 90°E in western Siberia. Fast-flying, our winter visitor Pochard and Tufted Ducks are genuinely long-haul migrants, and the likely origins of those that we see on our local reservoirs or gravel pits during the winter (even at city margins or centres) are as exciting and impressive as you could wish for.

Goldeneye

Pochard

Man-made waters

It is worth reflecting on the origins of many of our open freshwater sites which are so appealing to birdwatchers. Growing industrial complexes and urban populations demanded a steady supply of water, leading to the creation of mill-ponds along existing waterways, and reservoirs in the hilly catchment areas and on the outskirts of towns and cities. The creation of canals, themselves wildlife corridors, brought a further demand for reservoirs to top up the water levels across the whole canal network, located in habitats varying from relatively flat arable farmland to remote, steep-sided valleys previously watered only by high rainfall and fast-flowing streams. Lowland reservoirs in particular are one good example of the winter value of such areas to bird populations. Taking London as an example, often as much as one half of the small winter-visiting Smew population (often fewer than 100 in total) is to be found on the London reservoirs. Why this is the case for this small but extremely elegant fish-eating relative of the Goosander remains to be explained.

Sharing larger reservoirs, as a preferred winter habitat, with Goosander and Smew, are Goldeneye. Reservoirs are good places to view Goldeneye drakes, handsome in black and white with a dark bottle-green head, with white cheek patches and the golden eye of its name. The females are greyer-bodied with brown heads. Goldeneye, too, are diving duck, and are equally at home in coastal seas. A small but expanding breeding population (encouraged by the provision of nest boxes set high in trees) in Scotland now exceeds 100 pairs, the first pair having bred in 1970. The handful of recoveries from these Scottish birds suggests only limited movement in winter. However, recoveries of birds ringed overseas during the breeding season indicate winter visitors originating almost entirely from Fennoscandia and northwest Russia, spreading widely both inland and coastally throughout Britain and Ireland, where the habitat is appropriate. Late October and early November see the first arrivals, with numbers reaching a maximum (estimated at 10-15,000 overall) in midwinter, which is sustained until March, when the indications are that there may be pre-return migration gatherings off the northeast coast. There is more than a suggestion that groups or larger flocks move about during the winter, seeking better feeding or when a particular source of food runs low.

Reservoirs in winter also offer an excellent chance to watch the fishing techniques of all three divers as winter visitors (Chapter 8).

The hunting diver will patrol on the surface, often putting its head under water to scan for fish. If it sights likely prey, it seems to slip under the surface, just sinking gradually from view, leaving hardly a ripple. The various grebes (Chapter 9) may also be encountered on larger reservoirs and present even greater challenges in identification in winter plumage.

As well as these rarer waterfowl, a very significant proportion of wildfowl wintering inland are supported by man-made waters of one sort or another. In spring, these same lakes, reservoirs and gravel pits are the places to see the first migrant hirundines of the year, and, slightly later, for a chance encounter with a few of the small number of elegant Black Terns that passage through (mostly) eastern England. Two centuries ago Black Terns bred in southeastern England in some numbers, until driven out by drainage schemes, but today the population is centred in eastern Europe and Russia. We see the westernmost stragglers of birds moving north from winter quarters in the Gulf of Guinea through the Channel and North Sea. In autumn, although many thousands gather over on the Ijsselmeer and in the Elbe Estuary, we see even fewer.

Urban and industrial development demands cement and concrete, and the extracted clay, chalk, sand and gravel to produce these construction materials. One of the by-products of mineral extraction is a widespread range of wet or marshy areas, possibly going some way towards replacing wetland lost to agricultural drainage, although still not providing adequate habitat for all the birds displaced. Perhaps more importantly, these new habitats can be designed and managed from the outset or later 'converted' into nature reserves or multi-purpose recreational areas, where fishing and boating share, with nature, the addition to the landscape. However artificial, the provisions of islands safe from disturbance and predators like foxes, or the creation of shallow beaches for feeding or resting, and a mixture of deep and shallow waters, must certainly be far better than the wall-to-wall wheat crops that preceded them.

Little Ringed Plover – George H Higginbotham

During digging operations, these excavations provide nesting sites for an unusual migrant summer visitor, the Little Ringed Plover, and it is thought that most of the 1,000 or so pairs now nesting in Britain do so in man-made habitats. The first pair ever to breed in Britain did so in 1938, on a newly-excavated reservoir at Tring in Hertfordshire, one-time home town of the BTO. About 50 ring-recoveries give a pointer to a broad-front migration south in autumn through France and Spain, entering northern Africa from Morocco to Tunisia. There are no autumn recoveries to the south of this as yet, but it is thought that our breeding birds probably winter in the western Sahel, a contention supported by a single January recovery in Togo. From the viewpoint of the Little Ringed Plover, and illustrating an interesting conflict of needs, planning and social requirements lead to either a rapid back-fill after mineral extraction or flooding with water; so the dry excavation habitat available is not only limited but of short duration. Other birds take advantage of mineral workings, no matter that the opportunities are transitional; Hobby, Pied Wagtail, Sand Martin and Swallow feature in other chapters. Less mobile, Kestrel and Barn Owl hunt small mammals, and many finches exploit weedy patches. Overall, much excellent conservation work takes place on these sites.

The wild swans

When we come to look at areas of permanently or occasionally waterlogged soil adjacent to rivers and lakes (marshes, reed beds, bogs, water meadows or wet grazing), the immediate reaction is one of loss in recent years – perhaps at most over four centuries in the Fens and much less in many areas. Reclamation and drainage has amended British and Irish wetlands very considerably. Where the commercial pressures demanding a high return from every acre of land are less, as in areas of the extreme north and west, the modification and up-grading of poor wet land has been carried out on a correspondingly reduced scale. In all probability, the bulk of the impact comes from wet-meadow drainage, rather than from the loss of extensive reed bed areas that the conservationist and environmental ecologist prize so much today. The technology and ecological know-how to restore wetlands and reed beds is now substantial and continues to advance, as these areas remain of prime importance, and a number of conservation bodies have restoration or re-creation programmes actively in hand.

Open marshy areas attract some spectacular migrants, none more so than the Whooper Swan, one of the heaviest of all regular migrants, weighing in sometimes at more than 10 kg. Whooper Swans very occasionally breed in northern Scotland, but mainly in a broad sub-Arctic belt from Iceland east as far as Mongolia and northern China. They are winter visitors to Britain and Ireland, primarily in the north and west, with regular but lesser numbers in East Anglia and the southeast. Whooper Swans are catholic in both food choice and habitat, the latter ranging from estuarine flats to lochs, lakes, grassland and increasingly general farmland, although they always seem to need a large enough water body nearby for safe roosting.

Whooper Swans – Jennifer Gill

Ring-recoveries indicate that British and Irish winter migrants stem from two sources. The great majority in Ireland, Scotland and northern England are of Icelandic origin, but others (mainly down the east coast of England) come from breeding grounds in Fennoscandia and Russia. Rings, colour rings and collars combine to give a relatively detailed picture of Whooper Swan movements. They normally travel in family groups, which stay together through the winter until adults and immatures return north separately.

Arriving Whooper Swans trumpet their reappearance with their wonderfully wild calls, an audio-visual spectacle of the highest order. First landfalls are in late September/early October in the northwest of Scotland and Ireland, followed by increasing numbers of records further south in Scotland and northern England. These, it is thought, indicate a southward shift of early waves of arrivals, rather than new birds, and certainly both ring-recoveries and sightings of colour-marked birds indicate a substantial degree of

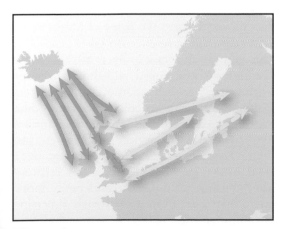

Whooper Swan

within-winter movement throughout and between Britain and Ireland. Departure northward in spring spans March and April.

Satellite tracking of individual Whooper Swans fitted with radio transmitters has helped to determine the flying times for the 800-1,000 km oversea journey from Iceland at 13-42 hours in autumn and 32-100 hours in spring. One of the benefits of radio tracking is that an individual journey and the weather *en route* can be matched. Birds with longer journey times met headwinds on the way, confirming that even the largest migrants have hazards to overcome, while in better conditions one autumn bird flew the 1,100 km from southeast Iceland to Co. Donegal in 36 hours. In particularly bad weather, water birds (Whooper Swans included) do have the great advantage of being able to land on the sea, resting and sitting it out until conditions improve.

Bewick's Swans, the smallest of our three swans, traditionally favour natural shallow freshwaters surrounded by grazing grassland, but are increasingly visiting stubbles and root crops on adjacent farmland. Once here, they tend to remain on traditional wintering areas, visited by parent birds year after year, each year (with luck) with a new brood of young. Bewick's Swans have been well-studied using ringing, colour rings and neck collars and, on an unusual individual basis, by variations in their yellow and black beak patterns. The late Sir Peter Scott, his family and colleagues compiled a huge amount of detailed family history information about the Bewick's Swans at Slimbridge and Welney in this way.

Bewick's Swans breed in the High Arctic of Russia, from the Kanin Peninsular at 45°E to the Chukchi Sea at 145°E. The track of our winter visitors is clear to see and on an unusually narrow front. The first leg from the breeding grounds takes the family parties via the White Sea, thence through the south Baltic, Denmark and the Low Countries to Britain and Ireland, where they arrive in October/November. Calculated with assistance of some satellite-tracked birds, it is

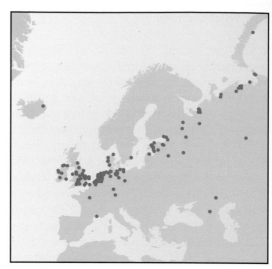

Bewick's Swan

thought that the journey of 3,000 to 3,500 km is made with two or three stop-overs. Energetic calculations suggest a flight range of around 1,500 km before a pause for rest and refuelling becomes necessary, which equates to 24 hours at 60 k.p.h. The spring return journey begins in February and March and takes several weeks, allowing for feeding and rest *en route* and timed to finish as the spring thaw frees the tundra breeding areas of ice. Radio tracking, by the Wildfowl and Wetlands Trust, coupled with meteorological records suggests that, in both spring and autumn, Bewick's Swans wait for favourable tail-winds (southwest and northeast respectively) before departing on any journey leg.

What of our third swan, the Mute Swan, so called because of its restricted grunting, hissing vocabulary? We think of Mute Swans as a year-round presence on lakes near us; is this always the case? Over 80,000 Mute Swans have been ringed, and almost a quarter of these recovered. In addition, large numbers have been fitted with colour rings and some with neck collars. To all intents and purposes the answer to the question is most often, yes, Mute Swans are sedentary. Certainly, once adults have established a breeding territory they remain faithful to it and rarely move more than 2 km from it. Although dispersing juveniles and individuals from non-breeding flocks move further, the typical recovery distance remains less than 20 km. Young birds become independent during their first winter but do not breed until they are at least three years old, this age being dependent to some extent on a territory becoming available. Adult birds with youngsters moult on their territories but immature birds, which gather in non-breeding flocks, can travel 100 km or more to safe, food-rich moulting waters. Northwestern European populations do have a regular migratory pattern, reflected in about 60 exchanges between Britain and France, the Low Countries, Denmark and the Baltic States, so birdwatchers in the south and east may (just) encounter the occasional migrant during the winter.

Wetland waders

Waders, too, appreciate the rich and comparatively easy feeding offered by the moist margin between water and its reedbed or grassland surrounds. Here you will see Black-tailed Godwits and Curlew, which feature in the chapter on estuaries, but two others, Ruff and Snipe, are most appropriately discussed here. Each is intriguing in its own right, each fascinating and each part of the overall charisma of the marshes. Snipe are marshmen's birds, the sort of bird you can imagine leaping from beneath a startled Pip's feet, as he walked through the murk of the North Kent Marshes towards his assignation with the escaped convict in Dickens' *Great Expectations*. In brown, black and buff stripes, they are supremely well camouflaged amongst the broken reeds and sedges at the water margin, and they fly only at the last moment. As they go, towering rapidly away in characteristic zig-zag flight, they shriek a harsh warning to other birds nearby. Amongst other claims to distinction, they must have just about the longest beak for their body size of any of our birds.

The Snipe must be one of *the* most typical waders of all sorts of marshes, bogs, fens, swamps and wet meadows. Britain and Ireland have a breeding population estimated at 40,000 pairs, about a quarter of them in Ireland. Though this is a great reduction on past numbers, they remain widespread, but

their breeding distribution is biased towards the north and west.

British and Irish breeding Snipe are short- to medium-haul migrants, some moving only a few kilometres but with a median ring-recovery distance around 270 km. Autumn migration begins in August, first in Scotland and northern England, where the trend is to move southwestward to Ireland. More southerly birds move within the country but may occasionally winter on the Continent. There are reports from Finland and Germany but the bulk are in France and Iberia, with one in Morocco and one, presumably both wind-blown and relieved to make landfall, on the Azores, out in the Atlantic.

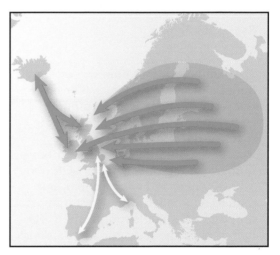

Snipe

In winter, those of our breeding birds that remain are greatly outnumbered by migrants. Though Snipe are notoriously difficult to count, most estimates suggest hundreds of thousands of winter immigrants, some more than one million. These migrants are of astonishing wide origin and begin to arrive in September. Huge numbers of the Faeroese race *faeroeensis* cross from Iceland (and presumably some from the Faeroes) to northwestern Scotland and (primarily) Ireland. Appreciably milder during mid-winter than Britain, Ireland also receives large numbers of Snipe from Fennoscandia, the Baltic States and the Low Countries. Greater numbers from the same group of countries plus those from Russia

Ruff

Ruff – Colin Varndell

The Ruff breeds in Britain but with only a handful of nesting females (Reeves) on our wetlands each year. Two hundred years ago, before wetland drainage reached devastating levels, the indications are that Ruff were far more numerous. Today, compared with about 150,000 pairs in Fennoscandia, our minute population is the westernmost outpost of the Ruff's range. The male Ruff in breeding plumage are amongst the most spectacular of birds, the huge ruff of feathers (black, white or chestnut) the more conspicuous because the males gather in groups (leks) to display collectively at traditional lekking grounds. Display is largely aggressive with much leaping and rushing toward each other, ruffs flared to the full. In contrast, the females watching the performance are dressed in subdued browns, as are the males once breeding is over.

We know very little indeed about our Ruff population and its movements, but rather more of them as passage migrants, passing south through Britain (mainly in the east) and Ireland in autumn, and in lesser numbers northwards in spring. Autumn passage runs from August to October, Ruff from Fennoscandia and Arctic Russia moving southwest to Britain, thence to the Low Countries, France and Iberia and into west Africa, on a broad front, to wintering grounds stretching from Senegal east into Mali. Throughout Africa, where Ruff winter widely, there is a lot of evidence that the further south the sample, the greater proportion of females, reaching 90% in Kenya and South Africa, interesting as yet another case where females are substantially smaller and lighter than males but travel further. Spring passage seems to run on a more easterly track, indicated by numbers of recoveries in Italy in March and April.

and Central Europe come to England, Wales and Scotland. Some of these continental migrants pass on through Britain to France and Iberia. All in all, though our breeding Snipe may be a relatively small part of the northwest and central European population, numbers here through the winter underline once again the importance of our islands (in this case our wetlands) to European bird populations.

The fringing reedbeds

Among the most conspicuous components of freshwater marshland, particularly lakeside and ditch margins, and probably the feature showing the greatest reduction in area over the last millennium, are reedbeds. In smaller ponds, reedbeds are often of the highly invasive bulrush *Typha*, but of greater ecological diversity so far as birds are concerned are the larger and more visually pleasing expanses of the reed *Phragmites*, tall, with plumed flower-heads flexing with the wind. Difficult terrain for birdwatchers to scan other than from a hide, usually on the margin, reedbeds demand care from researchers in minimising damage to the reeds and avoiding disturbance, but for both researchers and viewing birdwatchers, the rewards of sustained vigil can be great.

Reedbeds have a number of highly characteristic birds (with summer migrants predominating), many of which may be vocal (some tunefully so), some charismatic, but most not only secretive when it comes to appearing in vision, but also very well camouflaged! The most obvious bird, although rarely vocal, is the Marsh Harrier. Broader-winged than Hen or Montagu's Harriers, it uses the same hunting strategy, tirelessly quartering its hunting territory on wings held in a stiff shallow V, with wing flaps only when necessary. Flying only a few metres above the ground – or water – the Marsh Harrier takes prey, ranging from amphibians and fish, through small mammals to birds, by surprise and seizes them in talons at the end of long legs to keep the wings out of harm's way when making the kill. Few sights are more exciting than watching the tumbling mid-air

Marsh Harrier – Tommy Holden

food-pass of prey from the outstretched talons of the male to the female.

The Marsh Harrier breeding population, with strongholds in East Anglia and Kent, now well exceeds 100 pairs, and is a tribute to the efforts of conservation bodies which have raised the population from just a single pair (at Minsmere) in 1971 to the current level. Marsh Harriers traditionally nest on a platform of vegetation deep in the reeds, although increasing numbers have moved into crops like oilseed rape in adjacent fields. They are long-haul migrants, although a few remain in England through the winter, mostly the larger females better able to compete for a lessened food supply. It may be that some roam within Britain and Ireland before departure, but most seem to have left on their southward journey by October. Ring-recoveries outline a route through France and Iberia to northwestern Africa, where some overwinter while others move further down the west African coast. Most are back on their breeding grounds by April.

Given its size, at not that much smaller than a Heron, few birds can be as elusive as the Bittern. A sighting of this reedbed specialist, streaked black, brown and buff plumage providing near-perfect camouflage against the reeds, really makes the day, whether it is flopping away over the reeds in broad-winged flight, hunting stealthily or (and maybe particularly) when you have just managed to distinguish its motionless shape from the surrounding reeds! The Bittern's rather more conspicuous fog-horn-like booming calls, produced from January into late spring, must once have been a widespread feature of wetland Britain. The shopping list for a Boxing Day banquet organised by Richard III in 1399 includes amongst a wide array of items five 'bitores', and they featured regularly on menus between the 14th and 16th Centuries. Today, five for the table would make a detectable hole in winter Bittern numbers.

We know little about our breeding Bitterns from ringing and radio-tracking, save that our breeding adults seem to be relatively sedentary while young birds do disperse from their natal reedbed soon after fledging, and in no particular direction. Winter Bitterns in Britain and Ireland have a widespread but unpredictable distribution. Numbers are augmented by overseas birds from September onwards, with a detectable peak in December and January, but are unlikely to exceed 200 overall. Ring-recoveries from continental schemes indicate that this 'influx' is likely to be birds from Sweden, Germany and the Low Countries, as variations in the timing of their arrival broadly coincide with the year-to-year variations in the onset of cold weather in those countries. We can but hope that current conservation interest in Bitterns and a better knowledge of their detailed habitat requirements leads to an increasing population, winter and summer, of this fascinating bird.

Water Rail

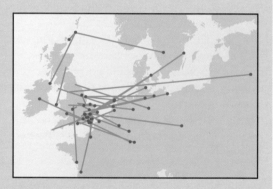

Water Rail – John Harding

Water Rails are more often heard than seen, and 'squeaking like a stuck pig' is entirely appropriate as a description of their calls. With a leaden-grey belly and mottled brown upperparts, Water Rails are sombre in plumage, relieved only by boldly barred black and white flanks, a white undertail, and a longish downcurved red bill, which is used to lethal effect to stab any unwary rodent or smaller bird, especially in freezing weather.

When, seemingly rarely, they do fly they do so on feebly fluttering wings, legs trailing, low over the reeds. Ring-recoveries therefore come as a surprise. Though there are only about 100 of them (30% ringed overseas) they do provide a clear indication that Water Rails are capable of long-haul migration. It seems that most of 'our' birds, those ringed in Britain and Ireland in the breeding season, are sedentary and rarely travel more than 20 km. The recoveries of birds ringed elsewhere indicate an autumn immigration into Britain and Ireland from central and northwestern Europe. Difficult though it is to census Water Rails in summer or winter, it would be fascinating to know just how large is the winter influx, which includes birds turning up in unusual places, like city centres.

Smaller birds, some conspicuous ...

Though specialised as a habitat, the scrubby or grass and sedge margins of wet areas, and particularly fully developed reedbeds, are not without small birds too. Year-round, the most prominent of these is the Reed Bunting, the male strikingly black-headed, white-collared and chestnut-backed in summer but as well camouflaged as the female in winter. Reed Buntings can be found in most swamps and reedbeds but are less restricted to this habitat than their name implies, venturing onto farmland and even young forestry plantations. The males' raucously repetitive song and choice of prominent perches makes them difficult to miss in summer, but in winter and in drabber plumage, when they may be the only passerines in the reeds, they are far less conspicuous.

Ring-recoveries show that the great majority of British and Irish Reed Buntings are sedentary, and also generally site-faithful in the breeding season. Post-breeding dispersal is normally in the order of only a few kilometres or less, but some (often females) move further; 300 km would be the extreme. The tendency for these longer movements seems to be of more northerly birds moving generally south towards a warmer climate. During the winter, just over 50 ring-recoveries from European schemes indicate that some (probably not many) Fennoscandian-breeding Reed Buntings overwinter in Britain (and maybe Ireland) and that rather more of these birds passage through eastern Britain *en route* to France and the Low Countries.

Reed Bunting – Tommy Holden

Much scarcer and pretty well confined to English reedbeds, with an easterly bias even there, is the Bearded Tit. Attractive to watch, because of its agility among swaying reed stems, the male elegant with a blue-grey head and black moustaches, the Bearded Tit is not a tit at all. It is usually classified as the solitary representative in Europe of the parrotbills, a family typical of southeast Asia. From only a couple of pairs at Minsmere after the cold winters up to 1947, our population has risen to about 400 pairs, despite occasional setbacks due to severe winters. Some of this increase may be the outcome of the draining of the polders in the Netherlands.

Looking like oversize Long-tailed Tits, Bearded Tits share the short rounded wings, long tail and apparently feeble flight of that species. Ring-recoveries indicate that, while some may be sedentary year-round in their home reedbeds, many are better classified as short-haul migrants. After the breeding season there is a general dispersal broadly westwards from the east coast, initially over a few kilometres but by October journeys of 100-400 km occur. During the winter, birds may move (over similar distances) between reedbeds, but remember even small patches of *Phragmites* along a ditch may hold, albeit briefly, a small flock of Bearded Tits. Between March and April, most have returned to their home reedbed. As yet, no British-ringed Bearded Tit has crossed to the Continent, but more than 20 ringed in the Low Countries, France and Germany (and one from Switzerland) have crossed to England. Many of these have been associated with occasional eruptions from continental reedbeds as populations reach bursting point.

... some inconspicuous, but vocal

Five species of warblers make regular, rather than casual, use of our reedbeds and swamps. Four are summer migrants, the fifth (Cetti's Warbler), resident year-round. Cetti's Warbler is interesting not just as one of the two (with the Dartford Warbler) year-round warblers, but also as a recent colonist. Continuing a spread through Europe, a handful of British records occurred in the

1960s, with first nesting (in the extreme southeast of England) in the 1970s. Since then, the population has fluctuated (dropping dramatically during severe winters) but increased to several hundred pairs, now centred more in south-central England than near the initial colonisation. With its explosive 'churr-hink' call, this russet-plumaged warbler is not easily overlooked in reeds and damp scrub, despite its secretive habits.

Of the four migrant warblers, the streaked and mouse-like Grasshopper Warbler is the most difficult to see. It is, though, far easier to hear. The song is an extended high-pitched and monotonous churring, often likened to the noise of a fishing reel ratchet as the line is drawn out, and out ......, sometimes for minutes on end. As the male, singing from a hidden perch, turns his head, so the reeling becomes ventriloquial and difficult to pinpoint. No bird better underlines the adage 'you never know', as Grasshopper Warblers can turn up in a variety of habitats, usually but not always damp, from rough grassland and scrub to young forestry plantations. This is reflected in its wide breeding distribution across Britain and Ireland, though it is never numerous.

Surprisingly, about 17,000 Grasshopper Warblers have been ringed but, more in line with expectations for so notoriously secretive and inconspicuous a bird, only 30 recovered. These though, coupled with observatory and other observations from focused studies, do provide a surprisingly reasonable picture of their movements. Southbound migrants appear in July on the south coast with the first of three waves of migrating juveniles, presumably representing three broods of young. Adults depart at the same time as the second wave of young in late August and September, before the last wave of young leave in late September. Scandinavian breeding birds passage through Britain and Ireland, and move with British and Irish breeders in comparatively short stages through France to Iberia and northwestern Africa. There, contact is lost until birds appear in west Africa, south of the Sahara, where a major

wintering area has been located in Senegal. Birds leave Senegal in February on what appears to be a steady-paced return journey, it is thought making use of ephemeral wetlands in northwestern Africa to feed up for the onward stages, arriving back in late April and May.

Reed Warblers, as their name validly implies, are strongly associated with *Phragmites*, but not necessarily in reedbeds, as pairs can be quite at home in the fringe of reeds round gravel pits or in marshland ditches. Their repetitive and metallic song, with interspersed phrases of mimicry of any nearby songbird, is a summer feature of reeds in a distribution biased heavily towards southern and eastern England.

With over half a million Reed Warblers ringed and about 6,000 recovered, a reasonable picture of their migration can be built up. Departure seems to be on a broad front across the North Sea and English Channel into the Low Countries (particularly Belgium) and France, thence in steady stages down the French Atlantic coast to Iberia, where recoveries in Portugal again show a coastal bias. It seems likely that clusters of recoveries are indicative of regular stop-over areas, where traditionally good feeding is available to fuel the next stages of their journeys. The crossing into northwestern Africa seems to be on a broad front, but regrettably we know little of the departure weights of southbound migrants from this point on. Until the Mediterranean crossing, all the evidence from birds weighed

Reed Warbler – Kevin Carlson

while being ringed is that Reed Warblers put on comparatively little pre-migratory fat at each stage, increasing in weight by 20% or less, supporting the view that their migration is in short-haul stages.

Reed Warbler

Precise information on Reed Warbler winter quarters remains to be discovered, although a number of recoveries from Mauritania to Guinea-Bissau point to this area in west Africa, maybe for wintering birds, maybe as a staging post prior to an eastward extension (indicated by a mid-winter recovery in Ghana). In March, ring-recoveries indicate that return movement is under way, and that it may well be on a broader front across northwestern Africa and both more rapid and possibly in longer stages than in autumn, borne out by the relative scarcity of spring recoveries in Iberia and France. Unusually, it is not just the adults that return faithfully to their breeding areas; ring-recoveries suggest that many returning juveniles head to their natal areas to breed.

There is good evidence that in autumn British and Irish migrant numbers are swollen by Reed Warblers departing from breeding areas in Fennoscandia. It may be that these individuals are drifted to the west of their normal route by easterly winds, as there is no evidence of a similar return route to the breeding grounds via Britain and Ireland in spring.

In several ways, the Sedge Warbler shows interesting differences, even contrasts, to the Reed Warbler, although their songs are similar. A little experience will tune the ear to the Sedge Warblers' slightly chirpier, less metallic song, rather more tuneful and with longer phrases than the Reed, but still with plenty of mimicry. The briefest of glimpses of a Sedge Warbler's dark-streaked upperparts, dark crown and striking eyestripe will suffice to confirm its identity. Sedge Warblers are far more catholic in their habitat choice than Reed; almost any damp, vegetation will do, and not always damp, as sometimes they may nest in brambles on quite dry areas. In consequence (at least in part) Sedge Warblers are far more widely distributed across all of Britain and Ireland except the uplands, and four or five times more numerous than the estimated 40-80,000 Reed Warbler pairs. Unlike the neatly woven nest of the Reed Warbler, constructed within and suspended from a group of reed stems, Sedge Warblers build a typical cup nest buried deep in vegetation. Perhaps ease of access is why Reed Warblers feature so much more frequently as Cuckoo hosts.

Differences between the two warblers in migratory pattern may be more subtle, but are just as fascinating. On the face of it, the map shows more similarities than differences, apart from a rather wider range of ring-recoveries from Africa, although the African recoveries need to be viewed with unusual caution. Overall, of over 4,000 Sedge Warbler recoveries 80% or more have been recaptured live by ringers, some of these in Africa on special expeditions investigating the winter quarters of British and Irish birds. In consequence, the map not only reflects where Sedge Warblers were, but where they and ringers coincided in time and space.

It is thought that autumn migration begins in late July, with Sedge Warblers searching for reedbeds with high infestations of plum-reed aphids, common enough but erratic in quantity and appearance. Feeding largely on these, Sedge Warblers lay down pre-migratory fat in southern British and northwestern French reedbeds, to the extent that on average they put on an additional 50% of their bodyweight as fat, and some may almost double in weight! The fat is stored in the body cavity round the kidneys and just beneath the skin, in the hand often visible as a whitish pad in the fork of the 'wishbone', and even beneath the eyelids, reducing the eyes to slits. Departing in August/September, with this fuel load on board, Sedge Warblers can undertake not only long-haul but rapid southerly journeys.

In contrast to Reed Warblers, there are comparatively few autumn recoveries in southern France and Iberia. Most Sedge Warblers may migrate across France, Iberia,

Sedge Warbler

northern Africa and the Sahara in long stages, with little need for further intensive feeding stops. Winter quarters (bearing in mind any possible bias due to ringing expeditions) south of the Sahara are reached in September, with the majority of reports in Senegal. Significant numbers have also been reported in Mali and Ghana, with occasional records from several other countries in that region. Interestingly, there are enough ring-recoveries to indicate that Sedge Warblers from Ireland and western Britain winter in Senegal, while recoveries of birds from eastern Britain are in the main from Senegal eastwards to Mali and Ghana. A handful of recoveries show that an unknown number of breeding birds from southern Scandinavia passage through Britain in autumn, to similar wintering areas, and return through Britain in spring.

Return migration in spring begins in late February/early March, with pre-migratory fattening placing heavy dependence on the wetlands south of the Sahara within the basins of the Senegal and Niger Rivers. Sedge Warbler passage is again fast and direct, with a handful of recoveries in northern Africa and movement through Iberia and France, apparently on a broad front. Many are back on territory early in April, with a possibly unusual tendency for adult males to be site-faithful but not adult females or year-old birds – another contrast with the Reed Warbler. All in all, a phenomenal performance for a bird weighing in mid-season around 12 g, less than half an ounce!

Freshwaters and their associated wetlands encompass a diversity of related habitats with as broad a range of migrant visitors as any other. Each has a fascinating migratory story and surprisingly few of these stories are in any way repetitive, such is the way of both ecology and evolution. Over open freshwaters will fly the first Sand Martin, then Swallow, of the year – and in the willows nearby the first Chiffchaff and later Willow Warbler will sing. The nearest lake, reservoir or gravel pit is the place that many of us go in March and April, not just out of interest but for that uplift in spirits provided by the spring, and by those early migrants.

Mountain, moorland and heath

Wild open spaces

With all their remoteness and grandeur, it is easy to imagine that the mountain areas of Britain and Ireland have persisted almost since the dawn of time unchanged, untouched by the works of man. This is rarely the case and, with increased leisure time and vastly improved travel facilities, these areas are today subject to the frequent human presence of walkers, climbers, naturalists and winter sports enthusiasts. However inadvert, there is disturbance, perhaps the more noticeable because of the previous isolation, and inevitably also litter and food scraps. The ski-lifts provided for winter sports provide easy access to the high tops which previously would only be visited by those whose fitness, endurance and enthusiasm carried them up extremely arduous and sometimes dangerous mountain tracks.

At the highest altitudes – 2-4,000 feet (600-1,200 m) – exposure to the extremes of climate (rain, low temperatures, and strong winds in particular) affects not just visiting humans but also the plant life of the mountain tops themselves. Plant growth is often scanty (but often extremely beautiful in the case, for example, of the saxifrages) and always very slow. Thus damage, even minor, be it due to grazing by Red Deer or the introduced Reindeer, to the trampling of human feet or the passage of ski-lift construction vehicles, can take many years to restore. In those years,

erosion may scour away the scanty traces of soil, leaving bare rock upon which nothing will thrive, save perhaps a few lichens.

It may be obvious but it is still worth noting, that the further south from the North Pole you travel, as a generality, the milder the climate gets but also that as you ascend a mountain range, the cooler the weather gets. Thus, in ecological terms, a low altitude rocky outcrop in the Icelandic tundra is matched, in terms of vegetation and climate, by a mountain top in Scotland, and a rocky outcrop in lowland Scottish moorland roughly equates to the highest points in the Pennines. Birds fit into the niches available to them, and thus it is that the Snow Bunting, widespread from sea level upwards north of the Arctic Circle, is confined in Scotland to the highest of mountain tops.

Moorland magic

Surrounding the real mountains of the north and west are vast areas of moorland, usually characterised by heathers, *Vaccinium* (Bilberry and its relatives), grasses like *Molinia*, and mosses like *Sphagnum*. Over time, considerable areas of moorland are regularly reshaped, particularly in Ireland, by the activities of local peat cutters seeking domestic fuel and, more recently, by commercial companies extracting vast tonnages of peat to fuel power stations or to improve the heavy or chalky soils of lowland gardens, hundreds of miles away.

What is less often realised is the size of the moorland acreage – or better square mileage – that resulted from forest clearances. These clearances, mostly in recent centuries, were carried out with the initial aim of increasing grazing land and replacing non-profitable (at that time) timber with more profitable stock. In upland areas, man-made impacts of this nature are exacerbated by the climatic conditions, primarily by heavy rainfall. Such a devastation has produced much of the moorland in Britain and Ireland, and in many cases it is easy to find the old pine stumps half buried and semi-fossilised in the peat. Thus, as with the conversion of lowland forests to farmland, although it is possible to regard the initial limited clearances as beneficial to birds in general, the continual clearance of moorland has ultimately resulted in an impoverished bird population, leaving the Meadow Pipit predominating. In many ways, much as large moorland areas are essential to the ecological and habitat balance of our countryside, it could be argued that there is scope for reversion and many 'moorland deserts' would only be improved by sympathetic forest replanting programmes.

Moorland, especially at lower altitudes in the far north, is not the unbroken expanse of heather and *Vaccinium* that it might appear. In many areas, viewed from the air, moor and water are mixed in roughly equal quantities, forming an intricate jigsaw puzzle so irregular are their outlines. Here Red-throated Divers, though scarce, are characteristic breeding birds, favouring remote smaller lochs in northwestern Scotland, the Northern and Western Isles, and with a small Irish population. Elsewhere, Red-throated Divers breed to the far north of North America, Greenland, Fennoscandia and Russia. The nest, with its distinctive olive sausage-shaped eggs, is usually within a metre of the water. Divers in general are supremely well adapted to life on and under water – slim and streamlined with legs and feet (with lobed toes for swimming) set well back towards the tail. This makes them clumsy on land, hence the proximity of the nest to water, and provides one clue to the divers' colloquial name 'loons'. Discussion centres upon whether loon stems from *lomr*, the Icelandic name for lame (the link to clumsy), or whether loons feature so much in folk lore because of their wild barking cries linking the birds with lunacy.

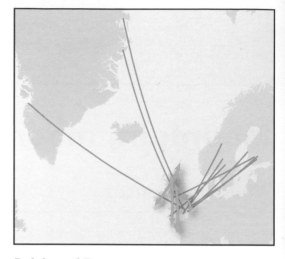

Red-throated Diver

Just under 3,000 Red-throated Divers have been ringed in Britain, and just under 200 recovered. The ring-recoveries, coupled with recoveries of birds ringed overseas and direct observations, allow a picture of their movements to be composed. The Highlands and Islands breeding population disperses widely in late summer round the British and Irish coasts, across the Channel to the Breton coast and across to the North Sea coast of the Low Countries. Occasional birds also fetch up on inland fresh waters. They are strongly site-faithful, and begin to return to their nesting lochs in March and April. Ring-recoveries of migrants from elsewhere indicate that wintering numbers of Red-throated Divers

Red-throated Diver – Derek Belsey

round our coasts may be augmented by birds from breeding populations in Greenland and Fennoscandia, and no doubt also from Iceland.

Redolent though Red-throated Diver calls may be of the Highlands and Islands, they are nothing compared to the eerie yodelling of the Great Northern Diver, which must be one of the most evocative of all bird songs from wild places. Though it has bred in Scotland, Great Northerns are scarce winter visitors from their northern breeding grounds to British and Irish offshore waters, occasionally seen inland on larger freshwaters. The Black-throated Diver does breed on larger lochs in northwestern Scotland but, with only about 150 pairs, the population is barely 10% of that of the Red-throated. Few Black-throated have been ringed in Britain and Ireland, and none recovered, but observation indicates that our birds generally winter offshore round the coastline, where they are joined and outnumbered by birds presumably from the northern European population centred largely in Russia.

Small bird survival

Relatively few small birds find the windblown and often wet expanses of moorland an acceptable home, but the Meadow Pipit is perhaps the most characteristic small bird of the mosses, heather, bracken, bog and rough grassland. For much of the year, wherever they are, pipits seem to spend a lot of time on the ground, running along at high speed snapping up insects. They are small birds, like elongated Dunnocks with athletic legs and dusky buff underparts. The back is a tweedy mixture of dark streaks on a brownish or olive background, sometimes quite golden in autumn. This gives excellent camouflage in a peat or dry grass habitat. One exception to this earth-bound way of life is the display flight, when the male rises steeply 50 feet (15 m) or more into the air, then slowly descends – wings extended and fluttering rapidly, tail fanned – just like a parachute, producing all the while a cheerfully tinkling trilling song.

Meadow Pipits are numerous and widespread from southern Greenland, Iceland and the

Faeroes eastwards through Europe to western Asia around the Ob River. Estimates put the breeding population in Britain and Ireland at about three million birds, and the wintering numbers at more than half this. Substantial numbers (almost 200,000) have been ringed, but fewer less than 1,000 recovered. This may be because, even when dead, they are concealed by their camouflage, or because of the low chances of finding them in the remote areas Meadow Pipits frequent. On the plus side, however, Meadow Pipits are amongst the most conspicuous of daytime migrants, not least because of their piercing 'seet' flight calls, and this assists in plotting their migratory flyways.

Meadow Pipit

Ring-recoveries and direct observations at bird observatories and elsewhere indicate a steady southward movement extending from July through to October or November. Some of our birds do not leave Britain and Ireland, and simply move from the inhospitable uplands to milder lowland areas. Those that leave Britain and Ireland head broadly south into France and then southwest into Portugal and Spain, some crossing over into north Africa. The severity and timing of the winter has a considerable influence on both migration seasons and on the northern limits of Meadow Pipit winter quarters. Numbers peak around the Straits of Gibraltar in October/November, and again in March/April, as birds return north. Movements of British and Irish birds are augmented in both migration seasons by birds *en route* to and from Scandinavia and Iceland, and certainly northern birds have longer wings and more marked migratory tendencies. It seems that birds from further east in the breeding range head directly towards the Mediterranean. There is as yet no evidence that foreign birds overwinter in Britain and Ireland.

In the absence of suitable song posts in the treeless moorland terrain, the use of song flights for display and for marking territorial boundaries seems logical for birds like the Meadow Pipit and the Skylark. Although to us both are pleasant songsters, these smaller birds take their lives in their hands during display flights, as they become conspicuous targets for the two moorland falcons, the Peregrine (which also inhabits mountains proper and which would probably find them too small a meal to be worth the hunting effort) and the smaller Merlin. Clearly, in the course of evolution the benefits of advertisement in this

Merlin

way to the population as a whole must have outweighed the hazard, as the technique is so widely used.

The sight of a Merlin in hunting action makes the day for birdwatching beginners and experts alike. Merlins are normally low-level strikers, cruising often not much more than a metre above the ground and taking their prey (mostly small birds) by surprise after a short high-speed chase. Merlins are birds for all seasons; in summer they are very much moorland birds of the north and west of Britain and Ireland, while in winter the best chance of seeing them is hunting over open country, often marshland or rough grazing, inland or near the coast. It would be easy to suppose that the breeding population simply leaves the moors, by the onset of winter almost devoid of small birds, to overwinter nearer sea-level, where their small bird prey is still abundant, but ring-recoveries demonstrate that the picture is far more complex.

In winter, some of our breeding Merlins do stay within Britain and Ireland, often only 100 km or so from their breeding grounds, but others migrate, sometimes fairly long distances south or southeast. Those from the north head

Merlin – George H Higginbotham

towards Denmark and the Low Countries, more southerly breeders down into France and Iberia. During the winter, our breeding birds are not truly replaced but simply boosted in numbers in their changed habitat, sharing their hunting niche with birds of the slightly larger and darker Icelandic race *subaesolon,* for which Britain and Ireland are probably the main wintering grounds.

The other and most conspicuous moorland bird of prey is the Hen Harrier. This is the most widespread of British and Irish harriers in summer, over much of north Wales, northwestern England, Scotland and Ireland, never common but rarely too difficult to find. Hen Harriers are also our most numerous winter harrier, when many still range over the moors and nearby farmland, while others are to be seen further south, outside the breeding range in the English lowlands, often coastal but also over rough country inland. Whilst a displaying pair of Hen Harriers is a spectacular sight, the male almost silver in the sunlight over a heather-clad hillside, so too in a different way is the steady dusk assembly (sometimes by the dozen) of winter Hen Harriers coming to roost in reed beds or rough cover.

Hen Harriers are well-studied, with ring-recoveries augmented by sight records of birds fitted (as nestlings) with conspicuous colour-coded wing tags. After the breeding season there is a general dispersal, often for no great distance and in no particular direction. Actual migration patterns are quite complex, due to the differences between the sexes and to different behaviour patterns depending on breeding location. The breeding population in southwest Scotland is the most sedentary, with little distant dispersal and even less migration – by either sex.

More-northerly Scottish breeders disperse, but not necessarily far, and around half of the males and three quarters of the females overwinter. Not only do more males migrate than females, but they tend to migrate considerably further (in one study, average male movement was 67 km against the female's 25 km) and generally migrants are more likely to be immatures than

adults. Those of either sex that do make medium-haul migrations head initially to southwest England, and from there to Brittany and Iberia, it seems in a direct oversea flight. The suggestion of a direct routing is supported by the absence of sightings of wing-tagged birds in northwest France, where substantial numbers of Hen Harriers overwinter, presumably of Fennoscandian origin. There are very few sightings of tagged birds among the wintering population in south, southeast and eastern England, which suggests that these birds too are of continental origin, an idea supported by some 15 ring-recoveries from Fennoscandia and the Low Countries. This routine westward movement into England in autumn may be amplified by an overspill from the adjacent continental winter population, when severe winter grips Western Europe.

Wader highlights

Though a possible target for Peregrines, Curlew are too big for Merlins to tackle. The Curlew's display flight must surely rank as one of *the* moorland sights and especially sounds for the birdwatcher, a continuous stream of the most thrilling calls, gurgling, bubblings and

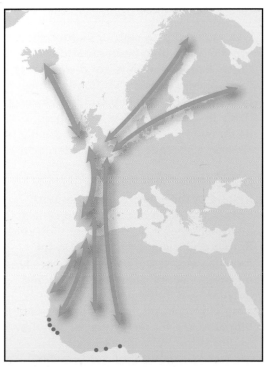

Whimbrel

whistling, ending in the evocative 'coo-er-leew' from which its name is derived. Curlew migrations are dealt with in Chapter 9.

The substantially smaller, shorter-billed Whimbrel, still Curlew-like and equally distinctive for its seven-fold fluting whistling call (the 'seven-tattler' of old) is a rare breeding bird in Britain and Ireland, with the couple of hundred pairs across the Northern Isles residing at the southern extreme of the Whimbrel's boreal range. Occasional individuals winter on western estuaries, but the birds most of us see quite regularly on spring migration (April/May) through our estuaries are heading towards breeding grounds in Iceland, Fennoscandia and Russia. Ring-recoveries, though few, also support the view that southbound migrants in autumn (July - September) are primarily from those same major breeding grounds, with our breeding birds intermingled, heading for wintering grounds on the West African coast from Mauritania east to Nigeria (Map: p107).

Golden Plover

Golden Plover – George H Higginbotham

The soulful piping calls of Golden Plover are typical of high open moorland. Once located, which is not always easy, the Golden Plover's own flamboyance becomes apparent. The Golden Plover is richly flecked on the back with gold, as its name implies, set off by apparently striking white-edged black underparts.

Golden Plover breed from Iceland to Ireland at the western extreme, east across moorland and tundra to central Siberia. They winter throughout lowland Britain and Ireland, both on coastal marshes and estuaries and extensively on open, usually damp, farmland and pasture. Are these our breeding birds simply dropping to lower altitudes and unfrozen soil for the winter, or are they migrants from elsewhere? Ring-recoveries suggest that our breeding birds, from the northwestern parts of each of Ireland, Wales, England and Scotland, disperse soon after the young have flown but may not immediately travel far. Actual migration starts in early autumn, and immature birds may migrate some weeks later than adults. Probably Golden Plover are best described as partial migrants, as some British and Irish breeders will remain on farmland and estuaries across lowland Britain and Ireland through the winter, while others will make moderate-haul migrations, primarily into France and Iberia (where hunting pressure is high) but also, and probably in lesser numbers, to northwestern Africa and northern Italy.

There is some evidence that some of the Fennoscandian population migrates through eastern England, especially in the autumn, most of these it seems routed through the Netherlands. The more northerly breeders may well leapfrog over populations such as our own, also heading for Spain and North Africa. The return of our birds in spring is comparatively early, with many of the British and Irish breeding population back on their breeding grounds by late February (weather permitting) or early March. More northerly breeders migrate up from the Mediterranean, departing in mid-February, passing through Britain and Ireland and the Low Countries in April and May, then onwards to Iceland or Fennoscandia. Siberian birds are

Very special as breeding birds to most British and Irish birdwatchers, Greenshank are confined in the breeding season to the remotest parts of northern Scotland. Here a tiny population of somewhere between 1,000 and 2,000 pairs is established as the western outpost of the Greenshank breeding range, which extends in wet boreal forest and taiga east through Lapland right across greater Russia and Siberia to Kamchatka beside the Bering Sea. Scottish Greenshank breed in more open terrain, where bogs and pools are

thought to travel on a direct route from North Africa, across the Mediterranean and northeastwards through eastern Europe to their destination.

What is perhaps most striking about the migration map is the marked movement of the Icelandic Golden Plover population to winter (almost to depend on wintering) in Ireland and to a lesser extent in western Britain. Just what proportion of the Icelandic population stays in Ireland and western Britain and what proportion flies on to Iberia and northern Africa we do not know.

punctuated by rocky outcrops. To some ears rivalling the Curlew, the male proclaims his territory with a blood-tingling sustained yodelling melody, delivered in a swooping song flight. Greenshank maintain different territories through the breeding season, for display, for nesting, and for feeding and chick rearing, to which the chicks are escorted soon after hatching.

In spring and autumn, the picture is different. Greenshank are widespread, if never common, across Britain and Ireland, using a variety of sheltered coastal and inland freshwater habitats and giving away their presence by their striking pale winter plumage and diagnostic trisyllabic 'tew-tew-tew' call. Some overwinter, especially in mild years in Britain, and greater numbers regularly winter on sheltered Irish coasts and estuaries.

We know relatively little about the movements of our breeding birds. Observation and colour marking studies indicate that adults are site-faithful and that, while some young may breed in their first year, others may simply return to the breeding grounds in spring without nesting. Yet others may stay in their winter quarters or part-way between. As to the migrants that we see; while some may be our breeding birds the likelihood is that they are mostly from the Scandinavian population, these migrating at a leisurely pace, between July and October, pausing for some weeks to moult on our estuaries before heading south to Iberia and northern Africa.

Other Greenshank pause far more briefly, not moulting but putting on weight quickly to fuel a swift departure on migration south. It is conjectured that these are the birds wintering in west Africa, south of the Sahara, and possibly of more distant origin, leap-frogging over the British and Irish birds. Timing of migration would suggest that our breeding birds generally undertake a shorter journey, perhaps to northern Africa. Their return migration in spring is difficult to define because of the presence of overwintering birds, but collectively for birds of all origins, seems to span February, March and April.

As the moorland rises towards the mountains, penetrated by rocky buttresses and screes, and dissected by mountain streams, so it becomes the habitat of the Ring Ouzel, which is very much the 'mountain Blackbird' of the north and west, though strangely not numerous in vast tracts of apparently suitable high ground terrain in Ireland and southwest England. Ring Ouzel territories are usually far larger than those of Blackbirds, reflecting the difficulties of finding adequate food supplies in the harsher environment. Upland pairs usually choose stretches of land with

Ring Ouzel – Tommy Holden

Ring Ouzel

occasional crags and isolated trees, often Rowan or Mountain Ash which serve as song posts for the male, as well as a source of berries, and with sheltered gullies in which to build the nest. Only rarely will they colonise a stretch of moorland uniform in slope and nature and without some distinctive features. In the far north, a few pairs may breed each year almost at sea level, nesting on ledges on the cliffs, but most Ring Ouzel nests lie between 750 and 1,750 feet (230-530 m) above sea level, the highest on record at a staggering altitude of 3,750 feet (1,150 m) in the Cairngorms.

Ring Ouzels are relatively long-haul migrants, mostly wintering in the western Mediterranean basin and interestingly again choosing montane regions like the Moroccan and Tunisian Atlas Mountains for their winter quarters. Here they live a nomadic life, roaming in search of the juniper berries that are their dietary mainstay. They are amongst the earliest of our summer visitors to arrive back, departing from North Africa in late February, many reaching the south coast early in March and the breeding grounds a few days later. Passage, including birds passing through Britain on the way to Fennoscandia, may continue until early May. Autumn migrants begin to gather in flocks to meander southwards in late August and September, with occurrences at southern bird observatories through October, and a trickle often continuing into November. The southward journey lacks the urgency of spring migration. When numbers are swollen by migrants from Fennoscandia and the year's crop of young birds, Ring Ouzels may occasionally be met with almost anywhere in lowland Britain favoured by migrant thrushes, the prime requisite being a plentiful supply of suitable berries including Elder, Hawthorn, Rose and Rowan. The harsh 'tchack' call and the conspicuously grey wings are always useful recognition features.

Life at the top

Over much of Britain and Ireland, the Raven is considered to be a bird of mountain and moorland or rugged coasts, but before intensive persecution by shepherds and gamekeepers during the 19th Century, the Raven was widespread even in the lowlands. Ravens are probably best classified as sedentary. Those from the bleakest terrain may move lower in severe weather, unless sustained by carrion from other casualties caused by the weather, and young birds will often disperse from breeding territories. Movements in excess of 30 km are unusual, over 100 km exceptional.

British and Irish breeding Peregrines remain faithful to their territories but, as these are so huge (often in excess of 20 sq km), weather-induced movements only involve flying to more sheltered parts of the territory. Young birds disperse more widely and usually in a broadly southerly direction. Ring-recoveries suggest an average movement of around 50 km, but a more than negligible 7% travelled over 200 km, including one each to Brittany and Portugal. Thus far, 16 Peregrines ringed overseas as nestlings in Norway and Sweden and moving southwest to winter have reached Britain, most of them in lowland England. So the bird you can see on an Essex or Kent estuary may well be of continental origin.

Golden Eagles, in popular view the avian symbol of the Highlands, are largely sedentary. Once adults have established a pair bond and a territory, they remain faithful to both while still alive. With fewer than 40 ring-recoveries of nestlings to go on, our knowledge of their

dispersal is scanty, but some young have now been fitted with radio transmitters which augment our information and support the view that in their first year, dispersal movements may exceed 50 km, while in the next two or three years, recoveries are to be expected an average of about 30 km from the place of ringing.

Another sedentary bird of the high tops that occasionally features in the diet of the Golden Eagle is the Ptarmigan. Over much of its breeding range in the Highlands, the Ptarmigan is confined to the arctic-alpine heath vegetation zone above about 2,000 feet (600 m). Here Bilberry and Crowberry, mixed with Heather, provide its main food year-round, because the Ptarmigan has evolved adaptations to living in this zone even during winter snows. In summer, its mottled greys, browns and fawns blend perfectly with the stunted, sparse vegetation and lichen-covered rocks. Camouflage is vital for a terrestrial bird, rarely flying far and thus very vulnerable to a hunting Golden Eagle as it sweeps at speed round the shoulder of a hill. As winter approaches, the Ptarmigan in its autumn moult gradually becomes whiter, until (save for its black tail feathers) it is snow white and ideally set up for winter camouflage. This is not all, however; during the winter snows Ptarmigan happily forage amongst the vegetation, burrowing down and living beneath the snow covering, which provides concealment from predators and good insulation in an apparently totally inhospitable environment. Ptarmigan feet are feathered to the tips of their toes so, should they venture out onto the snow, heat loss is minimised by the insulation the feathers provide at this point of contact.

Perhaps because humans are something of a novelty to them, and such humans as they meet on the high tops are not showing any obvious intent to persecute them, Ptarmigan and the two other high tops specialists, Dotterel and Snow Bunting, are extremely approachable. This confiding nature allows such superb views of the birds that the arduous business of climbing up to their high-level habitat is forgotten.

Dotterel – G Olioso

Dotterel are in that handful of birds where the role of the sexes is largely reversed. The female is slightly larger, certainly more brightly plumaged, and takes the lead in display. Having laid the clutch, a typical well-camouflaged wader foursome of eggs, she may share incubation but often leaves it to the male alone to raise the chicks. Not infrequently, she will find another male and will mate again, leaving him to handle their offspring.

Our comparatively tiny breeding Dotterel population, mostly in the Scottish Highlands, is the western outpost of a discontinuous distribution right across Eurasia. Although it is well studied, inevitably ring-recoveries are scarce. Such as there are, support visual observations that overwintering birds roam the semi-arid farmland and Atlas foothills in north Africa, from Algeria to Morocco, perhaps in company with Scandinavian migrants. Departure south from the Highlands is in late summer, and individuals may be seen, usually at coastal sites, during the autumn. The return passage begins in north Africa in late February and March, with passage across Europe during April and into May. In spring, small flocks (delightfully called 'trips') of Dotterel are regularly seen at traditional sites in lowland England and Scotland. The numbers seen are small, compared with the breeding population, so perhaps many fly directly back from Europe to their breeding grounds.

Heathland

Though never in the same altitude league as mountains and only rarely in the same remoteness league as moorlands, heaths and heathland birds probably fit more appropriately in their company than in any other habitat grouping. Primarily, though not exclusively, a habitat feature of England and Wales, heaths share several physical and botanical features with moorland. Usually located in rolling or reasonably flat countryside, heaths are characterised by sandy soils (often extremely sandy and often but not always acidic) lying over impervious rocks or clays, so the drainage is impeded and marshes and pools are commonplace. Like moorland, Heather and *Vaccinium* are regular botanical features, together with Bracken, but unlike the moors, Gorse is often the dominant shrub and small trees are present, the dominant ones being Silver Birch and Scots Pine.

Heathland birds are varied in their attributes, a typical mix of migrants, partial migrants and year-round residents. The mixture contains some unusual birds: one of our two largely sedentary warblers; one of our fastest-flying falcons; perhaps the best-camouflaged of our birds; and the bird with the more dubious distinction of suffering the most calamitous population crash of any British or Irish bird during the 20th Century. So, what are their origins and destinations, their migratory habits and flyways?

Genuinely sedentary birds typical of heathland (but as always not exclusively) include the Yellowhammer, Carrion Crow and Magpie, to which can be added those moving only in extreme circumstances like the Dunnock and Wren, most of which on most heaths are year-round residents. The local breeding Kestrels usually move little between the seasons, although their young may disperse post-fledging but to no great distance.

Dartford Warblers are scarce breeding birds in southern and eastern England which, except when singing, seem to spend much of their lives lurking deep within gorse clumps. By 1990 these areas contained a population of

Stonechat

Stonechat – Derek Belsey

Winter and summer alike, British and Irish Stonechats show a distribution biased towards the west and north, and equally heavily towards the coast. For such apparently confiding birds, Stonechats are notoriously difficult to catch and much of our information is derived from ringed nestlings. In one way, this is unusually useful in that precise details of origin are available, but in another it is a problem, as nestling mortality is high, as it is in most other passerines. The consequence is that fewer than 200 ring-recoveries are available on which to base any analysis of Stonechat movements. What is clear is that our Stonechats are partial migrants, although we can only speculate as to the possible reasons (age, sex, location, population pressure, weather, may all be contenders) why some migrate and others do not.

The Stonechat has a long breeding season, producing commonly three and occasionally four clutches, so juvenile dispersal is ongoing from mid-summer. Genuine autumn migration, for those birds leaving their breeding territories, begins in September. Birds occur at south coast bird observatories from mid-September sometimes until November. Some of these may remain in this country, but ring-recoveries (including birds from Ireland) indicate that others migrate through France to the western

Mediterranean basin, with winter quarters in southern France, Iberia, the Balearic Islands and North Africa. Most will return in February and March to be establishing territories alongside those pairs that remained overwinter.

There are three other interesting facets to Stonechat migration. First, there is little or no evidence of weather-induced migration. In a severe winter there is heavy mortality amongst those birds that do not migrate, which serves to underline the 'insurance' value of partial migration, as recolonisers will be available in spring. Second, a large number of nestlings ringed in Cumbria in the 1990s produced about half of the British and Irish grand total of recoveries in excess of 100 km and, while most moved south or southeast, strangely none crossed to the Continent. Third, also strange, is the absence of evidence of continental-ringed birds in Britain and Ireland. The only evidence of exchanges with other populations of this remarkably widespread bird is the rare but annual occurrence of a few wandering individuals of the eastern race *maura*, the Siberian Stonechat, which is recognisable in the field.

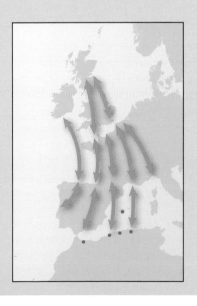

around 1,000 pairs and about double that a decade later. This is in dramatic contrast to 1963, when after a harsh winter only 11 pairs could be found, and highlights the extreme sensitivity of our outlying population to severe weather. Heathland is a comparatively scarce habitat, threatened by a range of encroachments, and of conservation interest and concern. In consequence it and its inhabitants (including the Dartford Warblers) are relatively well-studied. The great majority of English Dartford Wablers are sedentary, but the breeding population responds with dramatic increases to the absence of cold winters, which has been the pattern of the last decade or more. In these circumstances the population spreads quite rapidly, recolonising heaths that were their ancestral home.

In all probability this recolonisation is due to dispersing immatures, possibly forced out by established adults as they set up territories again in autumn after moulting. Dispersing birds may roam far, with records in Wales, Ireland, Scotland and even Fair Isle in Shetland. As yet, there is no evidence of any exchanges with continental populations but the Fair Isle birds could possibly be wind-blown overshoots from Europe, and the rare but regular occurrences at Dungeness and elsewhere on the Kent and Sussex coasts are close indeed to France, even for a bird whose flight abilities appear rather limited.

Out of Africa

Swallows and terns make some tremendous migratory journeys and usually make the headlines too, but spare a thought for the unsung Wheatear. Wheatears are without doubt migrants, moving north to breed in summer from winter quarters in Africa, but that dramatically understates the case. Three of the four races of Wheatears (the fourth is a sedentary north African resident) breed in a broad circumpolar belt, extending in places well north of the Arctic Circle, and elsewhere as far south as the Mediterranean. That belt extends from Alaska and arctic Canada across Eurasia to eastern Siberia, but what is perhaps most remarkable is that (apart from a few stragglers in North America and in the Middle

East) *all* Wheatears winter in Africa, Mauritania east to the Indian Ocean and in eastern Africa, south as far as Zambia.

Wheatear – Tommy Holden

A quick glance at an atlas, or better a globe, indicates just what this means in terms of migratory journeys. There are some extraordinary extremes; Siberian (and maybe west Alaskan) birds trek southwestwards the breadth of Asia before heading south into Africa, while birds from northern Canada and Greenland head southeast towards Iceland, Britain and Ireland and Iberia before turning south to cross the Sahara. Prodigious journeys in any context, not least for a bird which at 20-30 g is only a little heavier than a Dunnock! Departure weights and visual observations suggest that some (maybe many) Canadian- and Greenland-breeding birds of the larger and more upright race *leucorhoa* (colloquially the Greenland Wheatear) may, if the weather is right, get assistance from the autumn westerly jet-stream winds, which enable them to travel direct from southeast Greenland to Iberia or even North Africa, bypassing Iceland, Britain and Ireland. Conservatively a 3,000 km journey, this must surely be a leading contender for the longest regular transoceanic crossing by a passerine. Obviously this journey must be in a single hop with no refuelling stops, whereas overland migrants from Siberia, perhaps travelling an almost unbelievable 9,000 km or more just to reach the northeastern tip of Africa, at least can rest and feed on the way.

British and Irish breeding Wheatears (of the race *oenanthe*) are the first to arrive from Africa in early March, males a week or two in advance of the females, and soon establish territories. Passage migrants of *oenanthe* from Iceland and the Faeroes and *leucorhoa* from Greenland and further west can be seen in Britain and Ireland until May. In contrast to the autumn journey from Greenland, no favourable tail-wind conditions are likely in spring, so *leucorhoa* not only travels later but stages its return journey with stopovers in Britain and Ireland, with many also in Iceland.

Autumn departures of British and Irish Wheatears begin as early as mid-July, with most away by September. Ring-recoveries and radar tracking indicate a broad-front movement through France and Iberia, across the Mediterranean and into northwest Africa, thence it is presumed to sub-Saharan winter quarters in West Africa, arriving in mid-October. Later movements through Britain and Ireland in late September and October involve the race *leucorhoa*, migrating via western Europe rather than direct. Greenland birds do not leave until late August, which allows more feeding time post-breeding to put on pre-migratory fat deposits, and increases the chances of meeting favourable wind conditions.

In contrast to the western and northern bias of Stonechats and Wheatears in Britain and

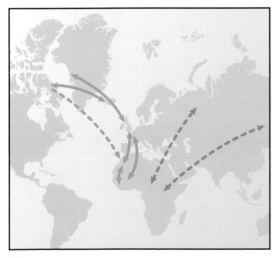

Wheatear

Ireland, the Hobby is largely restricted to the southeastern sector, roughly south of a line from the upper River Severn to the Humber. Hobbies are scarce as breeding birds, at only about 1,350 pairs in a 1999 estimate, but as they are mobile while hunting and often congregate over good wetland feeding sites, they are not too difficult to see within this range. They are also our only falcon whose population migrates to Africa in its entirety. With only just over 1,000 ringed, most of them nestlings, and under 40 ring-recoveries, our knowledge of Hobby movements has to depend considerably on observation and informed conjecture, better information coming from the more numerous ring-recoveries from other European schemes.

A handful of English recoveries, coupled with records from Scandinavia, the Low Countries and Germany, show Hobbies migrating south in autumn, collectively on a broad front across the Mediterranean rather than focusing on the short sea crossings at Gibraltar and the Bosporus, as might be expected. Hobbies tend to depart in August and September, it is thought initially heading for rich feeding on locusts and the like from Senegal to Cameroon after the October rains. There are suggestions that they have the flight capability to continue eastwards, possibly even as far as the savannah country of east Africa, in search of suitably rich insect feeding in the Zambezi basin, the species' main wintering area.

On their return journey, Mediterranean crossings occur during April, with birds reaching English breeding grounds in May. Like a super-sized Swift in flight silhouette, and amongst the fastest and most nimble of aerial predators, they hunt through the summer months for a mixture of large insects like dragonflies, not only caught but eaten on the wing, as well as birds. Their choice of bird prey is wide, all caught on the wing, and has included Swifts (a tribute to the Hobby's speed in itself) but more often focuses on the rather slower-moving hirundines that gather gregariously to feed on insects over lakes and marshes – Swallows, House and Sand Martins.

Sand Martins are colonial nesters in sandy areas, as their name suggests. Before the advent of the sand and gravel industry their colonies would have been in natural sand cliff faces like river banks. With extensive cement usage and the need for quarried sand, suitable faces for colonies became available as sand pits were excavated almost wherever the local geological profile brought seams of sand close to the surface. Nest holes (there may be hundreds, even thousands), are close together and often in a vertical or near-vertical sand face. Any local Hobbies (and Sparrowhawks) will exploit this ready food source. Gregarious habits, not only when nesting but when feeding and roosting, have also made Sand Martins relatively easy for bird ringers to catch, at least after the advent of mist-nets (Chapter 3) in the late 1950s. By the 1960s, catching expertise had advanced and an opportunity presented itself for really large-scale coordinated ringing, to the extent that over 400,000 Sand Martins were ringed in the decade. Recapture levels between ringing sites and at colonies were also unusually high and informative. Despite the remoteness and unpopulated nature of Sand Martin winter quarters, the information produced by ringing allowed a sharply-focused picture to be developed of the disaster about to happen.

Sand Martin – John Harding

In 1968/9 the Sand Martin population crashed dramatically, coinciding with a severe, and what was to become long-term, drought in the sub-Saharan Sahel, which severely limited overwinter food. Food shortage became critical as birds tried to fatten for the

northward migration in spring. Many failed to make the weight necessary to sustain a Saharan crossing. The 1968-72 BTO Atlas suggests that a pre-crash population of around 250-500,000 pairs, fell by about 80% following the catastrophe in the Sahel. Only now may numbers be struggling back. In many areas, instead of being an exceptionally common summer migrant as in the 1960s, Sand Martins are still seen only occasionally and colonies in sand pits remain small and few and far between. The sharp drop in numbers of Sand Martins ringed, and the experiences of bird ringers visiting colonies in spring 1969 to find them near enough deserted, were the first indication of the disaster that had taken place and ring-recoveries were able to outline the broad wintering problem area from Senegal eastwards to Mali.

Ring-recoveries indicate a departure south in August, often resulting in huge gatherings over freshwater for feeding and in adjacent reedbeds for roosting (one in the Ouse Washes in Cambridgeshire/Norfolk was estimated by Chris Mead to hold 2,000,000 in August

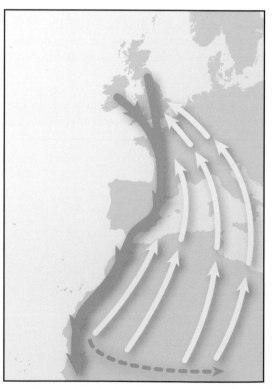

Sand Martin

1968!). Prior to departure, juveniles disperse to other colonies and are highly mobile, but adults leaving later, seem to travel faster. The route indicated by recoveries takes Sand Martins past the western end of the Pyrenees, then (and unusually for small passerines) down the east coast of Spain, the majority probably crossing to Africa around the Strait of Gibraltar. Most are into Africa by October, and move south across the western edge of the Sahara to Senegal, and later east towards Mali.

The return migration from the Sahel begins in March, usually with older birds under way first. Movement is on a broad front across the Sahara and takes place in less than favourable conditions, due to the prevalent northerly winds. This is a hazardous enough crossing at any time, but likely to be fatal for birds not in peak condition. Spring recoveries are numerous along the north African coast, from Morocco east to Tunisia, and along the northern Mediterranean coast. The sea crossing also may be on a broad front, not the narrow funnelling through Gibraltar seen in autumn. Amazingly, the first birds are back at British and Irish colonies in late March, yet another hazard in years when winter ends and spring begins with an extended spell of really cold weather.

In many ways, the Nightjars of our heaths and plantation woodlands on sandy soils are the antithesis of Sand Martins, although both are long-haul migrants wintering in Africa. For a start, fewer than 4,000 Nightjars have ever been ringed in Britain and Ireland (and 75 recovered) compared with the almost one million Sand Martins with over 16,000 recoveries, so our detailed knowledge of routes and destinations is inevitably comparatively poor. Like Sand Martins, Nightjars are insect feeders but, while Sand Martins are built for speed and hunt at speed, Nightjars (despite their long-tailed, hawk-like silhouette) fly comparatively slowly, making full use of their enormous mouths to catch rather larger prey like moths at dusk or after dark. Nightjars (and their nests and eggs) are amongst the most perfectly camouflaged of all birds. A nest on the ground amongst leaf litter or burnt gorse, with eggs, chicks or a sitting bird is astonishingly difficult to discern.

Although heavily biased towards the southeast, Nightjars breed right across Britain and Ireland. Considering its scarcity (around 3,000 pairs breed), general secretiveness and crepuscular habits, the Nightjar is a popular bird, with sightings much sought after by birdwatchers. The Nightjar is as rich in names as it is in folklore, many relating to its extended purring song, with both 'churr' and 'grinder' featuring frequently, others to its silhouette ('hawk') or habits and food ('night', 'moth' and 'dor'). Strangest is 'goat-sucker', derived from its mythical habit of sucking milk from goat udders, featured in Shakespeare's Midsummer Night's Dream but dating back to Aristotle. Even *Caprimulgus*, the Latin scientific name of the nightjar genus, is a literal translation of goat-sucker.

So what do we know of Nightjar migration? The few ring-recoveries, coupled with observations from detailed studies, indicate a departure south from the breeding grounds from late July to early September, the occasional later records into November perhaps relating to northern continental migrants passing through. Ring-recoveries indicate a south to southwesterly route through France and Iberia, with a couple of Moroccan recoveries as the southernmost. Here our knowledge, such as it is, ends until Nightjars return to the breeding areas in late April and May. So far as it is known, all Nightjars winter in Africa, probably south of the Sahara and south at least as far as South Africa in the east. Thus the Nightjar races breeding at the eastern end of the range in Siberia have a tremendous journey to undertake. Presumably European birds winter somewhere in West Africa, but observations are almost as scarce as ring-recoveries.

The Stone Curlew shows a number of similarities to the Nightjar. It too is a summer migrant, a bird of the dusk and night, and has a similar southeastern bias to its distribution in Britain and Ireland. Although lacking the rich folklore of the Nightjar, the Stone Curlew is equally mysterious in its ways, with an eerie

Stone Curlew – George H Higginbotham

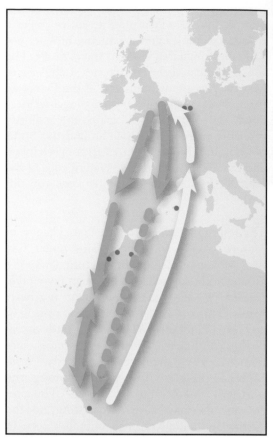

Stone Curlew

screeching call to startle the unwary evening birdwatcher. Huge, staring yellow-irised eyes assist poor-light vision, and streaked buff plumage helps concealment, as does the habit of remaining near motionless for long periods. When they do move, it is in exaggerated slow-motion.

Stone Curlews are atypical waders, favouring the stunted vegetation of the unusual alkaline sandy soils of the East Anglian brecks and the chalky fields along the Chilterns, and particularly on Salisbury Plain. Although considerably scarcer as a breeding bird than the Nightjar, over 2,500 Stone Curlews have been ringed, mostly as chicks, and more important, over 100 ring-recoveries are available to help plot their migration. Amongst other things, the reported causes of these recoveries include a number of collisions with overhead wires, a sad but inevitable hazard of flying around feeding grounds after dark. Departure south begins in late August and September, and the timing of over 30 ring-recoveries in France and Iberia indicates a swift transit. Recoveries in northern Africa

and Sierra Leone suggest wintering grounds in sub-Saharan west Africa, but even field observations are so far of scant help in defining these areas more precisely. The tiny handful of spring recoveries lie rather further to the east, and suggest the possibility of a more easterly return route, with breeding birds back in Britain in late March.

Although the Nightjat and Stone Curlew are popular species, both of which are of conservation concern, their are significant parts of the year where they can at best be described as enigmatic. For both species, birdwatchers operating in Africa may be able to provide as much new information as ringers in Britain and Ireland. Once more, these birds underline the fact that, though we know a great deal about some of our birds, a great, great deal still remains to be discovered. And that will be both challenging and exciting.

Estuaries

Sheltered shores

Beloved by birdwatchers, often lonely, few places can be so severe yet so hauntingly beautiful as an estuary, a flat landscape covered by an apparently limitless bowl of ever-changing sky. The mind's eye readily conjures up a picture of such wild places, the terrestrial evidence of man often vanishing as you near the sea. Better still, add a skein of geese in an open V formation against the sunset, or perhaps a burning line of sun running across the creek-interrupted mudflats. The mind's ear can add the distant laughing cackle of geese, with nearer at hand some wader calls; the musical lilt of the Curlew; or the plaintive whistle of a Grey Plover, redolent of wild places; or the shrill alarm call of an ever-alert Redshank, nicknamed years ago as the 'sentinel of the marshes'.

Estuaries are sheltered shallow inlets, often with a layout as complex as a river delta, where sea meets river at the turn of the tide. Shallow seas are warmer and rich in food, in the form of mineral and organic nutrients, and this richness is enhanced by the additional nutrient materials carried down, along with the silt, in the land water draining into the river. Thus an estuary, no matter whether it is sandy or muddy or somewhere between, contains copious plant life, and each square metre of mudflat usually contains literally millions of small animals, from worms, shellfish and crustaceans to the myriad nematodes and the like among the microscopic invertebrate animals. All of this forms part of food chains supporting larger animals like fish and (perhaps especially in the case of estuaries) birds, often in tremendous numbers.

The mudflats themselves, and the saltings islands laced with minute runnels, have much the same appearance year round. The saltings seem grey even in summer; the silica-rich leaves of the tough grasses and the ever-present oval-leaved Sea Purslane see to that. In summer this grey carpet is given some coloured pattern as plants flower; Sea Asters (like miniature Michaelmas Daisies), Sea Lavender (like a spray of blue 'everlasting flowers'), Golden-flowered Samphire, and Glasswort (thick and fleshy, with the appearance of a miniature but obese Christmas tree only a few inches high).

The vegetation has to be tolerant of a wide range of salinities, coupled with regular drying out and inundation with the tide's ebb and flow. On the mudflats themselves, an alga called Sea Lettuce often abounds, looking as limp as the worst real lettuce a motorway café could present; and an odd plant called *Zostera*, or Eel-grass, which like the Sea Lettuce is beloved by Brent Geese and Wigeon, helps spread a green sheen. Sea Lettuce, and the conspicuous clumps of *Spartina*, matching its name 'rice-grass', harbour millions of tiny snails, and these the Shelduck relish noisily.

Silt tends to collect around the bases of *Spartina* clumps, and over the years may accumulate enough to raise the soil level sufficiently for other plants to gain a roothold. Glasswort is one of the first of these, with surprisingly spectacular autumnal colours and in time a new island may form to replace those lost elsewhere in the estuary to wave erosion.

Wader flocks swirl over the estuary – Kirsty Coutts

Get the timing wrong, and the intrinsic beauty is all that you may find; get it right, and a bonanza awaits you. From the birdwatcher's point of view, estuary visits require more detailed planning than most. The pattern of bird behaviour is set not by the clock, but by the changing tides – normally two each day, and each day between 30 minutes and an hour later than the day before. So a tide table becomes essential. Then comes the question of when is the best time to visit. The estuary in summer, though not without its attractions, is rarely likely to match up to the estuary in autumn and winter for most birdwatchers seeking spectacular numbers and a wide variety of estuary birds. However, a spring visit may provide the chance to see some arctic birds in their breeding plumage. As for the best time of day, experience of the particular estuary must be your guide, as it should be in more precise determination of the best times of year. It may be that a rising tide will be the best, pushing ducks and waders towards the sea wall over the mudflats but, on occasions, it may be better to watch birds on a falling tide as they fly in to freshly exposed mud, eager to feed. At high tide, the ducks and grebes will be out in mid-stream and not easy to see but waders will usually congregate in a few roosts

on islands, or sometimes in fields just inland or on promontories remote from human disturbance.

There are few ornithological sights more spectacular, or more fascinating, than the gathering of several wader species at a roost, and their subsequent dispersal a couple of hours later. Many such sites are traditional and regularly used, and once located can always be borne in mind for a visit. Some species arrive in fast-flying skeins low over the water – Redshanks, not so noisy in these circumstances, and the ever-conspicuous Oystercatchers, which gather in an exclusive black-and-white huddle. Smaller waders like Dunlin and Knot arrive in dribs and drabs, then suddenly in a huge shimmering flock. Once Knot have landed, so close do they stand and so uniform is their plumage that it is very difficult to see where one bird ends and the next begins. Late-comers are received with ill-concealed annoyance by those birds already on one leg, eyes closed (or often just one eye closed), beaks tucked into the scapular feathers. Over an hour or so, little happens, but then small groups of birds begin to depart as the water level falls.

Time of tide is not everything, of course. There is little point in visiting an estuary on a fine winter afternoon if your view is always to the west, because there will be little to see save silhouettes! Equally, it can be impossible to birdwatch for any length of time looking into the teeth of a northerly gale. Nevertheless, at least the layout of most estuaries, with banks and sea walls, allows the birdwatcher either to get into a position comfortably, for example to watch over a roost at high water, or to approach feeding birds closely by dropping down out of sight until near at hand.

Clearly, estuaries are going to offer a kaleidoscopic display of birdlife, varying with tide, time and season and offering colour, spectacle and fascination. Within the fascination, lurk the questions surrounding not only the part that estuaries play in the daily life and survival of their birds but also the origins and destinations of those birds.

Rich pickings

Possibly more than any other group of our birds, across the full range of habitats, the waders highlight the position of Britain and Ireland at the crossroads of a phenomenal array of tremendous migratory flights. Between them, these stretch from the southern coast of the Republic of South Africa to the northernmost parts of Canada and Alaska and way across eastwards to arctic Siberia. Amongst waders are to be found some of the most challenging migrations; challenging physically to the birds because of the sheer distances involved, challenging to their navigational and 'logistic' capabilities. Challenging also to us in comprehending the magnitude of what the birds accomplish, year after year. Again and again we see the international importance of our estuaries and the challenges that face us in ensuring that these refuges are maintained in the face of the various (often apparently compelling) reasons to interrupt them with developments purporting to be for our general benefit.

Ringed Plover

Different species have adaptations which allow them to specialise in different parts of these estuarine food-halls. Largely it depends on beak length and, often related, on the choice of worm, shrimp or shellfish eaten. Among the short-billed feeders and to be seen on sandy or pebble beaches, often some distance above the high water mark, the sandy-coloured Ringed Plover darts about, picking up small insects and other animals. Ringed Plovers are widespread and not uncommon as breeding birds in Britain and Ireland, usually favouring coastal sand, shell or shingle spits, but also with a number nesting inland in man-made sites like sand or gravel pits, quarries or other excavations. As a general rule, these breeding birds disperse widely at the end of the season, although many remain in Britain and Ireland over winter. Some undertake moderately long-haul migrations; a general trend is shown by the ring-recoveries for a south or southwesterly movement into France and Iberia but individuals have also reached southern Norway and north Germany, possibly caught up with other migrants during the winter.

The picture for migrant Ringed Plovers passing through Britain and Ireland in autumn and spring is in spectacular contrast. These passage birds originate from breeding populations in northern Canada, Greenland, Iceland and Fennoscandia. Those from the west often use stopover points around the Irish Sea, while those from the east migrate through British east coast bays and estuaries. They are heading for wintering areas in Spain and west Africa as far round the 'bulge' as Benin and Ghana. Ringed Plover appear to 'leap-frog' migrate – birds from the farthest north migrating furthest south – which means that our sheltered shores and estuaries are staging posts to waves of migrants from August onwards in autumn and from February to May in spring. They also accommodate those northern birds that overwinter and augment the wintering numbers of British and Irish breeding birds.

On the mud or sand flats other short-billed waders probe for small animals just beneath the surface. One of the smallest of these is the Sanderling, usually found (as its name implies) on sandy substrates and easily recognised through most of the year by its white and silver-grey plumage, although in later spring you may be lucky enough to encounter birds coming into their rich chestnut breeding plumage. Even more characteristic is the Sanderling's run across the sand following the waves in and, spent, out again, when the black legs move so quickly that they become just a blur.

Sanderling do not breed in Britain and Ireland, or indeed anywhere near, as they are amongst the northernmost of arctic breeding waders. Thus any seen on sandy bays or at the seaward extremities of our estuaries are long-haul migrants, some prodigiously so. Sanderling are not only attractive to look at but interesting to study, so our knowledge of their movements and biology, through ringing and particularly through colour-marking is comparatively good. Britain and Ireland serve as a major staging post for Sanderling from two extensive breeding areas, to the west in Greenland and northern Canada, and to the east in Siberia. Many of these waders press on south in autumn to winter in widely scattered west African locations, and in some cases as far south as the Republic of South Africa. Studies show that many remain in Britain and Ireland through the winter, while others may pause to feed-up just briefly, or for days, even weeks. Site-faithfulness on migration seems to be part of a Sanderling's make-up, so colour-marked birds have a good chance of being seen repeatedly.

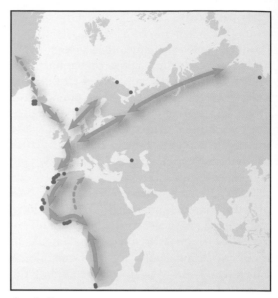

Sanderling

Autumn passage begins in July and peaks in August/September, while returning birds are seen first in April, peaking dramatically on our estuaries in May. Ron Summers, who made detailed studies of Sanderling movements, suggests that African migrants may return either north along the African coast or alternatively by a direct crossing of the Sahara to the Mediterranean. It is thought that the huge journey from winter quarters to breeding grounds is made in just three long stages, with two stop-overs to 'refuel' *en route*. Weights of Sanderling caught just before departure indicate that they carry a heavy load (maybe 50-100% additional to their normal 50-60 g) stored as body fat to fuel their journey, enough to give them a range of around 5,000 km! The view from energetics studies is that the total journey time, from South Africa to Greenland for instance, may be around seven weeks, and ring-recoveries broadly support this.

In most estuaries, the two most numerous species are Dunlin and Knot, both of which fall in the medium-length beak size range and both of which feed out on the flats. The smaller Dunlin seems to arrive mysteriously on the mudflats, materialising from twisting shimmering flocks looking almost like smoke in the distance. So precise is the timing of their aerial acrobatics that a dense-packed flock, with birds only inches apart, will turn as

Sanderling – Al Downie

one, giving a sudden change from white undersides to grey-brown backs. How this timing is achieved, and why collisions in mid-air are so few, is not properly understood, beyond the fact that birds' eyesight and reflexes seem far superior to ours. Dunlins are amongst the first waders to scamper about on freshly exposed mud as the tide recedes, leaving little lines of beak probe holes between their footprints as they feed.

Some Dunlin breed in Britain and Ireland, but relatively few compared to the vast circumpolar population, which has been separated by taxonomists into as many as 11 different races. Three of these occur in Britain and Ireland. *Calidris alpina arctica* is the smallest in size and smallest in population (about 15,000 birds), breeding in northeast Greenland. Ring-recoveries indicate that it passes through only briefly on passage to winter quarters in West Africa. Far more numerous (800,000 birds) is the race *schinzii*, slightly larger in size, which breeds in southeast Greenland, Iceland and northern Norway, with smaller numbers forming the British and Irish nesting populations. Most of these also pass through our estuaries on their way south to winter in west Africa.

The third, largest, and even more numerous race using our estuaries, some on passage, others forming the bulk of our wintering birds, is *alpina*, with a breeding range from Fennoscandia east into arctic Russia. Dunlin from the western part of this range provide the flocks so spectacularly evident on British and Irish estuaries as they twist and turn in flight. Normal arrival is from August onwards and, like Sanderling, Dunlin are faithful to their winter sites. For Dunlin, all our estuaries are valuable, but particularly so the major and spacious ones like the Thames, Wash and Morecambe Bay which are, with the Waddensee, also important as autumn moulting grounds.

Collecting these movements together, a picture for Dunlin emerges in Britain and Ireland at the fork of a Y-shaped set of flyways, similar to the maps for Sanderling, Ringed Plover and Knot. Although these flyways may

differ in length and detail, various key features are common to all. Simply put, Britain and Ireland's estuaries provide sheltered and rich feeding and resting grounds, staging posts, moulting areas and winter quarters to a very substantial proportion of Northern Hemisphere wader populations.

Dunlin: yellow – arctica; green – schinzii; orange – alpina

Similar to the Dunlin in winter colouration but larger in size is the Knot. Knot tend to feed in close-packed flocks, but they also pack in so close together on their roosts close to the water's edge that it is easy to see how they acquired their colloquial name. Their scientific specific name *canutus* is equally appropriate, recalling Canute, King of England 1015-35, who famously, but inevitably unsuccessfully, sat at the sea's edge and bade it cease encroaching on the land.

Knot may be static at the water's edge at high tide but, as migrants, they perform some of the longest non-stop flights of any wader. They breed on the circumpolar High Arctic belt of tundra, and are separated into several races, not readily distinguished in the field, of which two use British and Irish estuaries as staging posts or winter refuges. *Calidris canutus islandica*, which breeds in Greenland and northern Canada, is by far the more numerous, as confirmed records of the other, *Calidris canutus canutus* (which breeds on the Taimyr Peninsula in arctic Russia) are scarce. The habit that Knot have of roosting close-packed at traditional spots makes them an ideal target for cannon-netting (Chapter 3), which produces high catches but demands large teams of dedicated ringers. That we have managed to unravel this much of the undoubtedly complex flyways, timing and energetics of Knot is due very much to their efforts.

Knot from Canada and Greenland migrate southwards in autumn, via staging posts in Iceland, to reach Western Europe's larger

Oystercatcher

Oystercatchers – Tommy Holden

The Oystercatcher breeds widely in Britain and Ireland, on damp pastures in river valleys well inland, along the coast and on offshore or estuarine islands. Dubbed the 'sea-pie' for its Magpie-like appearance, and strident in its frequently uttered calls, the Oystercatcher is one of the familiar year-round birds of our estuaries, although substantially more numerous in winter than at other seasons. Oystercatchers do not breed until they are three or more years old, and many will not return to their breeding areas until then. Our summer Oystercatchers will be a mixture of nesting residents and non-breeding birds possibly originating hundreds of kilometres away. Ring-recoveries suggest that most of our breeding birds move only short distances, if at all, during the winter. For

southern England, Wales and Ireland, 35 km or less would be the average, but for northern England and Scotland, average movements are greater at around 200 km. This fits well with the evidence from across the Oystercatcher's range that more northerly populations migrate further than southernmost ones. Those of our birds that do move further are usually juveniles which, as with a wide range of other species, disperse further than adults. Ring-recoveries suggest the coasts of Normandy, Brittany, the Bay of Biscay and northwest Iberia as their destination, with a handful of recoveries in Spain and one in North Africa indicating that some may travel further.

In winter, those of our Oystercatchers remaining are joined by many more migrating south from Iceland, the Faeroes and Norway (where they regularly nest in gardens), which spread widely through our estuaries, sheltered bays and exposed rocky shores. Some will pass through Britain and Ireland to winter in the Low Countries and France. Ring-recoveries confirm a major dependence of Icelandic and Faeroese breeding birds on British and Irish estuaries for winter survival although, with the current run of warmer winters, it seems that more are overwintering near their breeding grounds.

There are some areas (e.g. Morecambe Bay, the Burry Inlet) where wintering Oystercatchers come into apparent

estuaries. Adults leave first, parents having shared the task of raising families but having departed before the young, in late July and early August. From the evidence provided by their heavy departure weights, it is suggested that the first leg is a single stage across Greenland to staging areas in Iceland, where they rest and refuel for two or three weeks, departing as the later-travelling juveniles begin to arrive. It may be that the

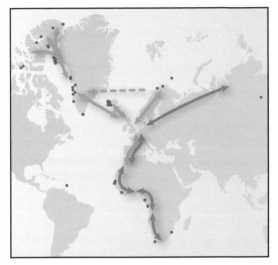

Knot: green – islandica; orange – canutus

inexperienced juveniles need longer feeding time on the breeding grounds to reach the necessary departure weight, and certainly the staggered arrival at the staging areas must help to 'spread the load' of feeding pressure on local invertebrate populations.

From Iceland, a second long hop takes the Knot to British and Irish estuaries and to the Waddensee, east of the North Sea, where they recuperate and moult. Most adults arrive here in August (although failed breeders may be earlier) and juveniles in September. By October, they are able to disperse to the estuaries on which they will overwinter, and some will continue passage further south.

Some south-bound Knot, mostly juveniles, will pause in southern Norway, Denmark or the south Baltic coast, where they coincide with arrivals of the race *canutus* from the Taimyr, *en route* to the Waddensee, where the two races seem to remain largely discrete. It is tempting to speculate that the onward passage as far as southern Africa of birds ringed in Britain involves *canutus* individuals crossing the North Sea to England while heading south as astonishingly South Africa is the usual destination for wintering Taimyr Knot.

Returning in spring, most *islandica* Knot cross again to the Waddensee in late March and moult into their spectacular rufous summer plumage, the remainder moulting in Britain

conflict with local shellfisheries, particularly of cockles. Without doubt, Oystercatchers eat cockles, but detailed studies have failed to confirm that they merit the 'damaging pest' status accorded them by cockle gatherers. Nonetheless, in the 1960s and early 70s, shooting was permitted on Morecambe Bay and the Burry Inlet. Although 27,000 Oystercatchers were shot, the cull failed to stem the decline in the cockle fisheries. The cull, instigated by fisheries pressure, provoked wide conservation concern and support for Oystercatchers, interestingly in particular from the Faeroes, where the Oystercatcher is the national bird and where strong feelings were aroused by the policy. Diplomacy at governmental level was needed to avert an international incident.

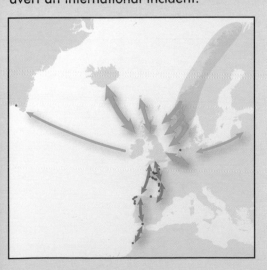

and Ireland. Departure north is in the first half of May, before *canutus* populations have returned from Africa. The *islandica* birds fly non-stop to staging posts in Iceland or northern Norway, where moulting is completed and food reserves garnered over two or three weeks ready for the long journey ahead. Departure from the two staging areas is remarkably well synchronised at the end of May, on another non-stop leg it is thought to the breeding grounds in Greenland and northern Canada.

Redshank may be present on estuaries year-through, ring-recoveries indicating that some are part of our breeding population, others migrants. Redshank breeding on estuaries and marshes from Ireland east to the Urals belong to the race *Tringa totanus totanus*. A proportion of our birds (though possibly not many from Scotland) remain with us through the winter, to be joined by migrants from elsewhere in northwestern Europe and from Iceland. Some of the Redshank present on our estuaries in early autumn move on southwards for the winter, reaching France, Spain, Morocco and west Africa, but it is difficult to assess from available ring-recoveries which of these were from the British and Irish breeding population. The general opinion is that our birds are probably relatively short-haul migrants if they migrate at all, and that those wintering furthest south originate in northern Scandinavia and have leap-frogged the bulk of the *totanus* population.

In Iceland, a slightly larger race of Redshank, *robusta*, breeds. The great majority of the substantial Icelandic population migrate southeast to winter almost exclusively in Britain and Ireland, with interesting indications that those from western Iceland winter in the west, those from eastern Iceland in eastern Britain. Thus, the Redshank on our estuaries in winter are a mixture of local residents, a few migrants from northwestern Europe, and many birds from Iceland. This mixing of different populations means that a birdwatcher on the Severn estuary will be seeing birds from Iceland, Scotland and northern England, while flocks on an Essex estuary will also include many local breeders and Scandinavian birds.

Further out from the shoreline and feeding in deeper mud or at the water's edge are the longest-billed of estuary waders, the Curlew and Black-tailed and Bar-tailed Godwits. Curlew, familiar for their exceptionally long down-curved beaks and haunting yodelling calls, also breed across northern uplands and boggy lowlands in Britain and Ireland, while Black-tailed Godwits are prized but rare breeding birds on wetlands in East Anglia and occasionally elsewhere. Bar-tailed Godwits are high arctic tundra breeders.

Ring-recoveries indicate that Curlews are site-faithful in both their wintering and breeding grounds. Unlike Oystercatchers, most Curlews breed inland so some winter movement coastwards is inevitable. Our breeding Curlews are best classed as short-haul migrants, often remaining within Britain and Ireland, with many showing a marked tendency to move west or southwest in autumn to Ireland, others generally south to coastal France and Iberia. In winter, the remaining native birds are joined and outnumbered by migrants from Fennoscandia and Russia. Radar studies by David Lack indicated that some might arrive as early as June/July, presumably failed breeders. Our breeding birds leave later in the summer for the estuaries, but may start to return to their breeding grounds as early as January or February, long before the longer-haul continental migrants begin their northeastward journey back, which starts in April and continues into May.

Curlew

The two godwits share long straight beaks (maybe very slightly upturned in the Bar-tailed) and similar feeding techniques but differ as strikingly in their plumage as in their breeding areas. In winter on the estuary, the two may seem outwardly similar in buffish grey. The Bar-tailed is subtly undistinguished overall, but dramatic differences are seen in flight when the Black-tailed reveals its identity immediately by showing its black and white tail and broad white wingbars. In spring, both moult into a superb cinnamon breeding plumage, more uniform in the Bar-tailed and covering the head, neck and belly, confined to the head and neck in the Black-tailed, which has a black- and buff-barred breast and belly.

Bar-tailed Godwits breed on the arctic tundra in several discrete areas in a discontinuous circumpolar belt. Ring-recoveries indicate that those passing through Britain and Ireland, or overwintering on our estuaries, come from two of these areas. One is Lapland and the Kola Peninsula by the White Sea in northwest Russia; the other, substantially further east, is around the Taimyr Peninsula in Siberia. In Britain and Ireland in autumn, winter and spring, spectacularly huge flocks of Bar-tails are a feature of really major estuaries, such as the Wash, but most estuaries shelter large enough flocks to provide substantial interest and enjoyment.

Bar-tailed Godwits arrive on the east coast in late July and August and use the rich estuary food supply while they moult. Some may disperse elsewhere on British and Irish estuaries, and others will migrate onwards to winter quarters around Mauritania in west Africa. Yet others, and probably the majority, will remain where they are through the winter. The return migration northeast in spring begins, it seems from ring-recoveries and colour-marking, with a short flight to the Waddensee to moult into summer plumage and fatten up, refuelling for the longer journey ahead to the White Sea. Godwits wintering on the Banc d'Arguin in Mauritania depart in late April, well fattened and probably able to fly non-stop to the Waddensee, arriving after the White Sea and Lapland population have left. In all likelihood, it is these migrants that

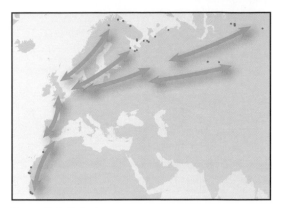

Bar-tailed Godwit

pass offshore up the Channel and are recorded, regular as clockwork, at seawatching points in Sussex, Kent and Norfolk in early May.

The Black-tailed Godwit differs substantially from the Bar-tailed in its more southerly breeding belt, from Iceland east across Eurasia to about 90° E. Our breeding population of around 100 pairs is but a tiny sub-unit of the race *Limosa limosa limosa*, which has its stronghold from the Netherlands and Denmark east across Russia. This race has a series of long-haul flyways to wintering areas, often well inland, from the Sahel eastwards to the Rift valley and Lake Victoria in East Africa, although thus far only a single recovery in Guinea-Bissau supports the view that our breeding birds are amongst those that winter south of the Sahara.

Most of the Black-tailed Godwits we see on passage and during the winter are of the Icelandic race *islandica*, for which ring-recoveries indicate that British and Irish estuaries are major wintering grounds, although others winter in France, Iberia and the Netherlands. The race *islandica* is more of an estuary bird than the wetland-favouring *limosa*, but also frequents coastal lagoons and flooded meadows.

Although some of our information on *islandica* comes from ring-recoveries, unusually these are overshadowed rather than augmented by sightings of colour-marked birds. With those long legs, Black-tailed Godwits lend themselves to sightings of colour ring

Black-tailed Godwit – Pat Wileman

On the estuary, they are joined by other Great Crested Grebes of north European origin, and perhaps by one or more species of the smaller, rarer grebes, Black-necked, Slavonian and Red-necked Grebes (in ascending order of size), also migrants but from the Continent.

Spectacularly colourful in breeding plumage (a few pairs of Slavonian and Black-necked Grebes breed every year in Britain), in winter plumage these rare smaller grebes provide an identification challenge together with a thrill of accomplishment once their identity is established. Winter migrant Black-necked Grebes originate in Eastern Europe and tend to occur mostly in southern England. Red-necked Grebes are more northeastern European in origin, although their breeding range does overlap that of the Black-necked. The Slavonian Grebe has a circumpolar breeding distribution, and although ring-recovery evidence is scarce, it seems likely that west European estuaries shelter migrants from Greenland, Iceland, Fennoscandia, the Baltic States and Russia. First arrivals of the rarer grebes can be as early as September, with return departures from late February onwards into May.

combinations, both on the mudflats and on their Icelandic breeding grounds. Migrants arrive from Iceland in late July and August and commence their moult. Those arriving in the (east) of England may later move south to (east) coast estuaries and on into Europe, while those arriving on the south coast tend to remain on their estuaries until their spring return to Iceland. Just as for Bar-tailed Godwits, the Black-tailed's dependence on relatively few major estuaries highlights the fragility of their ecology and the importance of estuaries in sustaining godwits on migration and over winter.

For the Grey Plover, the past few decades have seen big increases in the numbers seen on British estuaries. They arrive from their breeding grounds in arctic Russia resplendent in black and white plumage but soon moult into the grey feathers which give them their name. Some birds move further south later in the autumn to spend the winter on African estuaries.

Out on the water

The sheltered waters of the estuary provide a haven for many species of waterbirds, including the grebe family. The familiar Great Crested Grebe breeding on inland freshwaters across Britain and Ireland occasionally becomes a short-haul migrant, particularly those from the north whose breeding lakes may freeze over in winter. Displaced birds, together with others with a migratory urge, head for the sheltered, productive and rarely-frozen waters of estuaries, usually not far away.

Goose on the menu?

Most geese only resort to estuaries to roost or when driven off their grazing areas on adjacent farmland or marshes, and even the Brent Goose, now numerous on many of our estuaries, is no longer solely an estuary specialist. In the past, it was held that the Brent Goose and *Zostera*, the Eel-grass on which it feeds, were inseparable. Indeed, when *Zostera* beds were decimated by a disease, Brent Goose numbers plunged and a wildfowling ban was introduced to protect them. However, the *Zostera* slowly recovered, and a series of mild summers in the Arctic saw Brent numbers rise at an explosive pace after good breeding seasons, so much so that much of the available *Zostera* was eaten by Christmas. The geese then turned their attention to winter wheat, which advances in farming technology and land drainage had conveniently placed just a short flight away on the other side of the sea wall. Brent now favour wheat to such an extent as to be regarded as pests in some areas. This recovery is made no less remarkable because it is argued that Brent Geese have perhaps one of the most energy-demanding migrations of all waterbirds. Brent breed on High Arctic coastal tundra, in an interrupted circumpolar belt largely on the polar side of latitude 70° N and sometimes of 80°N. Breeding and wintering grounds are sometimes a massive 8,000 km or more apart (about 20% of the Earth's circumference!), and for some Brent each migratory journey involves non-stop, mostly over sea, flights in excess of 3,000 km.

Unlike the other estuarine 'black' goose, the Barnacle Goose, Brent Geese are taxonomically placed in three subspecies, each reasonably easily identifiable in the field. Two of these concern us, and we owe our understanding of a complex mix of populations and migratory flyways to the results of numerous ringing and colour-marking expeditions to their breeding grounds and, incidentally, to studies in the 1970s triggered by the threat to site an additional London Airport on the Maplin Sands, at the mouth of the Thames Estuary, a traditional Brent Goose location.

Brent Goose: green – hrota; orange – bernicla

In eastern, southeastern and southern England, the estuaries are winter home to the Dark-bellied Brent Goose, *Branta bernicla bernicla*, which breeds (mostly) on the Taimyr Peninsula in arctic Russia (at around 100-120°E, 75-85°N). These Brent migrate after the breeding season on a path heading broadly westwards to the White Sea, a staging post of crucial importance for feeding on both autumn and spring migrations. Their onward journey takes them to coastal marshes in Denmark and the Low Countries, especially the Waddensee area, where they arrive and stay during late September and October, before departing to English and French estuaries. Here they are centred from November until their departure in late February and March to gathering areas in the Waddensee, before onward movement to their breeding grounds (again via the White Sea) some weeks later.

The other Brent subspecies of European interest is *Branta bernicla hrota*, the Pale-bellied Brent. Two breeding populations are involved, according to marking studies, one from the tundra of northeast Canada, which winters almost exclusively around the Irish coast. As many as 75% of these Irish birds use Strangford Lough as an initial staging area before dispersing widely. This huge journey from Canada involves crossing polar seas, the Greenland icecap and the North Atlantic, none of them easy options! After crossing the icecap, it seems certain that pretty well the whole population heads for staging areas in west Iceland, where they feed up for two or three weeks in September, then on non-stop to Ireland. They also stop-over in Iceland in May on the spring return migration.

The second *hrota* population mainly nests on Svalbard in the Arctic Ocean, and again ring-recoveries outline well its autumn flyway, thought to be direct, to eastern Scotland and northeast England, with Lindisfarne in Northumberland as the most important winter site. Svalbard birds arrive from September onwards. The return journey begins in March, with departures to Denmark, and then possibly to staging posts either in northern Norway or on Bear Island (midway between Norway and Svalbard), but confirmatory field observations are still lacking. Some continue on from Svalbard to breed in northeast Greenland.

Barnacle Goose

Barnacle Geese – Mike Weston

The Barnacle Goose, pied in black, white and grey plumage, grazes the short, often sea-washed turf on estuarine marshes. Very much a bird of the north and northwest of Britain and Ireland, the Barnacle Goose is a traditionalist, with flocks of family groups frequenting the same estuaries and islands year after year. Another tradition, and a rather strange one, links the species with the Goose Barnacle, the stalked marine crustacean.

Few birds other than the Robin have such an extensive early bibliography: Giraldus Cambrensis, visiting Ireland with Prince (later to be King) John in 1185 testifies to seeing "...these small birds, hanging down on the sea-shore from a piece of timber." John Gerard in his famous *Herball* (1597) expands "... certaine shells ...wherein are contained little living creatures ...which falling into the water do become fowles, which we call Barnacles; in the north of England, Brant Geese ..." Returning to Giraldus, who probably hits the nail on the head: "...Bishops and religious men ...do not scruple to dine off these birds at the

time of fasting, because they are not born of flesh." Thus, Barnacle Geese conveniently became permitted eating in Lent and on Fridays, at a time when fasting on Holy Days was strictly observed.

Fascinating, but back to the equally interesting account of Barnacle Geese today, and their migrations. The map of ring-recoveries shows the movements of two major distinct populations. These recoveries are amplified by numerous sightings of colour-marked birds. Interestingly, although the two groups have both discrete breeding areas and winter quarters, unlike some other birds, there are no anatomical or plumage differences to establish racial or sub-specific distinction between the two populations. One group breeds in eastern Greenland (recently also establishing a

small colony in Iceland) and migrates in autumn to northwest Ireland and northwest Scotland, via staging areas in southeast Iceland. The other population breeds in Svalbard and migrates to overwinter principally on the Solway Firth, with occasional ring-recoveries elsewhere in Scotland and northern England. Small numbers from a third population, wintering in the Netherlands and breeding, mainly in arctic Russia but also on newly colonised Baltic islands, arrive in eastern Britian, as shown on the map.

When nesting, Barnacle Geese seek the additional safety from predators offered by screes and ledges on crags, even if the day-old goslings have to survive a tumbling precipitous descent to their feeding areas, with only their stubby wings as air-brakes to soften the bumps.

In Svalbard, family groups leave soon after the young can fly, moving to staging posts further south in the islands, sometimes (from radio-tracking results) also at various sites in Norway, before arriving at Caerlaverock on the Solway in late September or early October. The return journey in spring begins in late April or early May, with stops at regularly-used sites in Norway, before arrival in Svalbard in late May. Greenland birds depart south in late August or September, for staging posts in southeast Iceland, leaving for Scotland and Ireland from mid-October onwards depending on the weather. As an indication of how firmly established are the traditional wintering areas of the two groups, many of the Greenland birds winter on Islay, less than 200 km from the Svalbard birds on the Solway, a mere step along the Road to the Isles in goose-travelling terms!

Of the grey geese, it is the White-fronted Goose that is as a generality typical of our estuaries and their adjacent marshes and grazing land. White-fronts are as gregarious and noisy as other geese, but their double or triple barking 'kow-yow' calls, more musical than most geese, and the deep grumbling murmur of a feeding flock, are distinctive. Like the two black geese, White-fronted Goose populations show clear demarcations between breeding and wintering grounds, and in consequence migratory routes, and, like Brent, the races or subspecies can be separated with little difficulty in the field.

Britain and Ireland provide winter quarters for two of the four races of the White-fronted Goose, which breeds in the circumpolar tundra belt. Ring-recoveries amply demonstrate the importance of Ireland in particular for the dark-plumaged, orange-beaked Greenland White-front, *Anser albifrons flavirostris*, which has no important wintering areas outside these islands. Ringing results have been augmented by both colour rings and neck collars, readable or decodeable from a distance without the need for recapture. More recently, small numbers of migrants have been fitted with lightweight radio transmitters and tracked along their route; this is a well-studied bird.

At the end of the breeding season and after the adults have moulted, family groups depart their breeding grounds in west Greenland and embark on a 1,500-2,000 km flight, initially across the Greenland icecap and over the North Atlantic to staging posts in Iceland. Here they may remain for about a month, feeding energetically, before again taking off and heading over the open Atlantic in a direct flight to Ireland or northwest Scotland, a further 1,000 km or more away. Some will feed traditionally on bog plant roots and stolons, others on fields adjacent to estuaries. There is some evidence accumulating of leap-frogging, where birds from the furthest north colonies will overwinter furthest south in Ireland, while those from colonies in southern Greenland have shorter journeys to northwest Scotland. Detailed knowledge of timing is lacking, but departure for Iceland (it is thought overnight) is in late July/August, with peak numbers on Icelandic staging posts during September. Arrivals in Ireland and Scotland are normally in the second half of October.

White-fronted Goose: green – flavirostris; orange – albifons

Northbound in spring, *flavirostris* migrants begin to depart for Iceland in mid-April. Again, they may rest and feed on Icelandic staging areas for a week or two, but most leave Iceland for Greenland by mid-May. The evidence suggests a direct flight over the southern end of the Greenland icecap, which reaches altitudes of 2,400 m (7,500 ft) or more, making landfall in traditional early-thawing lowland areas. As the spring thaw releases the grip of the ice, they move on to their nesting areas.

The European or Russian White-front *Anser albifrons albifrons* breeds across the northern Eurasian tundra as far east as the Taimyr Peninsula. These birds migrate in late summer, initially southwest and then, for some, west, heading for wintering grounds stretching from western Asia to south and southeast England. The picture is not as well-defined as for the Greenland White-front, but departure from the breeding areas, after the adults have moulted, is during September. Groups make their way westwards steadily rather than rapidly, moving through Russia and central Europe, reaching England during November. Some may pass on into western France but more settle on English and Welsh estuaries and the adjacent grazing land and marsh.

European White-Fronted Geese favour the same areas year after year, unless some major habitat disruption occurs. Departures on return migration begin during March, via various staging areas in the Low Countries, Poland and Russian river basins, including the Volga, Kama and Oka. Their course then turns northwards, until the breeding grounds are reached in late May. Numbers of *albifrons* wintering here vary but are normally only a small proportion of the Russian population, which is in contrast to the complete dependence of Greenland *flavirostris* on wintering grounds in Britain and Ireland.

Estuary ducks

Smaller than the geese, but not as substantially so as our mental images would have us believe, are the various ducks that frequent our estuaries. Like the White-fronts, large numbers of them come to our estuaries in winter from northern European and Russian breeding grounds. They favour the really enormous tracts of boggy marshland in the river valleys running southwards from the White Sea and Barents Sea, and from the even larger wetlands of the West Siberian Plain, on the far side of the Ural Mountains, the north/south barrier between Europe and Siberia.

Estuaries are the province of the dabbling or surface-feeding ducks, rather than those that dive for their food, but not exclusively so. Across Britain and Ireland the five common dabbling ducks in winter are Wigeon, Pintail, Mallard, Shoveler and Teal and in all the species the drakes are spectacularly attractive. None more so than the Wigeon, also probably the longest-haul migrant of the five.

Wigeon – Tommy Holden

Wigeon breed in a broad belt of marsh and tundra from Iceland eastwards across Eurasia to the Bering Sea. Icelandic birds and those from the western half of their Eurasian breeding range head towards the Low Countries and Britain and Ireland for the winter, while those breeding further east head south to the Mediterranean and Black Sea and into southern Asia. Over 2,500 ring-recoveries shed a good deal of light on the origins of winter visitors to Britain and Ireland, indicating breeding grounds from Iceland east through Fennoscandia and across Russia and Siberia to beyond 40° E. Concentrations of recoveries (which may reflect local hunting pressure as much as anything) occur on the marshes adjoining the rivers Pechora (home of the pipit), Yenisei and Ob. Given that they survive the wildfowlers all along their route, this is a prodigious journey, for some amounting to 5,000 km each way.

Large flocks of these delightful wildfowl, the drakes easily identified with bold white wing patches and a penetrating wild whistling call, begin to arrive on our estuaries any time after August. Stragglers may not leave on the return journey (which ring-recoveries suggest may be further south than their autumn route) until April. As grazers not only on the mudflats but particularly on close-cropped marsh grasses, Wigeon are susceptible to periods of sub-zero temperatures and snowfall, when weather-induced movements west or south may occur.

The tiny Teal, like the Wigeon, breeds in Britain and Ireland, but in slightly larger numbers. By its habits more susceptible to trapping, many more Teal have been ringed than Wigeon (85,000 against fewer than 20,000) and correspondingly more ring-recoveries are available (13,000 from Britain and Ireland, 3,000 from overseas) to establish the origins and flyways of our winter visitors. As with Wigeon, it seems probable that Britain and Ireland are the primary winter quarters for Icelandic breeding birds.

Ring-recoveries indicate that Teal seem to be unusually adaptable as breeding birds, always ready to shift if old habitats have changed in water level or vegetation. The autumn migration from breeding grounds in Fennoscandia and east into Russia is similarly relaxed, and although some drakes may leave as early as June, our winter populations may not be in place until late in November. Some birds may pass through heading for France and Iberia. Once settled in Britain and Ireland, Teal remain on their chosen estuary unless driven away by changes in local feeding conditions or by freezing conditions or snow, when their weather-movement west or southwest is swifter than most other waterfowl. Depending on the weather, Teal return to their breeding grounds in spring, again flexibly, over an extended time scale from February to May.

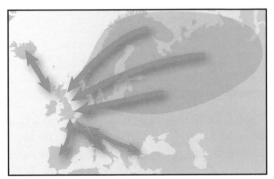

Teal

Ring-recoveries are often reported by letter; a Teal was the cause of one of the most poignant ever received by the BTO. It came from the Chaplain of a Cambridge College, telling how he and his fiancée had eaten a ringed Teal on New Year's Eve. He reported the ring number, together with a comment on how well it tasted and hoping that "all your other ducks have a Happy New Year"!

Elegant on the water and distinctively slim in flight, with a characteristically pointed tail, elongated in the drake, the vast majority of Pintail that overwinter in Britain and Ireland are migrants from northern Europe. While with us, they typically favour estuaries and adjacent grassland, especially flooded fields, occasionally occurring on or nearby inland freshwaters. The origins of our Pintail closely parallel Wigeon and Teal, migrants coming from breeding populations in Iceland,

Fennoscandia and across northern Russia as far as the Ob marshes and maybe beyond. Those breeding further east in the species' range (which is really huge, including northern Asia and North America) migrate towards the Black and Caspian Seas, into southern Asia or, in the case of North American birds, southwards into more temperate areas of that continent.

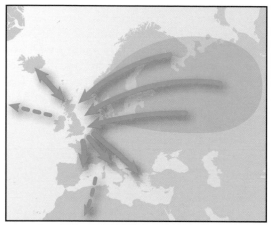

Pintail

Drakes leave their breeding grounds from late May and, after moulting (usually on large lakes nearby), head west or southwest, arriving around the North Sea coast from August until October. Females and young depart later and probably travel faster, so that all arrive on our estuaries at roughly similar times. Most autumn migrants remain on or around our estuaries until departure east, northeast or northward in March, although there may be some local movements during the winter, depending on weather and water levels.

Interestingly, a small number of Pintail pass through each autumn, *en route* to wintering grounds around the Mediterranean and in west Africa. The indications are that these birds depart south or southeast through Europe to the Mediterranean, not south-southwest or southwest as do other passage migrant dabbling ducks. More ring-recoveries are needed to put flesh on these tantalising bones. Clearly, Britain and Ireland are positioned on the margins (in migration terms) of Pintail populations, holding only around half the estimated 60,000 or so

wintering in northwestern Europe. Estimates suggest that one million or more Pintail from further east in northern Eurasia take flyways south to the Middle East, India, China and Japan for the winter.

Although the Pintail will grub in soft mud for rhizomes and other plant matter, most of its food is obtained by up-ending whilst afloat, where its relatively long neck gives it the advantage over other ducks in feeding in slightly deeper water. In striking contrast, the remaining member of this quartet of estuarine dabbling ducks, the Shoveler, is distinguished by its heavy spatulate beak and inelegant but effective slurping filter-feeding strategy in soft mud. Shoveler can be recognised at a distance by their head-down posture on the water and, perhaps oddly, by their head-up attitude in flight. Compared with the three others, the Shoveler has a more southerly winter distribution throughout Europe. Although occurring during the winter over much of England, Wales and Ireland, there are many fewer Shoveler in Scotland and, even in England, the winter distribution is biased to the southeast. As do the Pintail, Shoveler breed in a circumpolar belt across Europe, Asia and North America. Even for those breeding at the western edge of the European range, Britain and Ireland are very minor players in hosting winter flocks.

So effective is the filter-feeding technique of the Shoveler that, despite the tiny size of the ostracod and cladoceran zooplankton on which they feed, they can consume up to 10% of their body weight in a day, which allows a

Shoveler – Mike Weston

Scaup

Scaup – Mike Weston

marila marila is of concern to us (the other, *mariloides*, breeds from eastern Siberia across into North America). Ring-recoveries indicate that most of the Scaup wintering in Britain and Ireland are from the Icelandic population, mostly ringed at Lake Myvatn, the mecca for duck-watchers, and probably we are the major wintering ground for Icelandic birds. The remainder of our *marila* originate in Fennoscandia and eastwards into northwestern Russia at about the latitude of the Arctic Circle. These winter largely, but not entirely, along the east coast of Britain.

Surveys indicate that the Icelandic breeding population has declined in recent decades but may now be increasing again. Changes in Britain and Ireland are largely as a result of human activity in the Firth of Forth, which used to host the largest Scaup flocks (totalling in

One diving duck in particular, the Scaup, takes advantage of the sheltered waters of major estuaries, particularly in Scotland and Ireland, though flocks do also occur on the open sea and inland freshwaters such as Lough Neagh. Scaup have a circumpolar breeding distribution, often nesting in wooded areas, on the tundra at around the northern limits of tree growth. There are two races, not easily separable, but only one *Aythya*

excess of 30,000 in some years). These flocks fed on the various marine invertebrates – mostly molluscs – flourishing in the sewage-enriched sheltered waters of the Forth. Ironically, modernisation of sewage treatment plants has improved water quality substantially to meet European standards, but to the detriment of the mollusc population and, in consequence, many Scaup have moved elsewhere.

Shoveler

rapid build up of the fat needed to fuel their migratory journey.

Much of the Shoveler population breeding in eastern Europe heads south to winter in the Mediterranean and Black Sea basins, with substantial numbers pressing on into tropical Africa. Those overwintering with us are the minority from breeding grounds in Fennoscandia, the Baltic States and the Russian swamplands. More pass through and may be joined travelling south by some of the British and Irish breeding birds (possibly totalling over 1,000 pairs, mostly in the southeast). Ring-recoveries of our breeding birds indicate an autumn migration initially to the Low Countries and then broadly southwest, to winter in France and Iberia, with a single recovery in north Africa.

And passerines too

Although both estuary birdwatching and ecology are dominated by waders and wildfowl, it would be wrong to make no mention of smaller birds, albeit that they occur less often and create much less of a spectacle. For insect-eating birds on the estuary there is relatively little on offer in summer and even less in winter, although sedentary Rock Pipits, with their flexible dietary habits and an eye for a small shrimp, manage well. For seed-eaters, there is more on offer, not only on the banks and islands but particularly in the accumulated drift material along the tide line.

The small songbirds that do occur on a winter estuary are birdwatchers' red-letter-day birds

in their own right; Shore Lark, Lapland Bunting, Snow Bunting and Twite. All are difficult to spot because of their sombre, streaky winter camouflage plumage, and in the absence of ring-recoveries the origins of our Shore Larks and Lapland Buntings are a matter of speculation. The Lapland Bunting, a scarce migrant in Britain and Ireland, is one of the most numerous of arctic breeding passerines, where males can be seen in the full splendour of their black, white and chestnut plumage. In winter, the give-away is their rippling 'ticky-ticky-tew' call, revealing the presence of a sparrow-sized bird weighing around 25 g (almost one old-fashioned ounce). This is astonishingly small, given that the indications (particularly timing of arrivals) are that visitors to our northern and western coasts probably originate in arctic Canada and Greenland, while those on the east coast probably come from Lapland, appropriately enough. Shore Larks, subtly-plumaged with a distinctive 'horned' head pattern, are never other than scarce along the east coast. They probably also originate from Fennoscandian high ground (Lapland again), where breeding numbers are sadly declining, coinciding with lower winter numbers here.

A handful of ring-recoveries of Twite, inconspicuous even in this company, suggest that those breeding in Scotland and Ireland winter on estuaries and coasts relatively nearby, while the English breeding birds from the Pennines move to North Sea coastal areas for the winter. English and Scottish winter flocks are probably joined by birds from Norwegian breeding populations. On the ground, Snow Bunting too are well-hidden, often taking flight only at the last moment when disturbed. Once in flight the large white blocks on the forewings make them extremely conspicuous. Even more northerly than Lapland Buntings, Snow Buntings breed in a High Arctic circumpolar belt, and at higher altitudes the more southerly the breeding ground. Female Snow Buntings tend to migrate further south to winter than the males and are more likely to be found on the coast, males often preferring to stay close to their breeding sites, whether this be in Iceland or the small but flourishing mountaintop outpost population in the Cairngorms. Ring-recoveries show a number of exchanges with Iceland in particular, and in contrast only one from Norway. It seems reasonable to suppose that Snow Buntings migrating to spend the winter on our estuaries originate primarily in Iceland, the Faeroes and probably also Greenland and Canada, where a single recovery lends its support. Though faithful to their breeding sites, ring-recoveries north of the Arctic Circle are not easy to come by, and the nomadic nature of winter Snow Bunting flocks also inhibits achieving greater clarity as to their origins.

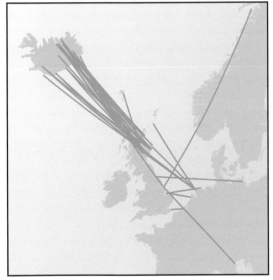

Snow Bunting

Small and inconspicuous the passerine birds of estuaries may be, but the migratory journeys particularly of some of the Snow and Lapland Buntings are extraordinarily long, prodigious feats for small songbirds about half the weight of the smaller waders whose flyways have already caused amazement.

Summer comes

What of the estuaries in summer? In late spring, the banks or islands will support some waders (Redshank and Oystercatcher), but usually many, many fewer than the autumn and winter populations. Only a few species are involved, as most ducks and waders are primarily adapted to an arctic or sub-arctic breeding regime. The strikingly-coloured

Shelduck – Tommy Holden

Shelduck is one bird with a year-round presence on many of our estuaries. Large and goose-like, Shelduck have a number of unusual features. For example, males and females are essentially similar in plumage, differing only in minor detail, so the female makes no concessions to camouflage. More interesting in the context of migration is the way Shelduck moult.

In true ducks, the male plays little part in family life once the female is ensconced on her clutch of eggs. Males then become secretive and spend much of their time in the reeds, taking on a camouflage plumage of mixed browns (called eclipse) as part of their moult cycle. Ducks, geese and swans become flightless while they moult their flight feathers, and male ducks moult in a special plumage for just a couple of months. When their flight feathers have been renewed they once more take on their colourful dress.

In Shelduck, the moulting strategy is very different. Once the ducklings have gathered into crèches under the care of a few guardian adults, which will moult later, the remaining adults and year-old birds gather to carry out what for them is their annual migration – to moult. From late June onwards, these birds from all over Britain and Ireland head for the Helgoland Bight and the Greater Knechtsand. Here, on the vast sandflats they gather with Shelduck from the Baltic and Scandinavia and undergo their annual moult, which lasts through August, after which the fresh-plumaged birds begin a leisurely return

Shelduck moult migration

journey to their home estuaries. The young of the year, once fully feathered, disperse from their home estuaries at the end of the summer, but only for short distances. Most will return as adults to the estuary of their birth. Obviously, this moult migration is a key component of their annual cycle, and adds yet another aspect underlining the international importance of estuary habitats. Interestingly, though the majority of our Shelduck take part in this traditional moult migration, a small but increasing proportion do not. These moult nearer home on particularly large sandy estuaries like the Wash or bays like Bridgewater Bay in Somerset.

There may be terneries on an estuary in summer, usually of Common Terns but occasionally of Arctic Terns in the far north of Britain, but terns are dealt with in Chapter 10. There will be gulleries too, almost always of Black-headed Gulls which are the prime gull exploiters of the estuarine habitat across Britain and Ireland, besides nesting in a variety of other situations close to water. A visit to a sizeable estuarine Black-headed gullery is an experience in itself, impressive in that the entire population and the non-breeding 'loafers' rise to mob the intruder. Colonies begin to re-gather in March and April, as the gulls forsake their winter preferences for wide open spaces (with a clear view of approaching predators) for areas with sufficient ground-cover to conceal their newly-hatched young. The whole

performance of a colony is geared to massive mutual stimulation, from the choice of the actual colony site, the sudden 'dreads' when the birds rise as one in a wheeling, calling flock, to the onset of courtship and egg-laying. Because of this mutual stimulation, a remarkable degree of synchronisation in egg-laying and hatching is achieved, presumably to the overall good of the birds.

A substantial number of ring-recoveries (about 16,000 ringed in Britain and Ireland, plus 8,000 ringed overseas) allow a good picture to be composed of Black-headed Gull post-breeding dispersal and migration. Our breeding birds are usually site-faithful in summer and the great majority of young return to their natal area when at two years old they begin to breed, although a handful of recoveries in the breeding season in Fennoscandia, Denmark and the Low Countries indicate that this is not inevitably the case. British and Irish breeders and their young disperse after the breeding season, immatures travelling further than adults. The majority of our breeding adults are likely to overwinter in Britain and Ireland, but some (again more immatures than adults) move in a generally southerly direction (from southwest to southeast) to Denmark, the Low Countries, France, Iberia and, on several occasions, north Africa.

The distinction between dispersal and migration is ill-defined compared to most true migrants. A picture emerges for our native Black-headed Gulls of a drift away from the colonies from June onwards, some birds moving further than others and with no striking regional differences, and a return in a similarly imprecise manner from the following February onwards. At a year old, immatures (see Chapter 1) move back some, but not all, of the way to their natal area, so most estuaries will hold non-breeding populations of diverse origins.

Movements of overseas Black-headed Gulls migrating to Britain and Ireland, where they substantially augment our own birds, are fairly well-defined as to origin and once again less so as to timing. There is a clear indication that

Black-headed Gull: orange – Icelandic;
green – Fennoscandian; yellow – British and Irish

much of the Icelandic population winters here, mostly in Ireland and Scotland. The remaining birds originate from colonies in Fennoscandia, Denmark, the Low Countries and the Baltic States, with a few from further east into Russia. Winter-visitor Black-headed Gulls seem to be site-faithful year-on-year, with their arrival spread over some months from mid-summer until Christmas. The return migration is rather more precise, departures beginning in February, peaking in March, with the majority of birds back on their colonies in April.

The vital link

In spring and late summer and autumn (the times of peak passage wader numbers), estuaries support a continually changing population of migrants, and it is to these birds that our estuaries are of inestimable value. Except for the natural hazards of predators and changing weather, they are more at risk here than either on the tundra or in their tropical wintering areas. Successful travel between their tundra breeding grounds and tropical wintering areas is imperative, so these staging posts on our estuaries are vital to the birds' survival. Not only do the stop-over areas allow recuperation after long flights from the north, but the birds also have time to feed and accumulate energy stores, mostly in the form of body fat, to serve as 'fuel' for the long

journey ahead. Also, for many species, the arctic summer is too brief to do anything but raise a brood of young; the vital process of renewing the body and flight feathers in an annual moult must be postponed, often until the waders arrive on our estuaries in autumn. Any major loss of estuarine habitat could be disastrous.

Given the widely varying origins of the birds involved, autumn migration to or through estuaries is spread out from early July, when failed breeding birds start to arrive back from the Arctic, until late October or November. The transition from birds on passage to those remaining for the winter is not always easy to detect. Much depends on the severity of the onset of the continental winter and the relative mildness of our own but, usually by December, the estuary birds will be those likely to stay for the winter, unless forced to move south or west by severe winter conditions. Although autumn, with almost daily migrant arrivals and departures, is numerically the peak season, wintering numbers are also spectacular, emphasising the continuing importance of our estuary habitats.

Spring passage is a much more hurried affair. It begins in March and continues well into May, by which time many waders may give us a glimpse – albeit brief – of their colourful summer plumages. In the spring, west coast estuaries are far more important than they are in autumn, with flocks of thousands of waders, such as Sanderling and Dunlin, in summer plumage, *en route* to Iceland and Greenland. These can be found on estuaries such as

Dunlin – Tommy Holden

Morecambe Bay and the Solway, many freshly arrived from Africa and desperate to feed up and move on. The arctic summer is so short that to arrive on the breeding grounds at its start and in good condition is of paramount importance; hence the apparent sense of urgency and the sometimes brief stays of the returning migrants on our estuaries. Brevity of stay makes the estuary no less important. On the contrary, with time of the essence, there must be an ample and rich food supply available. Not only is there a need to sustain the moult into breeding plumage, and for 'fuel' for the journey, but as weather (and thus feeding conditions) ahead are notoriously unpredictable, there has to be 'enough and to spare' to cushion the birds and their breeding capabilities as much as possible against such emergencies. On the tundra, after months of ice, food supplies are limited and adverse weather, such as frost or snow, can mean that nesting territories and food are inaccessible and that birds must wait for better conditions.

Most estuaries in industrialised countries, not just Britain and Ireland but the whole of western Europe, have similar yearly patterns of bird visitors. These estuaries' main importance must be in spring and over the autumn and winter months, and some idea of this importance can be gathered from the sheer numbers of birds involved. The Waddensee in the Netherlands regularly holds over half a million waders in autumn, with Oystercatcher, Knot and Dunlin each topping the 100,000 mark. In Britain, both the Wash and Morecambe Bay may hold in excess of 200,000 waders at peak times, with Oystercatcher, Knot and Dunlin again the most numerous species.

British and Irish coasts are well endowed with estuaries, internationally a relatively scarce habitat, and it would be difficult to name an unimportant estuary bordering the North Sea or the Irish Sea. Even some of the apparently rather birdless estuaries of the southwest of England and western Ireland would seem to have real importance in severe winters. There is plentiful evidence that many birds call routinely at the same estuaries each year on their way south or northwards in spring. The disappearance of an estuary, or even a single mud-flat, would affect not just the hundreds of birds seen to be using it in mid-winter but also passage birds, moulting for four weeks in September or feeding-up for ten days in May. In human terms, taking away a motorway service station would be a problem not just for the lorry drivers using it every week but also for those who only travel long distances on motorways occasionally.

Estuaries provide superb birdwatching, with spectacular birds performing tremendous migrations. 'Vital', though, is the key word linking estuaries to estuary birds. Estuaries are vital links in a chain often stretching between the tropics and the Arctic Circle. Remove a link and the chain is broken, its function jeopardised. Continued vigilance, good information and powerful presentation are imperative if the international estuary network is not to be imperilled, together with the birds it supports.

Exposed coasts

In the east and south of England the coasts are generally low-lying, the seas murky and much disturbed by shipping passing by or polluted by the concentrations of industrial development on many of our own estuaries and on the continental coast of the North Sea and the Channel. Add to these the summer disturbance, caused by expanding seaside resorts, camping and caravan sites and marinas, and it becomes easier to see why the sea birds of the east coast in summer are limited in number. From Yorkshire northwards and Dorset westwards, the position improves as cliffs reappear along the coastline, but in the southeast, even in the limited places where cliffs do occur, they tend to be of friable chalk and unsuitable for many seabirds to nest.

Much of the western and northern coastline of Britain and Ireland is rocky, often deeply indented by coves and bays and strewn with myriad cliff-girt islands of all sizes. This whole coastline enjoys access to the shallow seas of the Continental Shelf, for much of the year still rich in fish, despite dramatic reductions in a number of species of importance to ourselves (such as Cod) and to birds (Sandeels). This wealth of seabirds is very much a summer feature though. During the autumn and winter months, these coastal waters are often whipped into a frenzy by the prevailing southwesterly winds and most of our seabirds find less trouble feeding either by migrating south or by moving to less broken seas well away from the shore.

Just what is it that makes Britain and Ireland spectacularly fascinating for seabird enthusiasts? What is it about them ecologically that is so special that (for example) about 90% of the world population of Manx Shearwaters nest here? For the specialist seabirds, perhaps the answer lies largely in the nature of our rocky coasts and islands. Most good seabird sites are remote from human presence and feature precipitous cliffs, guarded by treacherous and often rough seas. Thus they are natural nature reserves in themselves, with little need for fences or notices, and this protection is effective even against birdwatchers seeking a better view.

Gigantic and magnificent as a spectacle as some of our cliffs and stacks are, rising 1,000 feet (300 m) or more sheer from the sea, they can still sometimes be devoid of birds. The rocks must be of the right type, with strata and fractures producing a terrain suitable for the wide variety of seabird nests. Caves, for example, provide sites for Black Guillemots and in some areas for Rock Doves and the spectacular Chough. This red-billed, red-legged member of the crow family, a sedentary resident like the Rock Doves, has a particular delight in riding the fierce updraughts of air at the cliff face, tumbling skilfully about on broad wings with conspicuous 'fingered' ends. Smaller crevices in the cliff face provide safe sites for Razorbills and Puffins to lay their eggs. Boulder screes house more Razorbills and Puffins, with Storm Petrels and Manx Shearwaters, Cormorants and Shags, for good measure. The cliff ledges themselves need to be more or less horizontal to be of use; hence the importance of the way in which the rock fractures. On Skokholm for example, off the Welsh coast, the Old Red Sandstone strata have come to lie in a vertical plane with successive movements of the Earth's crust. Erosion has removed the softer rock, leaving upstanding hard knife-edges set far too close together for the comfort of nesting seabirds. On nearby Skomer, where the rock is granite and the ledges horizontal, seabirds such as Guillemots, Kittiwakes and Fulmars abound.

Pelagic petrels

Gull-like in white and grey but actually a petrel, the Fulmar must hold the record as a seabird success story. Heavy-bodied but well-streamlined, Fulmars are masters of flight economy, flapping their stiff paddle-like wings only when necessary. The rest of the time they ride air currents off the cliff or over the waves, wings rigid and characteristically held at a slight downwards angle. Until 1878, remote St Kilda off the Outer Hebrides held the only British and Irish breeding Fulmars, but today they are fairly familiar right round our coastline, with even the lowest and crumbliest of cliffs holding at least a small colony.

Much debate centres on the cause of the population explosion that has spanned the North Atlantic; some say an advantageous genetic change, some a boost due to the increasing availability of whaling offal, and subsequently offal from an increasing fishing fleet gutting its catch at sea. What is most remarkable is that the Fulmar is a very slow-breeding bird. Most are well out at sea for the first four or five years of their lives, before starting to visit potential breeding areas in summer, perhaps pairing-up, but probably often not breeding until nine years old. Then, they only lay a single egg and, if that should fail, do not normally re-lay until the next season. Hardly the stuff of population explosions you might say, unless Fulmars live for an exceptionally long time.

Here, ringing is beginning to provide some exciting information. Prior to the 1960s, the soft aluminium rings fitted to Fulmars probably wore out and dropped off before the birds began breeding. Subsequent, much tougher alloy rings are showing signs of being able to last as long as the bird they are fitted to! It is already clear that many Fulmars may live for more than 40 years, and it would not be an unreasonable bet to suggest that, once sufficient time has elapsed from the late 60s, an occasional Fulmar may be proved to survive to reach our allotted 'three score years and ten'. With the sort of survival that is already being recorded, even at one egg a year, Fulmar populations do have the potential to expand explosively.

Fulmar

Migration is not the most appropriate word for Fulmar movements, which could better be described as dispersive and peregrinatory. For their first few years they wander widely around the North Atlantic, very rarely penetrating further south than northern Africa. Whilst some may eventually settle to breed near where they were born, others may aid the expansion by joining colonies a considerable distance away.

Another of our long-lived seabirds, already known to reach at least the age of 50, is the Manx Shearwater. Unlike the Fulmar which wanders the seas, this is a genuine long-haul migrant, providing a link between our western coast and Argentina. Manx Shearwaters are immediately recognisable by their black-above, white-below plumage, which flashes as they sweep and twist across the waves. All through the summer, but especially during spring and autumn migration times, Shearwaters delight seawatchers on headlands and islands, particularly down the length of our western seaboard.

Manx Shearwaters nest underground on remote and usually uninhabited islands and headlands, coming ashore only after dark to avoid the brutal attentions of predators like Great Black-backed Gulls. Most colonies are near the cliff edge or close to the shore of low-lying islands, but a striking exception is the colony more than a mile from the sea and high up in the rocky screes in the centre of Rum, in the Inner Hebrides. By day, walking along the cliff-top, there would be no reason to suspect that a Shearwater colony existed in the 'rabbit burrows' all round or in the screes nearby but at night there can be no mistake. The eerie caterwauling calls of the adults underground and as they fly overhead in the darkness, with a rush of air like the passage of a wartime shell, are absolutely distinctive. The tremendous cacophony of the large Manx Shearwater colony on the Calf of Man is described in one of the Icelandic *Sagas*, and in Norway in the past their mysterious and terrifying chorus was attributed to angry trolls.

Adult Manx Shearwaters depart from their colonies from August onwards, leaving their single chick to ready its plumage and muscles for the journey south. When it leaves, the chick is downy and very fat, too overweight to fly, and over the next couple of weeks it uses this stored fat to complete its development. The young fledge in suitable weather, after dark to escape gull predation. So far as we know, adults and young head down our western coasts and then set off southwest, down the eastern side of the Atlantic, crossing the Equator and possibly taking advantage of the trade winds to head west, to winter offshore along the eastern coast of South America, from northern Brazil to Argentina, where there are numerous ring-recoveries. A few recoveries on the coasts of North America and west Africa may possibly be indicative of a loop migration. The return journey begins in late January, signalled by a sharp drop in recoveries off South America, as the Shearwaters head north. There is some evidence from systematic oceanic surveys off the North American coast that this may be on

a more westerly track than in autumn, a concept also supported by an absence of spring recoveries off the west African coast. Our breeding birds are back in home waters from late March onwards after what can only be classed as a phenomenal journey.

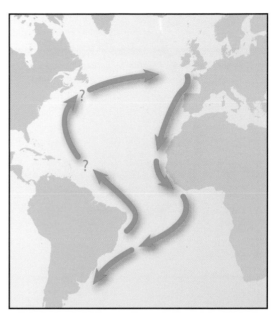

Manx Shearwater

Any analysis of the movements of a predominantly pelagic bird (the Manx Shearwater being an ideal example) using ring-recoveries is confronted by the obvious improbability of many mid-ocean recoveries from which to plot their route. Destinations and transit routes may be easier to define because most seabirds are seeking fish-rich waters in which to feed, and where there are fish-rich waters they inevitably encounter fishermen. The numbers of seabirds caught and drowned in nets or on long-line hooks is now a major conservation issue. Consumer demand for fish and fish products is rising steadily, commercial fishing is becoming ever more sophisticated and globally a number of seabirds (notably albatrosses) are now gravely threatened. Ring-recoveries are of great value not just in locating seabird winter quarters, but also in putting some qualitative and quantitative measure on this tragic toll. This is of immense assistance to the conservation bodies concerned.

Storm Petrel

Storm Petrel: green – migration; yellow – breeding season feeding movements

Storm Petrels come ashore under cover of darkness only to breed or investigate potential breeding areas. Weighing 20-30 g (about the same as a Greenfinch) the Storm Petrel is Britain and Ireland's smallest seabird. With a fluttering flight, and with legs and webbed feet trailing, Storm Petrels seem particularly unlikely as ocean-wandering long-haul migrants.

Being sooty black with only a white rump patch Storm Petrels are inconspicuous after dark. It is their song that gives them away; long drawn-out, slightly fluctuating purring, often accompanied on a still night by their characteristic musty smell. They are amongst the most readily attracted birds to tape recordings (lures) of their song, which has helped increase the numbers ringed and the understanding of their movements. Interestingly, non-breeding wanderers can be distinguished from experienced breeders because the latter carry many more ectoparasites (mites, feather lice etc.), which they pick up in the nesting burrows.

Storm Petrels leave their colonies, in burrows, screes and even dry-stone walls, from August onward, and both fledging and departure times seem well staggered until October. We presume they migrate south across Biscay to the seas off west Africa, where they appear from mid-November on. Probably most winter (December to early April) off the coasts of southern Africa, before returning north. Numbers increase off west Africa during March and Storm Petrels make first landfalls at their colonies from late April. It is thought that immatures stay south off Africa for maybe two or three years before returning to their general breeding area and roaming the colonies there. During the breeding season, established pairs move widely (ring-recoveries indicate up to 200 km in a single night) in search of food. The results of tape-luring indicate that they may be feeding near the Breton and Biscay coasts, in Norway and around Iceland and the Faeroes.

Storm Petrel – Stuart Newson

Size and spectacle

At the top end of the seabird size scale is the Gannet, streamlined, with a two-metre wingspan, adults elegantly white with contrasting black wingtips. Gannets tell another of the seabird success stories of the last 200 years. In the old days, they were harvested for food by remote island communities and, even today, a special provision in the law allows the islanders of Sula Sgeir in the Western Isles to take an annual harvest of young Gannets, called 'gugas'. There are now over 20 gannetries in Britain and Ireland, half or more founded in the last 100 years. Most are on remote islands or stacks, but that at Bempton Cliffs in Yorkshire is exceptional in that it is on the mainland. Bempton is an RSPB reserve and, although access is to some degree controlled for the protection of both the birds and the visitors, this is by far the easiest place to see Gannets on their nesting ledges.

The world population of the Gannet has trebled this century and, with some 250,000 breeding pairs, Britain and Ireland hold 70% of the world population. At a distance, their cliffs and rocks are so Gannet-encrusted that they look like a giant iced cake, snow-white with the birds and their guano. Gannets in bulk or in action must rank as one of the modern visual wonders of the bird world. The spectacle of hundreds of Gannets plunging headlong into the waves, often from 100 feet (30 m) or more, in pursuit of a school of fish is without equal. How there are not more collisions is difficult to understand, as birds are plummeting in from all directions at high speed, then bouncing back to the surface, heavily laden with fish, for a laborious take-off run, pattering across the waves.

By August or September the cliffs become deserted as the speckled inky-grey immatures have left for the sea. Ring-recoveries show that young birds disperse rapidly and widely southwards along British and Irish seaboards, one reaching Morocco from Ailsa Craig in the Firth of Clyde in 14 days from fledging. Gannets are a feature of visible migration, spring and autumn, at most coastal seawatching points, and also from ferries crossing the North and Irish Seas and the Channel. This wide dispersal takes young birds almost as far south as the Equator and deep into the Mediterranean, but not, so far as ship-board observations confirm, in any numbers far from the Continental Shelf and out into mid-Atlantic. More than half of the ring-recoveries of known cause result from accidental (fishing nets) or deliberate killing by man. The indications are that most birds return to their natal colony, but there are a few recoveries indicating that British and Irish birds may play some part in the establishment of new colonies, for example in northern Norway. This may not be too surprising, as the ring-recovery evidence indicates that birds from many countries, including some Canadian birds, gather wherever fish supplies are good.

As with a number of species, perhaps particularly seabirds, the evidence is that young birds disperse substantially further than breeding adults during the winter. Gannets do not breed until they are at least four or five years old, spending their time at sea. As they get older the young Gannets get more white

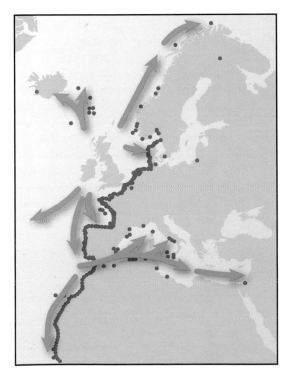

Gannet

in their plumage and spend the winter in higher latitudes, where their distribution increasingly overlaps with the adults.

The Cormorant is another flourishing species. Far more numerous and widespread inland than even 20 years ago (and reaching pest status on heavily-stocked commercial fishing waters), British and Irish birds are reflecting the long-established inland habits of Cormorants (of various races) over a large part of the globe. Ring-recoveries indicate that in winter some British and Irish breeding Cormorants are sedentary, while others are short- to medium-haul migrants, either moving within British and Irish coastal waters or overseas from southern Scandinavia south to Portugal. There are a fair number of inland recoveries across western Europe and a few into the Baltic and Mediterranean.

Immatures range further than adults (on average 220 km against 180 km) and begin to disperse soon after fledging from July onwards.

Most immatures seem to return to their natal area the next spring, the migration beginning sometimes in mid-winter and extending into May, at which times (like Gannets) they feature at seawatching points. Results from colour-ringing indicate that adults are generally faithful to their nesting area, and also tend to winter in the same areas year after year. Over 60% of immatures returning to breed do so at or near their place of birth.

According to ring-recovery information, dispersal of young is largely southerly and within Britain and Ireland, with a very few Scandinavian reports. Those ringed in southern Ireland, southern Wales and southwestern England make, on average, longer dispersive movements and account for many recoveries on the Breton peninsular, the Biscay coast, and in northern Spain and Portugal. Here they join birds from the north of Ireland and northwestern Scotland, which interestingly produce many more inland recoveries on a generally southeasterly bearing into southern and west-central Europe. Young birds from Little Saltee, off Wexford, not only show the south or southeasterly trend towards Europe, but also disperse north and west throughout Ireland.

Certainly not an inland breeding bird, and wedded to northern and western rocky coasts, Shags are more conservative in their movements than Cormorants and best qualify as sedentary or in some cases short-haul migrants. Shags are far more restricted than Cormorants in their global distribution too, with 40% of the world population breeding in Britain and Ireland, the remainder on rocky northeast Atlantic coasts and in the Mediterranean. Only the most northerly European populations can properly be classed as migrants. Immature Shags from Britain and Ireland disperse widely but not far, with a median mid-winter dispersal distance little over 100 km. Many adults, even in the north of Scotland, may move very little unless driven south by severe weather. There is a suggestion that a major factor restricting Shag movements is their comparatively poor waterproofing, which means that they must haul out, wings spread

Cormorant

characteristically, to dry off at frequent intervals. This confines them close inshore and may also inhibit lengthy sea crossings.

Shags ringed in the Northern Isles and northeast Scotland disperse more widely than most, with ring-recoveries across the North Sea from southern Norway, and a few south through Denmark and the Low Countries to northern France. Those ringed in southeast Scotland and northeast England have been recovered mostly down the east coast, sparingly in southern Norway and Denmark, and more plentifully in the Low Countries and northern France. Shags ringed in northern Ireland and western Scotland have produced large numbers of recoveries on local coasts but only a handful in Normandy, Brittany and into Biscay. Those ringed in the southwest quadrant – southern Ireland, southern Wales and the Cornish peninsula – have most recoveries in the Breton peninsula, with a few around the Iberian coast (including one in the Mediterranean).

The auks

Before they start to grow feathers, the naked nestlings of Cormorants and Shags are amongst the most reptilian of all young birds, and their leathery grey skin makes them seem even Pterodactyl-like. To most people, as a family, the auks (whether adult or young) are considerably more appealing in appearance. Ecologically, they are the northern hemisphere equivalents of the penguins of the southern hemisphere. One of them, the Puffin, has the ability to arouse wide enthusiasm and fascination, and not just among birdwatchers. Perhaps it is the upright, manikin-like stance, or the 'evening-dress' plumage and colourful beak that causes this, or perhaps it is the busybody enthusiasm to observe and participate in all the social goings-on in the neighbourhood that makes Puffins so endearing. Although an easy bird to watch, especially at colonies (like the Farne Islands) where it is used to human disturbance, for all its handsome charm and popularity, the Puffin is not the easiest bird to study.

Puffin – Jim Flegg

When they visited the huge puffinry on St Kilda, remotely situated 64 km west of the Outer Hebrides, the Kearton brothers, Victorian naturalists and pioneer bird photographers, recorded the Puffin flypast as sufficient to darken the sky and necessitate increased exposure times. Being well-equipped, they had with them umbrellas which they put up, not to protect themselves from droppings but from the showers of feather parasites dropping like rain from the birds overhead! Sadly, in parts of its north Atlantic range the Puffin decreased in numbers during the 20th Century, sometimes drastically. On some islands, particularly those close inshore and farmed, man caused problems to seabird colonies by introducing Brown and sometimes Black Rats. Lundy, the so-called 'Isle of Puffins' lost most of its Puffins in this way. There are cases where the Puffins themselves have played a part, too. On Grassholm, now famous as a Pembrokeshire gannetry, excessive burrowing by large numbers of Puffins led to rapid drying and fragmentation of the thin layer of topsoil, encouraging wind and water erosion and reducing the island surface to its basic rock structure. As yet, no clear overall reason for the declines has been identified, which is worrying. It may be that, because Britain and Ireland are at the southern extreme of the Puffin's range, climatic or oceanographic changes are adversely affecting their food supply.

Adult and young Puffins have almost entirely deserted their colonies and the seas nearby by the end of August. It is assumed that birds migrate swiftly or disperse to their wintering areas, but neither ring-recoveries nor sightings at sea offer many clues as to where British Puffins are through the winter. Ring-recoveries are frequently of birds found washed up on beaches, thus providing little precise information on when or where birds have met their deaths. They return to the area of their colonies between February and early April.

Only 2,000 Puffin recoveries have been reported to the BTO, a low percentage of over 200,000 ringed birds, suggesting that Puffins

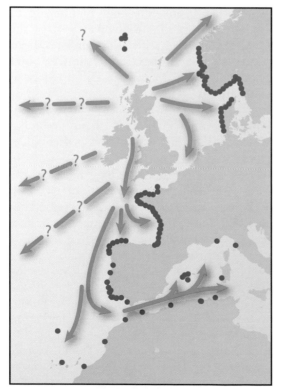

Puffin

spend much of their time away from shore. The map shows those shores on which recoveries have occurred and indicates some movement into the Mediterranean. Recoveries occur from northern Norway south to the Canary Islands and from Italy west to Newfoundland, where many Norwegian- and Greenland-ringed Puffins have been recovered. Just how many Puffins from Britain and Ireland cross the Atlantic (four recoveries in 50 years so far) and how many are wintering in mid-Atlantic we do not know; we remain very much in the dark in understanding Puffin migration.

Only 6% of Puffin ring-recoveries are reported as caught in fishing nets (a further indication of a pelagic life in deep waters away from intensive fisheries) compared with 27% of Razorbills, which spend the winter in much shallower, heavily-fished seas. Most Razorbill colonies are relatively small and often interspersed amongst those of other auks, especially Guillemots. Because the nest is hidden, observation can be difficult, but the confiding nature of the Razorbill more than compensates for this. Some consider the Razorbill the most handsome of our seabirds, an immaculate contrast in black and white. In summer the black head is offset by an elegant white trim on the beak and by a fine white line of tiny feathers running from the beak to the eye. It has been suggested that these white marks may form some sort of sighting device, helping Razorbills to catch fish when hunting under water. They catch smallish fish by the beakful, holding between 6 and 60 crosswise in the beak. The winter plumage is altogether drabber and greyer.

Though there are many more colonies of Razorbills than of Puffins, they share the same heavy bias towards the Scottish coasts and islands and the western coasts and islands of Wales and Ireland. Razorbill ring-recoveries indicate a gradual departure southwards after the adults have moulted and the young have completed their growth (at sea and reasonably near the colonies). This migration to winter quarters probably follows no defined routes, and it may be that most adults do not move as far south as the immatures, which certainly classify as long-haul migrants. Migrating Razorbills are amongst the birds encountered at traditional seawatching lookouts in spring and autumn, particularly when weather conditions force them close inshore.

In much the same way as for the Puffin, Razorbill ring-recoveries (about 3,000 from 90,000 ringed) must be analysed with caution, as dead birds may have floated some distance and for some time before being found. What emerges is a picture of birds wintering offshore over the Continental Shelf, south to Iberia and Morocco, and occasionally further to the Canaries, Azores and off Western Sahara. They return northwards in spring to gather near their colonies from March onwards. Systematic at-sea surveys in the Western Approaches lend support to this general picture. Significant numbers, mostly it seems immatures, move into the Mediterranean, penetrating as far east as Italy. Regionally, Razorbills from the southwestern sector of Britain and Ireland move south, with relatively few recoveries north of the Channel and in the North Sea.

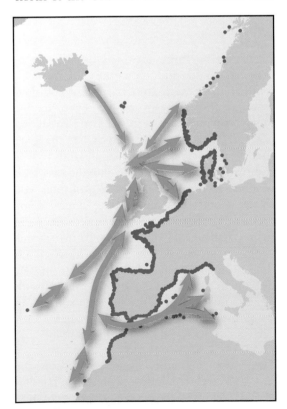

Razorbill

Those from the northwest tend not to travel so far south and move more into the North Sea, while those from the northeast move eastwards to Norway and Denmark, with relatively few moving south to the Channel and beyond.

Of the four auks that breed in Britain and Ireland, the Black Guillemot is the only sedentary one, with few movements exceeding 50 km. Much less numerous than its larger relative, it is particularly a bird of northwestern coasts and islands. In summer, jet black save for bold white wing patches and bright vermillion feet, the Black Guillemot is a cave or cavity nester, usually in colonies of only a few pairs.

The Guillemot itself is probably one of the most numerous North Atlantic seabirds. Just looking at the seabird stacks, for example of the Farne Islands, confirms just how tightly Guillemots pack onto stack tops or cliff ledges. Each new arrival, trying to find a space in which to land, causes noisy confusion as he or she blunders amongst fellow birds. The Guillemot has one of the simplest of all nests, merely laying its single egg on the rock, with no nesting material, not even a few sprays of seaweed for decoration. The egg that allows such simplicity is a masterpiece of evolutionary design. It is large and tapers sharply, rather like a pear. If knocked accidentally, as so easily happens in such crowded colonies, it rolls in a tight circle but stays on the ledge. In similar circumstances, the normally-shaped Razorbill egg would have as much chance of survival as a breakfast egg rolling off the kitchen worktop, but then Razorbills tend to be crevice nesters.

Guillemot (and Razorbill) chicks leave the nesting cliffs before they are fully fledged, usually when they are about two-thirds grown. They have plenty of subcutaneous fat and warm down, covered by a layer of water-repellent body feathers so they can safely swim. Their 'wings' are mere stubs at this stage, which makes their early departure from the nest all the more amazing, as they jump off the ledges into the sea, which may be several hundred feet below! Despite their inability to fly properly, feathers and blubber combined seem to have sufficient cushioning effect to allow them to bounce off the rock face on the way down without harm. The operation is made in one way more hazardous by taking place at night, but at least this allows the young birds a better chance of escaping the attentions of marauding gulls. Once off the cliff face, the chick swims with its father, and often in the company of others, out to the open sea, to long-established rich feeding areas where it completes its development away from the ever-present gull menace on the cliffs. Young Puffins are more mature when they leave the nesting burrows but they too are vulnerable, particularly to Great Black-backed Gulls, so they make their way to sea under cover of darkness and independently of their parents.

Once the young Guillemots can fly, usually by October, migration begins in earnest. Other than overall distance differences between adults and immatures, regional differences are not strongly marked. Northern birds more often head generally northwards, and tend to travel further on average than those from more southerly colonies. Those from northeastern England tend to remain in the North Sea area, few passing through the Channel, while Guillemots from western colonies tend to head towards Brittany and the Bay of Biscay. Pollution incidents are reported as responsible for more than one third of Guillemot recoveries, almost as many as are accidentally trapped in fishing nets.

Guillemots are sometimes considered to be simply dispersive, rather than migratory, not least because all year through they can be seen on the sea and at no distance from their breeding cliffs and stacks, and in most months some individuals will actually be on the breeding ledges. The only period of real absence is during the moult in August and September, when adults will be further out to sea for safety's sake whilst they are moulting and flightless. In reality, the distribution of Guillemot ring-recoveries is little different from that of the Razorbill (usually considered a long-haul migrant), but showing rather more northerly recoveries and fewer southerly

ones, particularly in the Mediterranean and off the northwestern coasts of Africa. Perhaps medium-haul migrant is the most appropriate classification.

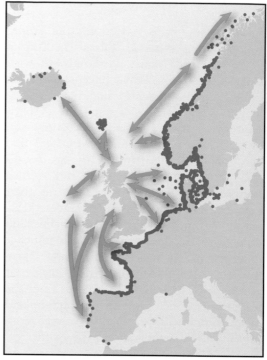

Guillemot

Once again, there are striking differences between adults and immatures. Many adult Guillemots remain in the vicinity of their colonies through the winter, even in the north, and many are recovered on British, but not Irish, beaches. It is tempting to attribute this absence of *adults* from Ireland to the comparative lack of human presence on Irish beaches, an essential component of their wild charm winter and summer alike, but *immature* Guillemots are found dead round most of the Irish coastline as well as the British. Some adults cross the North Sea or move south through the Channel, but recoveries are few in Norway north of Bergen or in France south of Brittany. In contrast, recoveries of immatures stretch from the Norwegian North Cape south to the Strait of Gibraltar.

The most enigmatic of our seabirds is the Leach's Petrel which breeds on only a handful of really remote islands off northern Scotland. Rare it may be for British and Irish birdwatchers, but it is an extremely numerous bird on a global scale. Unusually, ring-recoveries tell us little except that during the breeding season birds roam as widely or more so than Storm Petrels, usually in waters north of their colonies. Leach's Petrels make the day for autumn seawatchers, especially during and after stormy weather, but otherwise the indications are that this is the most pelagic of our seabirds in winter, distributed widely across the north Atlantic and well out of range of binoculars and telescopes.

Sea ducks

Whilst a range of ducks including Mallard, Wigeon and Pintail may be seen on coastal seas during the year, for three specialist 'sea ducks' it is their prime habitat. Eiders are one of our largest ducks and the commonest sea duck, heavyweight and seemingly placidly floating just offshore, dipping or diving occasionally for mussels. Drakes are black and white with a crooning grumbling song, ducks mottled brown with breast down feathers whose insulation properties are invaluable for both her eggs during incubation and for mankind, as the filling for quality anoraks, sleeping bags, eiderdowns and duvets ('duvet' is French for Eider). Over the last century, Eider populations have been steadily increasing, and they can now be found in winter around most of the British coastline, though they are less widespread in Ireland.

Eider – Jennifer Gill

Increasing numbers are breeding, especially in Scotland and the north of Ireland, which may account for the predominantly northern winter distribution. Many of our breeding Eiders are at best short-haul migrants, moving from scattered breeding areas to traditional food-rich winter sites such as the Firths of Tay and Forth. Some birds cross the North Sea in autumn to the seas off Denmark, southern Norway and Sweden, where they mix with birds of the Baltic population, with which some remain to breed.

The most obvious migrant of the sea ducks is without doubt the Common Scoter. Entirely sooty-black drakes and pale-faced, dull brown ducks fly in conspicuous and characteristic line-astern flocks over the sea, so low as to vanish behind wave crests as they go. From a higher vantage point, these 'lines' are revealed as the typical staggered V-formations of flying waterfowl. Little is known of the movements of the tiny British and Irish breeding population except that it deserts its northwestern loughs and lochs during the winter. The large flocks that we see in autumn, in relatively sheltered seas like Carmarthen Bay and the Burry Inlet in South Wales, are pausing to moult on their way (possibly from northern Scandinavia) to stormier wintering seas off France and Iberia. They, and the straggling lines passing south along British and Irish coasts in autumn, north in spring, breed in arctic Fennoscandia. Those from arctic Russia fly southwest in autumn overland to the Baltic, gathering there to moult before moving on south through the North Sea (where some overwinter) to become a feature of Channel seawatching spots.

Long-tailed Ducks are the neatest of the sea ducks wintering around the coasts of Britain and Ireland, particularly in the north and west. These 'Oldsquaws', as they are known in Canada and Alaska, have a circumpolar breeding distribution, mostly north of the Arctic Circle. Drakes are strikingly pied in winter, with very long tail streamers, but in summer become much darker, browner and drabber, like the ducks and immatures. Agile and active, and often confidingly close

Kittiwake

The Kittiwake is the most maritime of our breeding gulls, until recently with a breeding distribution heavily biased to remote western and northern coasts and islands. Kittiwakes have become successful birds, with the versatility, in areas lacking suitable cliffs, to turn to man-made alternatives, such as pier ledges and waterfront warehouse windowsills. British and Irish coasts are now ringed with colonies which are fascinating to watch. Kittiwakes' nests are so close together that, in the hurly-burly of comings and goings at the colony, any real fighting involving physical contact could be disastrous, dislodging eggs or young and sending them tumbling into the seas below. Instead, Kittiwakes seem to specialise in hurling vocal abuse at their neighbours if they venture too close. Each time an adult returns to the nest there is an effusive and vociferous greeting display to watch, with much head bowing and wing flapping.

Small and slender for a gull, the Kittiwake is elegant, with black legs and vermillion-lined yellow beak. It seems remarkable that many of these graceful birds will leave their colonies in July to spend the winter spread around the Atlantic Ocean, as far afield as the ice-strewn waters of the Newfoundland Banks. Although they may owe some of their success to our fishing activities, Kittiwakes remain literally 'sea gulls', arctic birds at home in the open ocean. Being genuinely oceanic through the winter months drastically reduces the chances of ring-recoveries at this season, but it is thought that the picture formed by autumn recoveries may not be too inaccurate. Although some of our birds move into the North Sea and south to

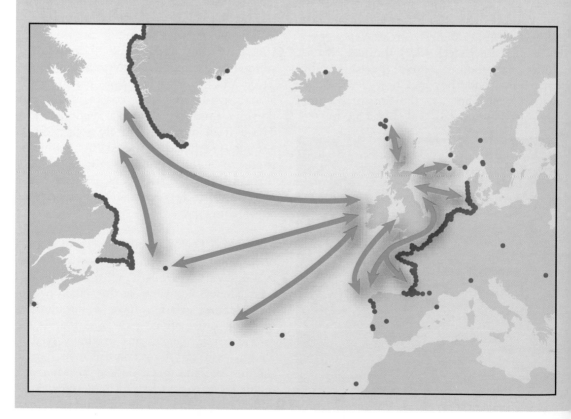

A ringed Kittiwake – Jim Flegg

the Bay of Biscay and beyond, ring-recoveries show a marked westerly trend towards Greenland and eastern Canada. On either side of the Atlantic, there is evidence that, as winter progresses, Kittiwakes tend to move southward.

It is likely that our immature birds stay in the rich feeding area of the Newfoundland Banks until they return east as potential breeding birds one or two years later; males returning close to where they were born, females dispersing widely. It may be some of these females that have produced recoveries in colonies on the far side of the Atlantic or in Scandinavia. Adults are strongly attached to their breeding colony, although not necessarily to their mate of the previous year if the pairing was not productive. During the winter at sea, Kittiwakes are mobile, moving extensively to avoid Atlantic depressions and the foul weather they may bring. This sometimes results in mass movements, visible from favoured seawatching points, and in the occasional anomalous recovery far inland in Britain, Ireland or continental Europe.

inshore, Long-tailed Ducks are a delight to watch, and (unusually for ducks) yodellingly tuneful as well as frequently vocal. Globally they are numerous birds, one estimate placing the Baltic Sea wintering population alone at fourmillion birds! Clearly the British and Irish wintering population, estimated at around 20,000 birds, is very much the southern fringe in both numbers and latitude. Migrants seen moving south in autumn along British and Irish coasts and back north in spring probably breed on northern Fennoscandian and Russian tundra. We know little about their origins and movements from ringing, but an adult caught and ringed on Fair Isle in Shetland was shot in Finland 20 years later.

Adaptability for all seasons

Until the 20th Century, members of the gull family were inevitably associated with the coast. Not for nothing were they colloquially called seagulls, with their occasional inland occurrences taken as indicators of stormy conditions out at sea. How things have changed! Several species are today commonplace inland, associated with refuse tipping, ploughing and rooftop nesting, sometimes far from the sea. However, most of the gulls are still sensibly considered in this chapter, associated with their true habitat, the sea.

The Great Black-backed Gull breeds around British and Irish coasts, although only sparsely in eastern and southern England. Our breeding population seems to be partly sedentary, partly short-haul migrant, on average moving just over 50 km, whereas the average recovery distance of immatures is more than twice this. Not only do immatures range further, but they tend to disperse further westward than adults, which show if anything an easterly trend. These movements may be inland as well as seawards, which accounts for the widespread distribution of Great Black-backs across Britain and Ireland in a wide range of habitats. In winter, the British and Irish population is augmented by substantial numbers of birds mainly from Fennoscandia, to judge from ring-recoveries of birds caught, usually on rubbish tips, using cannon nets.

Rather smaller and slate grey (rather than jet black) on the back, and with yellow rather than pink legs, the Lesser Black-backed Gull is genuinely migratory, although this status has changed steadily over the last 50 years. Lesser Black-backs are widely distributed as breeding birds, with colonies on coasts of all sorts from sand dunes to cliffs, and with some huge colonies inland on moorland. The British and Irish breeding population is probably about 90,000 pairs. Like the closely-related Herring Gull, Lesser Black-backs are adept opportunists when it comes to feeding, supplementing natural foods like fish and shellfish with piratical attacks on other seabirds, scavenging on fish offal ashore or at sea, and enjoying the bonus of food provided by refuse dumps and landfill sites. They are better than Herring Gulls at exploiting what farmland has to offer, particularly worms on grassland or behind the plough, and are enjoying the boom in outdoor pig-rearing too.

Lesser Black-backed Gull

Fifty years or so ago, bird books and county annual ornithological reports were quite adamant that Lesser Black-backs were long-haul migrants, heading south to Spain and west Africa for the winter, a clear distinction from the stay-at-home Herring Gull. Occasional winter sightings were recorded, but they were almost rarities. An analysis of over 300 ring-recoveries up to 1969 indicates a strong south to south-southwesterly trend, with plentiful recoveries from the Bay of Biscay, Iberia, northwestern Africa and west Africa as far south as Guinea. A similar analysis of almost 600 recoveries from 1970 onwards, augmented recently and most usefully by colour-ringing studies, indicates that the directional trend remains, but with fewer recoveries south of the Canaries. In striking addition, there are now numerous recoveries within Britain and Ireland during the winter months. The *Atlas of Wintering Birds* confirms that Lesser Black-backs are now widespread across inland England, Wales, Ireland and lowland Scotland in winter. Today it is probably true that Lesser Black-backs of all ages can be found throughout their range at all times of year. What has changed, we may wonder? Perhaps more enigmatic, why originally was the Lesser Black-back so distinctly different in its migratory habits from the so-closely related Herring Gull? Both questions remain to be answered.

At migration times, and probably through the winter, our Lesser Black-backs (race *graellsii*) are joined by the Scandinavian race *intermedius*, which has a subtly darker back, originating from Iceland and the Faeroes as well as Scandinavia and Denmark. The race *fuscus*, which is almost black on the back and breeds in Finland and the Baltic, migrates on a southeasterly track to Africa and is rarely encountered in Britain. Not surprisingly, with this mixture, migration times are imprecise. Autumn migration can begin in July and may be swift (600 km in four days), but some birds may linger near their colonies into October. Despite their changing migratory habits, it seems that immatures tend to travel further than adults, on average 1,700 against 1,200 km. Adults return between February and April, but immatures frequently stay south

Herring Gull in traditional setting –
Susan Waghorn

until ready to breed, usually at four years old. Adults are strongly colony-faithful, and many of the young return close to their birthplace when they reach breeding age.

This site-faithfulness is as true, or even truer, for the Herring Gull. Their population soared through the 20th Century, its expansion fuelled by the ready availability of fish offal and more particularly by land-based dumping of domestic and other refuse, which only recently has begun to be buried beyond the gulls' reach. For decades, the adaptable Herring Gulls seemed able to tolerate the various food-poisoning bacteria inevitably present in food waste as it decays, but over the last two decades increasing numbers of gulls have succumbed to bacterial toxin poisoning and their seemingly unending success and expansion has not only slowed but reversed in some areas. This is to the great relief of conservation organisations, seriously concerned at the predation and sheer pressure on nesting space that the gulls were exerting, for example on terns. Culling, however humane and however desirable, is an emotive topic and always has its vehement opponents, but in various locations it had seemed to be the only way to keep Herring Gull numbers under control.

Still essentially coastal breeders, Herring Gulls in Britain and Ireland are more abundant to the north and west. Some inland colonisation has occurred but it is in seaside towns where the adaptable gulls have noisily colonised rooftops and learned to pester (and sometimes attack) the inhabitants. Ringing, augmented by colour-ringing studies, indicates that many of our breeding Herring Gulls are sedentary, moving only a few tens of kilometres from their colony at most. A few others move rather further, putting them into the short-haul migration category, generally heading south after an initial dispersal to all points of the compass. As is often the case, immatures are likely to move further than adults, but fewer than 100 birds ringed as nestlings have been recovered overseas. They have been found in Iceland, Denmark, Germany, the Low Countries, France, Portugal and Spain, with no focal concentration other than along the closest stretches of the continental coast.

In winter, Herring Gulls are likely to be seen anywhere. Many of these birds will be our own population, moving to favoured feeding areas, but others will be migrants. Some 400 ring-recoveries indicate Iceland and (primarily) Fennoscandia as their main points of origin. Many northern birds pass on towards France, Iberia and the northern Mediterranean coast, perhaps in company with some British and Irish birds.

Small and neat, Little Gulls have the stature of a gull but habits and flight more akin to a tern, dipping down to feed from the water's surface. Their expanding breeding population is spread irregularly over the marshes of northwestern and north-central Europe, with outlying colonies to the west, for example in the Netherlands. Over the years, Little Gulls have made sporadic attempts to breed in England and Scotland, but it is as a regular passage migrant, increasing in numbers, that we see them most in Britain and Ireland, both along the coast and on larger fresh waters inland. Spring passage, generally northwards, is most apparent between March and mid-May, while in autumn two waves of migrants are sometimes detectable, in early and late September. That said, with the presence of breeding birds nearby and increasing numbers of wintering birds just offshore, Little Gulls are a possibility in any month.

Exposed coasts

Little Gull movements are not well understood. Dispersal from the breeding grounds is wide, mostly to coastal waters stretching from the North Cape in Norway to the Azores and North Africa, together with the Mediterranean, Black and Caspian Seas. In winter they are often out of sight of land but probably not truly pelagic, as poor weather may rapidly bring them close inshore. A handful of recoveries of birds ringed as nestlings overseas indicates that the origins of our migrants in the North Sea and Irish Sea are likely to lie in the Baltic States and northwestern Russian colonies.

Sea swallows

Among the principal victims of the gulls' expansion and predatory activities are the terns. Aptly deserving their popular name 'sea swallows', terns are perhaps the most graceful of our seabirds. Most are considerably smaller, much shorter-legged and slimmer even than a Black-headed Gull, with silver-grey and white plumage offset by darker wing tips and a black cap in summer. The dagger-like beak varies from black and black-and-yellow to black-and-red and blood red in the various species that breed in Britain and Ireland. All are long-haul migrants, travelling to fish in equatorial oceans or in the southern hemisphere during the northern winter, returning to our coasts to breed in summer. All terns are colonial breeders, and the colonies may be thousands strong, so predation or displacement under pressure from gulls may have a profound effect on tern numbers, not just here but around the North Atlantic as a whole. Often tern colonies are located on remote beaches and sand dunes, or on small islands offering the greatest security from human disturbance and from terrestrial predators such as foxes, rats and hedgehogs, all of which have a taste for their eggs and chicks. Eggs and young alike are remarkable examples of camouflage, nearly invisible against the background of sand, flecked with fragments of seaweed or shell.

Little Terns, with black-tipped yellow beaks and white foreheads, are one of the smallest terns and scarce even on a global scale. They have a wide but fragmented distribution in

Little Tern – Tommy Holden

small colonies round the coasts of Britain and Ireland. In the south and east they may breed on beaches popular with holidaymakers and, besides suffering almost continuous disturbance in fine weather, may lose eggs or young to the feet of unwary trippers, or to being buried by blowing sand on days when strong winds keep holidaymakers off the beach. With a little over 12,000 ringed and only about 150 recoveries to go on, a surprisingly good picture emerges of Little Tern migration and of the hazards they face. Almost half of the recoveries were reported as deliberately caught by man, usually trapped for food in Africa. We are familiar with Little Terns fishing just off shore with characteristic long-winged but jerky flight. It seems likely that they are similarly coastal on migration and in their winter quarters.

We have little precise information about the movements of adult Little Terns once their young are independent, but the juveniles depart during August in a dispersive pattern, possibly eventually heading for gathering grounds off the Netherlands. Thereafter, southerly migration seems to be swift, with one bird recovered in Portugal six days after ringing in Essex. Ring-recoveries are scattered along the European and northwest African coasts and the winter quarters for all ages lie off the west African coast, where they arrive in October and stay until beginning their return migration in February. The southernmost British recovery is from Guinea-Bissau, but birds from other European ringing schemes have been recovered further east in the Gulf of Guinea, off the Ivory Coast and Ghana. We know little of the summer whereabouts of one-year-old birds, which are thought to be off the African coast, nor of the passage of other populations through British and Irish waters. The indications are that adult Little Terns are colony-faithful when they return in spring, but several ring-recoveries indicate that young birds breeding for the first time may settle elsewhere, with reports from Sweden, Denmark, Germany and the Low Countries.

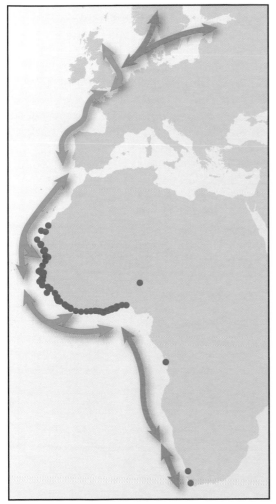

Common Tern: green – British and Irish;
orange – Fennoscandia

As its name suggests, the Common Tern (with a black-tipped red beak) is the tern we see most often and nearest home. Its colonies are widely distributed, coastally and inland, throughout Britain and Ireland. Analysis of ring-recoveries is easier than for the Little Tern, with over 2,000 recoveries on the computer. Well over half were reported as deliberately trapped by man, probably for food, a sobering hazard particularly in Africa for all British and Irish tern populations.

For young Common Terns, post-fledging dispersal may start in July, but most birds loiter near to their colonies for the first couple of months. There are indications that they then gather in favoured sites such as Dublin Bay and Teesmouth, and overland flights seem to be routine to reach these. During September and into October, strong passage is evident along the Atlantic coast of Iberia towards Morocco, and an 'average' bird will be about 1,300 km from Britain and Ireland. By November, this 'average' tern will be over 4,000 km along its migration route. Migration follows the coastline southwards down the eastern Atlantic, but not necessarily close inshore, as the presence of shoals of Anchovies and Sardines determines the location of the terns, particularly in the Gulf of Guinea. Adults follow the same route as immatures; in midwinter most are offshore between southern Morocco and Nigeria, although a few penetrate further south.

Adult Common Terns begin to return from February onwards, moving north at a calculated 80-120 km/day, leaving the immatures off west Africa and in the Gulf of Guinea for their first summer. Passage through the English Channel is a feature at seawatching sites like Portland and Dungeness in late April and early May, and birds are back at their breeding grounds soon after. In both spring and autumn, passage of British and Irish birds along our coasts is augmented by continental birds, mostly from Fennoscandia and the Baltic. Ring-recoveries indicate that these may migrate slightly later, in both seasons, than British and Irish birds, and frequently travel further south, some reaching the southern tip of Africa. One astonishing record is of a bird ringed as an adult in Northern Ireland in May 1959 and recovered (inland) in Victoria, Australia in October 1968. This could well have been a bird of continental origin, as nestlings from Sweden and Finland have also reached Australia.

Sandwich Tern

Sandwich Terns – Jim Flegg

Largest of our terns, with a spiky black crest, long yellow-tipped black beak, short tail streamers, a strident heavily disyllabic 'kay-wreck' call and vigorous diving action, the Sandwich Tern shows the most diverse overall migratory picture, derived from over 4,000 ring-recoveries (as many as all the other terns combined). Sandwich Tern colonies are widely distributed around British and Irish coasts, but often also widely separated. They are volatile, with some colonies moving after only a year or two, others after a longer interval, some apparently not at all. After the young fledge in late June or July, families disperse quickly.

By the end of August, family groups depart on their real migration south, the young being dependent (at least in part) on their parents until well into winter quarters. Birds from northwestern colonies appear to move down western coasts, with east coast birds migrating through the Channel. The journey south is through the coastal waters of western Europe and west Africa, with hardly any British and Irish birds entering the Mediterranean.

The major wintering areas appear to be in food-rich inshore waters, from Senegal east to Ghana, but heavy trapping pressure, especially in Ghana, may bias this view. There is another grouping of recoveries around Gabon, the Congo and Angola, and some Sandwich Terns push onwards to South Africa, rounding the Cape of Good Hope, and reaching Mozambique. Adults, probably three years old or older, set off north in March, on a speedy passage, with some back in British and Irish waters by later in the month. Breeding adults are site-faithful but birds of breeding age, returning for the first time, may settle anywhere within 500 km of their birthplace. The grey dots on the map indicate recoveries of birds able to breed for the first time and recovered during the breeding season, a pan-European scattering with few equals, and certainly one promoting genetic diversity?

Globe-spanning journeys such as this may be surprising for a Common Tern, but for the Arctic Tern they are more of a way of life. As its name suggests, the Arctic Tern is at the southern extreme of its breeding range in northern Britain and Ireland. Breeding well above the Arctic Circle, where the summer is nightless, they probably see more hours of daylight each year than any other creature. Having raised their young they migrate southwards along our coasts and on across the Equator. They spend our winter in the Antarctic Ocean, where once again they have the benefit of almost perpetual daylight and can enjoy a rich food supply of small fish and plankton.

Their route takes them offshore southwards along the western European coast, adults and juveniles travelling together, then onwards around the 'bulge' of West Africa and through the Gulf of Guinea, where hunters account for almost one quarter of recoveries reported. Passage continues to southern Africa and then on into the Antarctic Ocean, where they moult and apparently spread along the margin of the pack ice, the greatest concentration occurring south of the Indian Ocean. Return passage begins in March, with probably most birds retracing their autumn route. Once they reach Britain and Ireland they are regularly seen in numbers from seawatching sites, but there is also abundant observational evidence from inland freshwaters and elsewhere that overland travel is almost commonplace in spring. Even so, the suggestion that some may migrate north through the Indian Ocean and then onwards over the Eurasian land mass to the Arctic Circle is a little startling.

But then, that is the way of Arctic Terns. At its shortest, their migration 20,000 km each way must make them contenders as long-distance record holders; certainly so when their size is compared, for example, with the albatrosses. The oldest Arctic Tern that we know of was a ringed bird that lived for 26 years. Travelling almost from pole to pole twice a year, its lifetime mileage is unthinkably high – maybe more than one million kilometres.

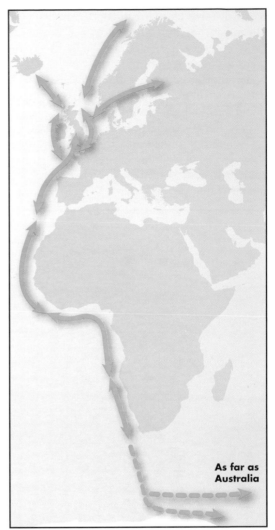

As far as Australia

Arctic Tern

Similar, faster, with longer tail streamers, and a black beak with blood red base, many birdwatchers would rank the Roseate Tern as the most elegant tern, and one of the world's most beautiful seabirds. Globally, Roseate Terns are widespread, mostly in the tropics, but sadly in Britain and Ireland they are rare, and alarmingly continuing to become rarer. The British and Irish population fell (crashed would be appropriate) by 80% between 1969 and 1991, when it totalled about 500 pairs, 400 of them in Ireland. Following heightened conservation efforts, both at the breeding colonies and in their African wintering grounds, almost 800 pairs bred in 1999. The breeding population centres on the Irish Sea basin, with only a handful of colonies elsewhere on the northeast coast of Britain.

Exposed coasts

Roseate Terns are maritime birds, rarely if ever venturing inland. They disperse randomly from colonies in August, though to go no great distance according to ring-recoveries, of which almost 900 are available for analysis. A gathering then occurs in Dublin Bay prior to departure, where adults and young (still largely dependent on their parents) put on pre-migratory fat deposits. It seems that, once they depart in September and early October, their journey south down the coasts of western Europe and West Africa is swift,

reaching winter quarters off the Ivory Coast, Ghana and Togo. Recoveries indicate that the great majority reside there from November until April, when adults begin their return journey, arriving back at their colonies from mid-May onwards. Birds entering their first summer remain in west African waters until the following year, when they reach breeding age. When they do return to the breeding grounds, they may prospect a range of colonies in northwestern Europe before settling distant from their birthplace. The suggestion is that all colonies in northwestern Europe form a 'metapopulation', within which exchanges are commonplace, but that exchanges with other metapopulations (e.g. in the USA) very rarely occur.

Clearly, our Roseate Tern population is in trouble. Ring-recoveries suggest that poor juvenile survival may be the reason, particularly due to increased killing for food on African shores. Of recoveries with an identified cause of death, 75% were deliberately taken by man. Such figures make disturbing reading, but do indicate the value of ringing efforts in highlighting conservation needs, pinpointing important localities and indicating possible conservation strategies to international agencies.

Collectively, from a birdwatcher's viewpoint, the terns have it all. They are easy to see and reasonably easy to identify, are a pleasure to watch both for their extreme elegance and incessant action, and possess one of the most amazing of all avian family travelogues. The saddest collective aspect is that they all suffer so severely from human predation in their African winter quarters.

Pirates under pressure

The terns are one of the major targets of a group of their relatives, the skuas, which have predation and parasitism as their main way of life. Two of them are only seen occasionally around our coasts; the Long-tailed Skua, little bigger than a Sandwich Tern but with very long central tail feathers, is an arctic-breeding rarity, but seen offshore every year in spring and autumn. The Herring Gull-sized

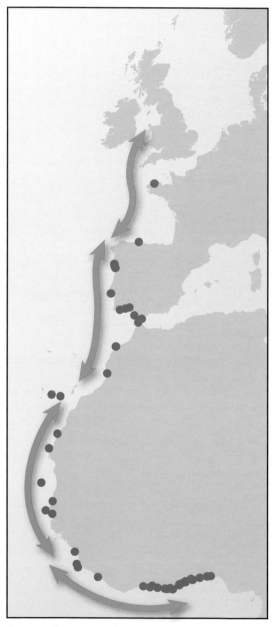

Roseate Tern

Pomarine Skua, with thick, blunt-ended and twisted elongated central tail feathers – 'spoons' – is a scarce but regular passage migrant in several areas, particularly in late spring in the English Channel. The May up-Channel passage of these skuas is a major feature of south coast seawatching from established lookouts like Portland, Beachy Head and Dungeness, as well as off the west coast of Ireland, but much depends on the prevailing weather. On autumn passage south, 'Poms' can be seen from more vantage points, widely spread round the British and Irish coasts, but rarely in the numbers occurring in spring.

The other two skuas, Arctic and Great, breed in Scotland, particularly in remote parts of the Hebrides, Orkney and Shetland, migrating south to equatorial waters for the winter. The Great Black-backed-sized Great Skua, brown and bulky, with the central tail feathers only just projecting beyond the rest of the tail, is quickly recognised from juvenile gulls by the large white patch in the centre of each wing. The Arctic Skua, Common Gull-sized, has central tail feathers projecting a few centimetres and, to make identification more difficult, comes in a variety of plumage 'phases', ranging from a buffish body with dark cap and wings to chocolate-brown all over. All phases, however, have the distinctive bold white wing patch.

Arctic Skuas are slender-winged and extremely agile in flight. They will harass (sometimes singly, sometimes as a team) terns, Kittiwakes and the smaller gulls, relentlessly chasing their victim until it drops or disgorges the food it is carrying. So quick in flight are they that normally they will swoop to catch the dropped item before it reaches the sea. Their migratory routes are to some extent shaped by those of their major victims, the terns. The 300 ring-recoveries available indicate that birds from Orkney and Shetland migrate south at the end of the breeding season, mainly down the east coast through the North Sea. Migrant skuas are a regular autumn seawatching feature along most of our coasts, some from our own colonies, others from elsewhere in northwestern Europe. Their southbound passage takes them along the tern routes in African coastal seas, as far south as the Cape of Good Hope, where most are thought to winter. A trio of recoveries in South America, one in Sudan, and two in the eastern Mediterranean add some tantalising questions. These, and the scattering of North American recoveries, may be roaming birds, mostly of breeding age but not breeding because feeding conditions have been inadequate through the winter. The return

Arctic Skua – Derek Belsey

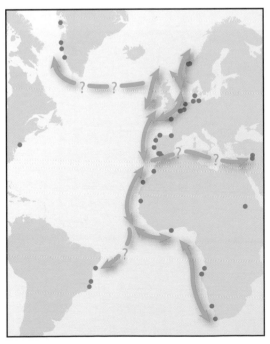

Arctic Skua

journey is thought to follow the same route (and also the terns) with birds arriving back on their colonies in the Northern Isles late in April. Seawatching observations of passage migrants usually extend well into May, as they also involve skuas heading for colonies in countries to the north. Recoveries indicate that while some immatures may remain in southern waters until reaching breeding age (usually at four years) others move north with the adults. Adults seem fairly frequently to exchange colonies between years.

Similar forms of piracy are the basis of the Great Skua's life-style. More powerful and more ponderous in flight but deceptively fast, Great Skuas will chase most gulls and terns, and even Gannets. Sometimes physical violence is used, and a favoured Great Skua tactic is to seize a Gannet's wingtip, in flight, and throw it off balance. Bigger though they are, Gannets are nowhere near so nimble in flight and cannot tolerate such treatment, coughing-up the contents of their crop, which the Skua usually catches before it hits the sea. Great Skuas often extend piracy to predation and can be a serious threat, killing, amongst others, Storm and Leach's Petrels, Manx Shearwaters and Puffins. Nor are they in the least shy of dive-bombing human intruders near their nests, regularly (and painfully) clipping them over the head with their wings or feet, sometimes sufficiently hard to knock over an adult.

Great Skuas are highly maritime, coming to land only to breed, and then on some of the most remote spots in the North Atlantic and Arctic Oceans. Our colonies are at the southern extreme of an essentially arctic breeding range, yet we accommodate more than half the world population, with around 10,000 pairs. For much of the last century, Great Skuas have been in an expansion phase, recovering from near-extinction in the 1890s. Protective measures and changes in fishing stimulated steady population growth but over the last 30 years occasional colony declines have become more general. Probably the decline is as a result of several factors, some linked to the shortage of sandeels around Shetland (impacting on other seabirds, notably Arctic Tern and Puffin), and yet more changes in commercial fishing technology and legislation, which have reduced the number of undersized discards thrown overboard from fishing vessels.

Overall, the Great Skua must be cast as a long-haul migrant, based on the analysis of almost 2,000 ring-recoveries. Durable metal

Great Skua – Jim Flegg

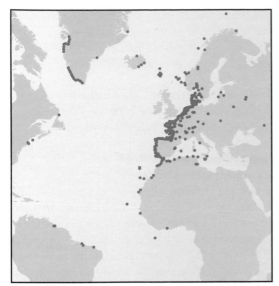

Great Skua

Life in the surf

Several wader species can be seen on exposed coasts and some, like Curlew, Redshank and particularly Oystercatcher, spend the winter in this rocky environment – but their migrations are dealt with elsewhere. There are two waders however that are completely at home on the wave-washed rocky outcrops and seaweed-strewn beaches – Turnstones and Purple Sandpipers.

Amongst arctic-breeding waders, Purple Sandpipers are distinguished globally by their overall northerly winter distribution, even occurring north of the Arctic Circle, where not only are temperatures low but daylight is minimal. As a fascinating adaptation to life in extremely cold conditions, those wintering in the far north have developed longer digestive tracts than those wintering further south, this allowing them to process the extra food they need to maintain sufficient body heat to survive the harsh conditions.

rings have been in use since the early 70s and have proved of great value, not least because some Great Skuas may be ten years old before they breed. Human pressures account for 60% of recoveries with known cause of death, mostly due to deliberate killing but also to accidental trapping and drowning in nets. Autumn migration starts in late June or July when colony-visiting (but not breeding) immatures, aged up to 8 years, depart and scatter widely across the North Atlantic as far south as the Equator and from Africa across to North and South America, so just about as widely as possible! Some also move northwards into the Arctic Ocean. Juveniles of the year are the next to leave, also dispersing widely. Adults need to remain on territory in defensive mode to avoid being usurped (a good territory is vital for next year), but they too depart in late August and September. Adults in winter seem to be substantially less scattered and less distant than immatures, being found around the Bay of Biscay, Iberia, Morocco, and the western Mediterranean. Return passage begins in March and territory-holding pairs are back in the colony around the end of the month. Younger birds (up to 3 years old) may remain in the south of the winter range, but others roam north, penetrating to arctic Canada and Greenland, in the west, and well north of the North Cape and on to arctic Russia in the east. All in all, an amazing life-cycle!

Purple Sandpiper – Tommy Holden

During the winter months, Purple Sandpipers can occur almost anywhere round the British and Irish coastline, although their main distribution is biased towards northern exposed rocky shores. Even where rocks, their favoured habitat, are absent, small groups will gather on man-made alternatives like lifeboat or boatyard slipways and harbour breakwaters, always inconspicuous but faithful to favoured localities.

Within Britain and Ireland, most ring-recoveries (and colour-ring observations) are along the rockier sections of the northeast coast of Britain, and the majority of overseas recoveries are within Fennoscandia. Measurements taken while birds are being ringed show that various breeding populations of Purple Sandpipers (from Canada, Greenland, Svalbard, Fennoscandia and Russia) have different wing and bill lengths. In each case and like many other waders, females have longer bills than males. Both sexes from the most southerly population in Norway have substantially shorter bills than those breeding further north around the Arctic Circle. Bill and wing measurements of birds trapped on Britain's east coast suggest that the majority of winter visitors there originate in Norway. These birds begin to appear during July, adults moulting as soon as they arrive. Most seem to be site-faithful until their departure northeast in April and May.

In the far north of Scotland and the Isles, long-billed birds predominate, and a scattering of recoveries in the north and northwest from Greenland, Iceland and Svalbard indicates that these birds have indeed travelled further. Measurements from these fascinating detailed studies suggest that Purple Sandpipers from arctic Canada may also be wintering in Britain and Ireland,

possibly in substantial numbers. As more birds are caught, ringed, measured and colour-marked, it is hoped that this story will unfold further.

The other wader characteristic of both seaweed-covered rocks and the drift lines of seaweed at the high tide mark on sandy shores is the Turnstone. Chequered black, white and chestnut summer plumage ensures that they are well-hidden among the rocks, mosses and lichens of their tundra breeding grounds. The Turnstone is familiar all round British and Irish coasts and equally effectively camouflaged in its more subdued winter plumage. Turnstones use their beaks as shovels, sometimes as their name suggests overturning small pebbles to reach the small marine animals beneath, but more often to probe for food amongst the seaweed fronds or to hunt fly maggots in the tide wrack.

Turnstones breed over much of the circumpolar High Arctic but ring-recoveries indicate that British and Irish winter migrants originate either from arctic Canada and Greenland or from Fennoscandia. Migrants begin to arrive in July, failed breeders and immatures arriving before successful breeders and their young. Detailed studies of birds trapped in Britain and Ireland indicate that immigrants from Canada and Greenland

Turnstones – birds ringed with coloured rings in Lincolnshire have been resighted in arctic Canada – Nigel Clark

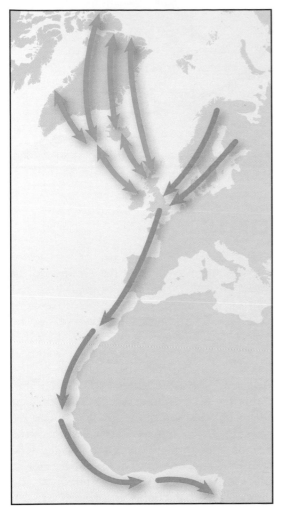

Turnstone: green – Greenland and Canadian; orange – Fennoscandian

Plover. Fascinatingly, from the lack of spring recoveries in Britain and Ireland, it seems that Fennoscandian passage migrants, which pass through Britain in autumn on their way to west Africa, return by another route.

Globally, Turnstones have an astonishing array of migrations. Alaskan birds migrate down the entire western seaboard of the Americas to winter as far south as Chile, and most Canadian birds head for the Caribbean, where they have learnt to beg for food at beach bars, scuttling round the bare feet of the holidaymakers! Greenland and eastern Canadian birds, we have just seen, move to Britain and Ireland, Scandinavian ones to west Africa. Central Siberian populations move south to southern Africa, the Middle East and the shores of the Indian Ocean, while to complete the array, the East Siberian/West Alaskan population winters in southeast Asia and greater Australasia. Simply prodigious!

Rocky coasts by their very nature hold more summer birdlife than the lower-lying shores and muddier waters of the south and east. The sight, sound and smell provided by seabird colonies in full swing must be difficult to equal. It is worth remembering that, for many seabirds, attendance at the breeding colonies can begin early in the year, with birds regularly on the cliffs on warm days even before spring has started. Equally, for most species, the breeding season is all but over when most of us elect to take our summer holidays; by August, many birds will have departed to the open seas for the winter. At migration times and during the winter, it may well be that the less spectacular south and east coasts will be more sheltered than gale-swept western and northern rocky shores of Britain and Ireland. Passage migrants seek these more protected routes (for example through the Channel) and the comparative shelter may encourage many more visiting seabirds to remain inshore during the winter months. Summing up, exposed coasts in winter, passage seasons and summer alike, present us with as rich a kaleidoscope of migrants as any other habitat, in summer often set against the most dramatic of scenic surrounds.

moult soon after arrival and tend to stay through the winter, moving little between sites. Those from Fennoscandia feed vigorously to put on fat, prior to onward migration to west African overwintering grounds.

Some, maybe most, one-year-old birds remain south through the summer, but breeding birds begin to leave Africa in February. For birds heading for the frozen tundra of Greenland and arctic Canada, there is no point in leaving Britain and Ireland until April or even May, on a journey that well-fed birds may be able to make in one flight. It is calculated that about half stop off to feed or rest in Iceland, alongside vast flocks of Knot, Dunlin, Sanderling, Purple Sandpipers and Ringed

Rarities and vagrants

Tales of the unexpected

The main aim of the preceding chapters has been to throw some light on the comings and goings of migrants that most birdwatchers are at least fairly likely to see. Some of them we may encounter almost daily in the right season, maybe around our homes or in the countryside nearby. Others may require a visit to a more distant habitat, but well within the range and reach of most birdwatchers. That said, one of the attractions of birdwatching is that birds are so mobile, so able to cover vast distances, that you genuinely never know what you might encounter.

This chapter cannot explore or identify all the rarities that might be involved, but aims to outline the possibilities. For most birdwatchers there can be little doubt that there is some *cachet* in seeing something out of the ordinary, even better a really rare bird. Fascinating as the daily comings and goings are of the various birds that are a routine component of the life of our countryside, it is especially intriguing to marvel at the arrival of a wanderer from afar and to replace the image on the page of a bird book with a fully-feathered memory.

Bird observatories

There are a few places where migration is so obvious that nobody could fail to notice what is going on. With lots of migrants passing through, chances are that the routine will be spiced with the occasional unusual bird, just waiting to be discovered. An excellent example of a migration hot-spot is the concentration of tens of thousands of birds of prey and storks crossing the narrow waters of the Bosporus, *en route* between Europe and Asia and Africa. Others are the autumn gathering of thousands of birds of prey at Falsterbo, in southern Sweden, prior to crossing the narrow straits separating Scandinavia from the main European land mass, and similar scenes at Gibraltar prior to the crossing into Africa. Inspired by the information that could be gathered in such circumstances, migration observation points were set up in Britain and Ireland, manned by a few enthusiastic pioneers such as Eagle Clarke, in the early 1900s. These were coordinated by no less than the British Association for the Advancement of Science,

The Bosporous: at the Narrows, Europe and Asia are extraordinarily close – Jim Flegg

and tended to be situated on islands, headlands, isolated lighthouses and lightships, that seemed to lie on natural migration flyways. The modern network of bird observatories is located in very similar places.

The first bird observatory proper was founded by one such enthusiastic amateur, Heinrich Gatke, who spent 50 years in the latter part of the 19th Century on the now German (but then British) island of Helgoland, off the German North Sea coast. His account of migration through the island (*Die Vogelwarte Helgoland*) makes compelling reading even today. Although some of the birds may be much rarer and others occurring today he would not have dreamt of, the overall pattern of events is much the same. What makes chilling reading are the gruesome accounts of shooting extreme rarities with a shotgun on the basis of "what's hit is history, what's missed is mystery". Horrifying today, but in those days not even raising an eyebrow.

Islands in general have several advantages as bird observatories. Often they have a lighthouse, which may attract night migrants, especially if the weather turns bad. Such an assisted landfall may be salvation for the many birds to be seen in nearby bushes at daybreak. Islands, too, can have the benefit of being of limited size, and often have relatively few patches of suitable vegetation to shelter migrants. Hence the birds can be easily located, trapped for ringing or counted, and a pattern associated with time of year and weather can gradually be built up.

The first British bird observatory was founded in 1933 on the Welsh island of Skokholm, off Pembrokeshire, by Ronald Lockley, whose family farmed the island, sharing it only with the lighthouse keepers. Over 70 years later the island is still an observation point, although no longer farmed or an official observatory. The network around the British and Irish coasts has grown, with 18 observatories represented on the Bird Observatories Council and most offering accommodation to visitors interested in participating in their work. These are augmented by numerous less formally

Heligoland trap on Skokholm – Jim Flegg

organised, but regularly manned, ringing stations. Many of the island observatories are slightly difficult to reach, because of their remoteness, which makes them especially attractive to those really wishing to 'get away from it all', but others, such as Portland Bill in Dorset, Dungeness in Kent and Gibraltar Point in Lincolnshire, are within easy reach of centres of population.

So what does an observatory do? In most cases the observatory area is carefully scanned to note arrivals, and a daily log is kept of bird species and numbers and of the direction of any movements. Depending on the weather, some of these migrants are trapped and ringed. This can be exciting work, sometimes because of the sheer numbers of birds arriving or passing over (as with an autumn 'fall' of thrushes on the East Coast); sometimes because a rarity from afar has appeared, blown off course. Located as they are in the best spots for migration watching, observatories seem to work like magnets to less usual birds as well as to the mass of common migrants. Fair Isle, in Shetland, sees an astonishing percentage of rarities from as far afield as North America, the Arctic and the Far East, and offers an experience rarely to be obtained elsewhere. Much the same can be said for any off-lying island in the right place; the Isles of Scilly at the other extremity of Britain and Ireland are a classic case in point.

Fall birds

Situated as they are at the extreme west of Europe, our group of islands is well situated to intercept lost or weather-assisted birds from North America. A glance at the autumn weather maps, with depressions looking like giant dartboards in the North Atlantic, shows how this occurs. To the north of these depressions sweep westerly winds, often reaching or exceeding 100 mph (160 kph) at high altitude. Some migrants (like the Wheatear travelling from Greenland) take advantage of these prevailing winds each year. But should any powerful-flying American migrant such as a duck or wader, normally on a north-south track, get caught up in one of these jet-stream tail winds, the crossing ('power assisted' by the wind) of the Atlantic is well within its flight endurance capabilities. Hence there are numerous records of such birds each year, plus an astonishing number of smaller birds that also manage to survive the journey. Although, for most of these species, sightings may be few and far between and not even at the rate of one a year, others, such as the Pectoral Sandpiper, are now annual, sometimes in numbers.

After a gap of five years, 5 American Robins turned up in Britain and Ireland in autumn 2003. One became so famous that its demise, in the talons of a Sparrowhawk, was reported in national newspapers – Su Gough

The range of vagrant American waders is substantial. At the lower end of the size scale are their 'peeps', including White-rumped, Western, Baird's and Semipalmated Sandpipers. The last has some webbing between its toes, and is very confiding. A delightful account records how one, trapped and ringed in Co. Cork, was positively

Ring-billed Gull – Dawn Balmer

identified when it obligingly pattered between pools of spilt stout on the bar, leaving part-webbed footprints! Slightly larger are the Buff-breasted and Stilt Sandpiper, and, at the top end of the scale, the Lesser Yellowlegs and Long-billed Dowitcher, both annual visitors. American gulls seem to be seen more frequently than in the past too; regulars including Bonaparte's, Ring-billed and Laughing Gulls, while Green-winged Teal, American Wigeon and Ring-necked Duck carry the flag for waterfowl. Amongst the more regular (though still very rare) small passerines are Red-eyed Vireos, Blackpoll Warblers, Rose-breasted Grosbeaks and White-throated Sparrows, almost always occurring in autumn. Even the Americans find New World warblers difficult to identify in autumn and, as most of those occurring are at best in winter plumage, at worst also immatures (always the longest-distance roamers), all small North American passerines present substantial identification challenges.

Hardly migration maybe, but there is one way that trans-Atlantic migrants can escape the hazards of the weather and accomplish a successful Atlantic crossing; on board ship! Several American small birds have accomplished the Atlantic crossing in this way. Some are non-migrants and unlikely to have the endurance, even jet-stream assisted, for such a prolonged crossing. Once on board ship, crew and passengers often lend a helping hand to survival by feeding scraps to the stowaways. For the bird concerned the voyage may even start with the vessel still in port, although it is easy to envisage a tired migrant, perhaps in difficult conditions, chancing on the boat out at sea. Once the boat docks, the stranger flies ashore. Ship-assisted crossings can occur at any time of year, creating a problem for the record keepers keen to sort genuine migrants or vagrants from birds that crossed the easy way.

Wanderers from the east

The west is far from being the sole source of our rare vagrants. Fewer than one-third of really rare birds (those necessitating identification ratification by the British Birds Rarities Committee) come from North America. Britain and Ireland also receive visitations of birds with a more easterly distribution, especially when periods of easterly winds blow birds off course whilst on their regular migration pathways. Typical autumn regulars *en route* from Scandinavia to Africa include Bluethroat, Barred Warbler and Red-breasted Flycatcher.

Sometimes freak climatic conditions, with a single massive weather system stretching across Europe and Asia, can bring oriental or Siberian wanderers to our shores – the

Pallas's Warbler – Jim Flegg

Chiffchaff-sized but more boldly patterned Pallas's Warbler for instance. Pallas's Warbler had occurred (or at least had been found and identified) only three times in Britain and Ireland before 1958. The influx of 6 in 1963 was considered astonishing at the time but palls into insignificance against the many dozens recorded since. That they should have been found and identified (often by no means an easy task) is a tribute to the enthusiasm and increasing skills of the growing numbers of birdwatchers involved.

In much the same size and plumage category and with similar identification problems are Greenish and Yellow-browed Warblers, which occur in autumn in very small numbers more or less annually. The Aquatic Warbler is another rare but regular autumn visitor. The only globally-threatened passage migrant occurring in Britain, Aquatic Warblers breed in swampy areas in central Europe. Rather than occurring along the east coast, autumn records are unexpectedly centred in the southwest, where the reedbeds are obviously of key importance for feeding prior to the next southbound stage of their migration. Rarer and more difficult to identify is the Desert Wheatear, subtly sombre in plumage in all seasons, a bird of desert areas in North Africa and the Middle East. This seems to occur more often in Britain and Ireland than its near relative, the Black-eared Wheatear, which breeds as close to us as southern France and Iberia. Desert Wheatears are perhaps the prime examples of not only "you never know" but you never know *where*, as they have an extraordinary predilection for the least prepossessing of landscapes, including spoil tips, refuse dumps and demolition sites.

Larger, easier to identify and regular in occurrence (though still in the unusual-to-rare category) are several tundra-breeding waders passing through in spring and, more often, in autumn *en route* to wintering grounds largely in eastern Africa and around the Indian Ocean. Of these, Little and Temminck's Stints are the smallest, and Britain and Ireland's smallest waders. Bigger and more colourful in spring are the Curlew Sandpiper, which is rich chestnut, and the Spotted Redshank, jet-black with white flecks, slim and elegant and to some birdwatchers the most handsome of waders. From Siberian breeding grounds, these two species migrate widely to winter quarters ranging from Africa east to Australasia, some Spotted Redshanks occasionally staying with us over winter. These two are noteworthy not just for their plumage but for the efficiency of their feeding, swiftly accumulating substantial body-fat deposits to fuel their migratory journeys, which ringing evidence suggests are made in unusually fast and long stages.

During the winter, eastern wanderers are represented on an annual basis by Jack Snipe, probably more numerous than we think because they are so secretive, flushing silently and at much closer range (almost underfoot) than their larger relative, the Common Snipe. Also annual but rather more picturesque are waterfowl like Red-crested Pochard and Ferruginous Duck, both sporadically distributed across eastern-central Europe. Their larger relatives include the Bean Goose (annual but quite scarce) which winters in scattered sites across western Europe, the rare Lesser White-fronted Goose and even rarer (and most colourful) Red-breasted Goose. Neither of the last two is necessarily annual in Britain and Ireland, and both are great attractions when they do occur, having wandered far from their major wintering grounds in the Black and Caspian Sea basins.

Red-crested Pochard – Mike Weston

Arctic specialists

Gulls and sea ducks feature strongly among regular rarities from the High Arctic and Arctic Ocean to the coasts and coastal seas of Britain and Ireland. Another rare arctic visitor which might be seen swimming on the sea or a coastal lagoon is actually a wader, the Grey Phalarope, which is pelagic in winter and floats buoyantly, swimming expertly with lobed toes to assist propulsion. Of the gulls, the larger and quite similar Iceland and Glaucous Gulls not infrequently spend much of the winter in a favoured fishing port or nearby refuse tip. Smaller and altogether more exciting are the extremely rare, arctic-breeding Sabine's, Ross's and Ivory Gulls. Sabine's Gulls are trans-equatorial migrants, those breeding in northeastern Canada and Greenland passaging to the west coast of Africa and occasionally getting storm-blown into British and Irish waters. Ross's Gull, dove-like and delectably pale pink in the breeding season, is an eastern Siberian gull, routinely wintering around the Bering Sea, while the all-white Ivory Gull (dumpy-bodied, short-legged and short-beaked as befits an arctic specialist) stays close to the pack ice margin all winter. The last two are scarce indeed, a very real thrill for those who find them.

Of the sea ducks, Velvet Scoter are annual visitors, widespread round the coast but scarce, while Surf Scoter and King Eider are much rarer and confined to the far north. As if to emphasise just how well adapted many of these birds are to pelagic life, it is often only in the roughest of weather that we see them. One of the species to look out for after winter storms is the Little Auk, blown here from northern seas, sometimes in very large numbers.

Mediterranean overshoots

Last in this catalogue of the unexpected are the Mediterranean overshoots. For some, a spring wind from the south may have carried them too far north and west. Perhaps the classic examples are colourful birds like Golden Orioles (which have established a small breeding population derived from such spring migrants); Hoopoes (regular but scarce as migrants); and Bee-eaters (most rainbow-hued of all, but breeding only extremely rarely). Just what happens to these overshooting migrants if they do not stay on to breed is a matter of conjecture; it may well be that many manage to re-orientate successfully. Indeed, it would almost come as a surprise if lost birds, relatively near to home and with excellent navigational abilities, were not able to relocate.

Smaller overshoots include Melodious and Bonnelli's Warblers from the Mediterranean. Others, like the scrub-loving Sardinian and Subalpine Warblers, are more prevalent after

Bee-eater – Su Gough

the breeding season, maybe in dispersive mode or seeking to expand into new terrain. Overshooting, drifting off-course, or a combination of the two would account for passage migrant Wrynecks and Red-backed Shrikes (now sadly virtually extinct in Britain and Ireland as breeding visitors) and for, amongst others, spring and autumn Ortolan Buntings, Woodchat Shrikes and the Kentish Plover, extinct now for over half a century in the county of its name.

Other scarce migrants from the south may be travelling to 'outpost' populations. Our breeding Golden Orioles could also fit this category, but other good examples are Quail, Montagu's Harriers and Honey Buzzards, all at the northwestern extremity of their range. All

maintain tiny breeding populations; Montagu's Harrier's being the most precarious and confined to the south and east.

Pioneers

In a period of substantial changes in land use and with subtler fluctuations in climate, it is not surprising that our bird communities also change. It may be that the comparatively recent extinctions or near-extinctions in Britain of the Kentish Plover, Wryneck and Red-backed Shrike reflect more than anything contractions in these birds' mainland European distribution. In contrast, recent colonisations (or re-colonisations) of Britain and Ireland are probably due to population expansions, if not explosions (Collared Doves for example).

The Avocet, internationally recognised symbol of the RSPB, is more than appropriate as an example of recolonisation following expansion, and of ringing as a tool for conservation. Since recolonisation in East Anglia in 1947, the British Avocet population has grown to around 500 pairs, spread over a number of sites mostly from the North Kent Marshes to The Wash. Wintering numbers are also increasing, mostly on estuaries from East Anglia through Kent and along to the southwest peninsula and the Severn. Although only 30 British ring-recoveries are available, they indicate that some British birds join moulting flocks in the Netherlands, involving birds from across northwestern Europe, whilst others move to estuaries adjacent to their breeding grounds. Avocets in the Netherlands disperse at the onset of winter, southwards to a handful of wintering grounds in France, Portugal, Senegal and Guinea, those moving furthest south using the famous wader areas of the Banc d'Arguin in Mauritania as a staging post. British ring-recoveries reflect this distribution, but thus far none have been reported south of Morocco. Overall, it is calculated that just ten wintering sites hold 90% of European Avocets, clearly indicating how important it is that these sites are effectively conserved, and that conservation must be an international, not simply national, concern.

Not far behind Avocets as colonists came Mediterranean Gulls. Their northwestern European numbers began to build in the 1960s, resulting in colonisation attempts in southern England, which led to regular breeding from the mid-1970s and a current list of well over 20 colonies, usually in close association with Black-headed Gulls. For a species in expansionist phase, ring-recoveries

Little Egret – Al Downie

are difficult to interpret but a well coordinated colour-ringing programme has helped establish that even breeding birds are mobile, changing colony from year to year. They also show an autumn influx, from July onwards, of migrants from as far afield as Hungary, the Baltic and the Low Countries, to provide a steadily growing winter population around the English and eastern Irish coasts. Return departure east stretches from February to May, with adults moving well in advance of non-breeders.

For a bird scarcely mentioned in British and Irish field guides 20 years ago, recorded in one

10 km square in the *Winter Atlas* (1981-84) and as 'present' in just 3 squares during the *Breeding Atlas* survey period (1988-91), the Little Egret has now made its mark, breeding widely (if still in small numbers) across southern Britain and Ireland and present, sometimes in dozens, occasionally more than 100, on many sheltered southern and western estuaries in winter. Their arrival from southern European marshes is doubtless the outcome of dispersive movement, but as yet with no return migration that we are aware of.

Today any sighting of a rarity will be swiftly broadcast on pagers and web sites, guaranteeing the bird concerned a large and appreciative audience. By such means, 21st Century birdwatchers are far better informed than their forebears, with much information available within minutes of the original sighting and regular updates on location provided. Optical equipment, too, is far superior to even 20 or 30 years ago (particularly telescopes). Identification manuals, field guides and specialist handbooks are at such levels that birdwatchers of 50 years ago would have been bemused at their number, content, quality and functional effectiveness. In consequence, identification skills are at far higher levels than in the past, and continue to improve, but this also serves to put into proper perspective the accomplishments of those earlier birdwatchers. Increased mobility (some will even charter a light aircraft to see something really special) and dramatically increased birdwatcher numbers make it substantially harder for a rare bird to escape detection. So changes in the numbers, seasons and locations of unusual birds need to be assessed with caution as they may be more apparent than real; they could be just the outcome of more, better-trained, better-informed pairs of eyes on the lookout.

How do birds migrate?

The search for knowledge

The preceding chapters leave no room to doubt birds' abilities to migrate. They do it extremely well and, despite the hazards, it is obviously worthwhile both for individuals and in an evolutionary sense for the species. So, *how* do they migrate? What abilities are necessary for success? Where are those abilities located within the bird?

We can without too much difficulty grasp the differences in anatomy and in physiology that empower birds to be such successful migrants, performing feats of strength, endurance, and even eating, that are way beyond human abilities. However, these are just the mechanics of migration. What we are seeking to understand is the way a bird gets from A to B (and in due course, back again) and how it knows where B and A are when it arrives.

Perhaps now is the time to suggest that we disregard as far as possible human attitudes and abilities, or at least look at them in a different way. In our development from hunter-gatherers to our present society, with its dependence on things mechanical or electronic, we have shed, or partially shed, some of our sensory abilities. How often do we talk about a 'sixth sense'? What is it? What about telepathy? May there be something in it? How come some of us have a photographic memory, others a memory like the proverbial sieve?

There are amongst us 'haves' and 'have nots' when it comes to a sense of direction; some of us have 'an eye for ....'; is it simply experience telling? We recognise birds by their shape, their plumage and their songs or calls, but often all of these are integrated subconsciously. Without a detailed analysis of the steps leading to an identification, we *know* that it was a so-and-so. Birdwatchers have even coined a word for this subliminal analysis – jizz. When you step back, we know relatively little about the detail of our own brain anatomy and function, so it should come as no surprise that we find it difficult to grasp what birds' brains are capable of. It is all too easy to comment that a migrant Goldcrest's brain is 'just too tiny' to handle the navigation that it performs. But pause to think a moment; our grandparents, familiar with the grandfather clock mechanism, could not have conceived the workings of a quartz watch. The pace of progress is reflected in many things; satellites in space, a man on the moon, the development of the computer and the extraordinary diversity of opportunity opened up by the microchip. What we find puzzling or even insoluble today, our children or grandchildren may in the future take for granted. So it may be with migration.

As simple as the question 'How?' is to pose, that simplicity masks a complex array of sub-questions, for some of which we may have an answer or the beginnings of an answer, for others, the search for enlightenment continues, or may have only just begun. In some areas, we may not yet even know the questions. Trying to put some structure to this; what is it that a bird must have, or be able to measure, or to sense, to be a successful migrant? Migrants need a sense of where they are and where they want (need) to be; an ability to navigate from one to the other; a sense of direction; a sense of time, both seasonal and by the hour (essential for accurate navigation); and a sense of the oncoming weather. In short, maps, compass, calendar, chronometer and weather forecasts.

Timing

A migrant's yearly 'calendar' is dominated by four or five major biological events; its spring and autumn migration; the breeding season between them; and one, sometimes two, moults. During these periods of moult, old worn feathers are discarded and replaced by new, flexible and strong ones, and fresh plumage (especially the flight feathers in the wings) would appear to be of substantial value to a migrant about to depart on a long and hazardous journey. Obvious though this may seem, the range of moult strategies evolved by migrants is surprisingly variable. Some moult before the breeding season, most moult after it, some do both. Those migrants moulting after the breeding season may do so on or near their breeding place; or at established sheltered and food-rich communal gathering sites; or partly before departure and partly after arrival (as migrants rarely fly with a gap in their flight feathers).

Sandwich Tern in suspended moult. The outer five flight feathers are old, contrasting with the crisp new inner feathers – Rob Robinson

On the face of it, this is a surprising diversity for such an important process. However, on consideration, perhaps each moult strategy may be an adaptation well-suited to the pressures of the migratory schedule of the bird concerned. It may well be that the onset of autumn moult, for instance, is triggered by the cessation of the breeding season. Perhaps changing day-length is of just as much importance, with the influence of temperature and consequent changes in food supply playing secondary roles, and that the 'moult now' switch cannot be turned on until breeding is over.

Preparation for migration involves relatively major changes to a bird's daily routine, and also to its anatomy and physiology. Over the preceding chapters, there have been frequent references to 'feeding-up', 'putting on fat to fuel the journey' and to the importance of stop-over points or staging posts. How do migrants handle this process?

Fat is the most suitable and efficient of stored fuels, releasing when metabolised about eight times the energy of a comparable weight of carbohydrate. Thus the majority of migrants use fat reserves, deposited in their body cavity and subcutaneously, to fuel their migration. The quantity of stored fat varies, usually with the length of the migratory stages as well as the overall length of the migration. Clearly migrants that can feed while on passage (Swifts, for example, or terns) need not carry so much fat, nor devote much time to accumulating it. Nor is it simply a matter of the length of the migratory stages; a Wheatear travelling over the open sea from Greenland to Iceland (or even Britain) non-stop will obviously need to set off with a 'full tank', whereas an overland migrant, with opportunities to pause and feed and no long sea crossings, may not need to fatten so much. Some do fatten well though, because the journey ahead (and the stages that they undertake it in) may take them through relatively inhospitable habitats or leave them relatively little time to stop and feed. Better to depart on a 'full tank' and top-up reserves when and where possible.

Whatever the fuel load, migrants are very efficient at laying down fat reserves, usually by eating well and effectively. Many migrants can add 10% each day to their weight pre-migration, and Garden Warblers may double in weight in the two or three weeks before their departure south. In many migrants it is not just a matter of eating furiously. Many can increase the efficiency of their food intake by changes in their metabolism, particularly in the liver, which increases the rate of fatty acid production and fat storage. In others, the intestine may lengthen, improving food uptake. Yet others use 'dietary shift' to increase their rate of fat deposition, changing their diet seasonally. In autumn, wild fruits (like Blackberries and Elder berries) are readily available, easily and quickly gathered and digested, low in fibre and rich in sugars which convert easily to fat. Many migrant warblers which feed through the summer on insects switch to fruit pre-migration. Interestingly, for those passerine migrants stopping-over near the Mediterranean prior to crossing to Africa and on over the Sahara, many of the Mediterranean fruits are richer in lipids than those in Britain and Ireland, so fruit-feeding is even more efficient.

Blackcap (female) – Tommy Holden

Two warblers that do not turn to fruit are the Reed and Sedge Warblers, which seek *Phragmites* reed-beds in southern England in late summer in which to fatten. They search for reed-beds with particularly high aphid infestations and feed avidly on the aphids. The aphids themselves suck plant sap, which is sugar-rich (hence their 'honeydew' excretions) and, engorged with this sap, are excellent food for the warblers.

We have seen (Chapter 2) that birds are very well adapted, both anatomically and also physiologically, for migratory flights. The stored 'fuel' is destined to power that flight through the breast muscles operating the beating wings. In some birds these muscles have been shown to increase in size prior to migration, providing greater power for the long journey (as opposed to day-to-day flights) and allowing the bird to carry the greater weight created by its fat deposits. In a 'worst-case' scenario, the extra muscle bulk can itself be metabolised to keep the bird alive and flying, for example through unexpected hostile weather or if a stop-over area does not, for some reason, provide the expected re-fuelling opportunity.

These differing metabolic and physiological strategies linked to migration are controlled hormonally and linked to the migratory schedule as a whole. The processes of evolution will have dealt with a number of trade-offs, such as to migrate at night or by day, or to travel in short stages or long – or a mixture moderated by the various habitats along the way. Yet another trade-off is involved in the weight issue. A migrant with a heavy load of fat as fuel can travel further, but the cost of this is in the energy expended in carrying the load, which is higher than that of a lightly-loaded bird. Such cost/benefit scenarios are yet another illustration of how many factors are involved in the complexities of bird migration.

On a much finer time-scale, there is wide agreement among researchers that a highly accurate daily 'clock' is vital to birds, probably essential if visual clues like sun or star positions overhead are to feature in their navigation. It is also generally agreed that birds, in common with many other creatures, possess an intrinsic circadian rhythm which establishes an effective and accurate internal 24-hour clock. Experimental results strongly support the idea that this clock is under the control of secretions from the tiny pineal gland in the brain, which is responsive to light but not as perceived through the eyes. There are indications that there may be several such clocks. Accurate time-keeping was the key to successful global navigation for mankind, and accomplished only two centuries ago by clockwork, though much enhanced since. The prime reason for accuracy is to allow for the Earth's inexorable rotation, a movement of about 1,800 km each hour on the Equator. The navigating migrant must make allowance for this rotation. For a trans-equatorial migrant, Chris Mead of the BTO calculated that to be five minutes out in timing would confer an error of 150 km on the navigational track!

Maps

Adult migrants will have experience of the topography of both their summer and winter quarters, and very probably of at least some of the terrain between, unless of course it is open ocean. A flight in a light aircraft at altitudes of around 1,000 m provides for us a panoramic vista of an area, interestingly far superior and more useful than the view from an adjacent hilltop of comparable height. This sort of view would be available and could be memorised as a 'map' by migrants, as for example could 'leading lines' like ridges of hills and mountains, major rivers (and roads) and coastlines. In this way, the wildfowl wintering on the North Kent Marshes would only have to make a brief exploratory flight to twice this altitude over North Kent to see whether, say, the winter floods on the Ouse Washes in Cambridgeshire were reaching attractive levels. A great many birds, however, would not routinely be able to take advantage of this facility. For example, a Willow Warbler or Chiffchaff spending its breeding season deep within woodland will reach and exceed such altitudes on migration, but day-to-day will hardly ever fly higher than the treetops.

Whilst it seems intrinsically obvious that birds are likely to learn 'map' information, in detail around their home area and more generally for the surrounding countryside, confirmatory evidence is technically difficult to obtain. Homing Pigeons have been used to test these map-reading skills and, whilst some head straight for their loft once they can see it, researchers have met with varying degrees of success in trying to establish how much use is made of the knowledge of local topography and landmarks and how much they use other navigational systems.

Whilst juveniles, the young of the year, may learn about their immediate environment soon after fledging, and their broader environment on post-fledging dispersals, they could be expected to be naïve when it comes to the actual migration journey and to recognising when they have got to the 'other end'. A substantial body of experimental evidence continues to accumulate suggesting that many species of migrant birds have an innate navigation 'vector'. In other words, they are born with a genetic 'setting' for their migratory direction and possibly also for the elapsed time of their journey. Maybe the location of their migratory target is also innately marked in some way.

Starlings – Mike Weston

This innate directional vector was very effectively demonstrated by Perdeck in the Netherlands in the 1950s. He trapped thousands of adult and juvenile Starlings from breeding populations in northeastern Europe whilst they were migrating through the Netherlands in autumn, and transported them swiftly to Switzerland before ringing and releasing them. On release, the juveniles continued on their innate broadly southwesterly track, as if nothing had happened. Subsequent ring-recoveries in the winter indicated that they reached southern France and Iberia, areas from which no recoveries from these northeastern populations had previously been reported. However, the adults, by means that at present remain a matter of conjecture, set off northwestwards at right-angles to their innate track, many of them reaching their normal wintering areas in northwestern Europe, including Britain.

Clearly the experienced adults were able to over-ride their innate setting in some way, and correct for their displacement, whereas naïve juveniles lacked the means (experience?) to do this. However, the story takes yet another fascinating twist, which provides another piece of the jigsaw puzzle. The young Starlings that wintered (not typically for their origin) in Spain, returned north in spring, not as might have been expected on a parallel course towards Switzerland, but towards their birthplace. Thus, despite the autumn displacement for which the young birds were unable to compensate, their sense of location of their place of birth was firmly enough lodged in their navigation system for them to relocate it, over-riding their innate return vector.

Come wind, come weather ...

Perdeck had fortunately ringed large enough numbers of Starlings for there to be a further winter's recoveries. The displaced juveniles that later re-orientated to their natural breeding area this time over-rode their innate migratory orientation and returned to winter once again in Spain. This gives us an indication that the innate directional impulse (vector) actually proved weaker than the urge to follow the learnt path. Additionally, the displaced juveniles learnt that path in the reverse direction. Were the displacement force to have been a natural one, like a storm with strong winds, we can see how colonisation can occur and new migration routes open up, particularly for a flocking bird like the Starling.

Apart from recording the arrivals, for example of a storm-driven Leach's Petrel on an inland reservoir or an Asiatic Pallas's Warbler on the east coast, we know little of the ultimate fate of 'lost' birds. Observational evidence supports the view that if migrants run into hostile weather they head for the nearest landing point and shelter. They then take cover and resume their journey when conditions improve, often not having lost much body fat in the process. If the storm or other hostile conditions strike while the migrants are well out over open seas or over a major desert, the presumption must be that loss of life, sometimes perhaps huge, is likely. Perhaps this is one of the reasons for comments like "not many Swallows back this spring". In rather less adverse conditions, cross-winds for example, radar studies show that many migrants can cope and hold their direction, implying that they cannot only sense the wind force and direction in some way, but also compensate for the displacement.

In general, migrants seem well able to predict the weather, and to select favourable conditions, particularly wind directions. These can have substantial beneficial effects on journey times and energy expenditure. For Britain and Ireland (and elsewhere) summer migrants tend to return on rising temperatures and falling barometric pressures, whilst autumn migration south accompanies falling temperatures and rising pressures. There must be innumerable occasions when migration occurs in less than ideal circumstances, as exemplified when clear still weather in spring or autumn triggers movement. At times migration becomes a necessity, as for instance when in autumn a sharp drop in temperatures, and the accompanying sudden absence of insects, persuades insect-eating hirundines that it really is time to leave. Sometimes, heading into adversity seems to be the rule rather than the exception; a spring northbound crossing of the Sahara (hostile enough territory anyway) presents many smaller migrants with an apparently incessant north wind into which they must head. A marked contrast to the autumn Wheatears in Greenland, awaiting with reasonable leisure the predictable annual strong trans-Atlantic northwesterly tail-wind to speed them on their way.

Greenland Wheatear – Tommy Holden

Compasses

How migrant birds orientate and navigate with the accuracy of which we know they are capable has intrigued and challenged biologists for centuries. Although numerous researchers have tackled the problem, none has made the breakthrough necessary for us to be able to claim anything like a full understanding of the process. Despite what has been discovered, that question 'How?' remains as one of the (if not *the*) major unanswered questions in the whole of ornithology. Researchers and theories are numerous indeed, and even a summary of their experimental results (let alone a critical analysis) must be the subject of a whole book, not a chapter. But some idea of where we stand is an imperative component of any book on bird migration, with the proviso that it is inevitably highly condensed. No single researcher or research team could have the capacity, equipment or funding to investigate all possible avenues simultaneously or indeed in sequence. Despite their individual focus on one or two aspects, it is enlightening that the general view is that birds make use of several forms of compass, depending upon circumstances.

To us, and probably also to birds, the most obvious visual cue for orientation (other than a knowledge of the landscape) is the sun. Over half a century ago, Gustav Kramer and his team, working in Germany with Starlings in large circular cages, discovered that at times when the birds should be migrating and when they had an unimpeded view of the sun, Starlings hopped repeatedly in the direction that they would expect to take on migration. If the sun was obscured by an overcast sky, the migratory urge subsided. By the simple but brilliant idea of using mirrors to make the sun appear from a different angle, Kramer discovered that the migratory restlessness was directed at an angle to their natural track, that angle being equal to the angle that his mirrors had 'moved' the sun. Further experiments showed that this innate knowledge of where the sun should be also has a built-in compensation factor to allow for the Earth's rotation during the day, set by the accurate timing of the circadian rhythm.

Simply using the sun's position in the sky is only a crude compass; as with human navigators' use of the sextant, accuracy is achieved through measurement of the sun's azimuth (its movement on a horizontal plane) and its altitude (the vertical component). Birds are able to do this, in one experimental case simply by reference to the shadows cast rather than by observing the sun itself. It is suggested that an innate knowledge of sun position is amplified and made more accurate by experience through the year in changing latitudes.

Interestingly, similar experiments investigating the possible role of the moon in navigation have revealed hardly any likelihood that moon position is used by migrants. This is not, though, the case for stars. Kramer again initiated experiments showing that the migratory restlessness of migrants in his cages under the stars was in the expected migratory direction. Using a planetarium to 'shift' the night sky, Kramer and later researchers found that migrants adjusted their direction accordingly.

The experiments showed that the key factor was the rotation of the night sky about the Pole Star (for centuries the key to stellar navigation for human voyagers) and that even an extremely simplified and reduced star pattern would suffice, as long as it rotated about the Pole Star. No defined migratory restlessness occurred under a static night sky. More subtly, nestlings raised under an artificial sky with the star Betelgeuse (in the constellation Orion) as the point of rotation, treated this as the Pole Star when subsequently tested. Stephen Emlen, working with Indigo Buntings reared from the egg in isolation, showed that without access to the night sky they were unable to orientate in the planetarium. This suggests that (at least in this case) knowledge of the night sky was learnt rather than innate. Wiltschko and his team obtained similar results working with Garden Warblers.

Garden Warbler – Tommy Holden

It is easy to assume that birds' sensory mechanisms are the same as ours, but they may well be able to use their eyes, ears and brain in very different ways. There are anatomical differences too, such as the heavily-pigmented pecten (an organ found only in birds' eyes), which J D Pettigrew suggested might cast shadows on the retina, thereby acting as a navigational aid. Working with honey bees, von Frisch almost magically demonstrated their use of polarised light in orientation towards food sources. We know that birds can perceive both polarised and UV light, and experiments have shown that the disappearance of the sun on the horizon at sunset provides useful visual orientation clues to migrants and enables them to reset their internal compass.

Hearing might play a part too. We know that most birds hear extremely well, compared with ourselves, and that even the simplest of calls or songs appears to be far more complex when listened to at quarter- or eighth-speed. Other of course than in 'communication' between migrants actually in flight, could low- (or high-) frequency sound play some part in their route finding? Similarly smell; although the majority of birds apparently make little use of their olfactory organs, these seem anatomically normally developed. Bizarre as the suggestion might seem, even we, with our impoverished senses, can detect aromatic differences (perhaps largely due to the nature of the vegetation) as we journey south from Britain and Ireland through Europe and the Mediterranean to Africa – maybe birds could do likewise? Experiments have shown that pigeons, at least, are highly sensitive to changes in barometric pressure. Such a sense would assist migrants in weather forecasting prior to and during migration, but pressure also changes with altitude, and Kreithen and Keeton found pigeons able to detect barometric change equating to altitude differences of a startling 10 m or less.

Last, but certainly not least, of the contenders for a major role in providing the compass is the Earth's magnetic field. As early as 1859, von Middendorf speculated that the Earth's field might be of importance, but really only in the last half-century have the researchers and the equipment been available for extensive experimentation. Wild birds, migrating at night, usually maintain an accurate course if the sky becomes overcast, and experimental birds in test cages show the expected directional preferences outdoors (or indeed in wooden sheds) with no sight of the stars. The ability to maintain directional preferences in a wooden shed but show no such preference within a reinforced concrete building is indicative that a magnetic field may be playing a part. As Peter Berthold, responsible for much recent orientation research, points out, we find the fact that birds can do this amazing more than anything because we ourselves have no ability to detect the Earth's magnetic field.

How do birds migrate?

Our understanding of bird migration is improving all of the time. Recent research by Wolfgang Wiltschko has shown that the ability of Robins to detect a magnetic field is centred within the right eye and left brain hemisphere. A Robin wearing a temporary blindfold over the right eye could not orientate itself using the Earth's magnetic field but had no such problem when the left eye was covered. Photo – Tommy Holden

A

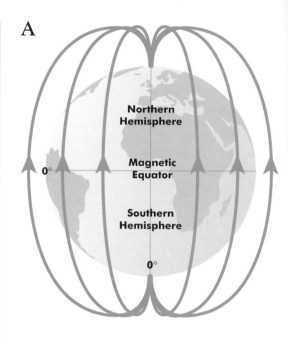

The Earth's magnetic field

The experimental breakthrough came in 1968, when Wiltschko and colleagues in Frankfurt isolated caged migrants within a massive electromagnetic coil, blanking out the earth's magnetic field. They were then able to establish a series of new and false 'North Poles', and were able to manipulate in a predictable way the migratory tendencies of the experimental Robins. The concept is based on the Earth as a hugely powerful magnet, whose north magnetic pole is situated fairly close to the geographic North Pole, and south magnetic pole likewise close to the South Pole in Antarctica. Running through the atmosphere between the two magnetic poles are the invisible lines of magnetic force of the Earth's field. These circle the globe and are uniform in shape, and best regarded as in the shape of a slightly elongated letter C, a little like the segments of an orange. Conventionally, the force lines leave the magnetic south pole at right angles to the Earth's surface, then bend towards the north, steeply at first, then more gently, before bending in, initially gently, then steeply,

finally vertically, to the magnetic north pole (Diagram A).

The magnetic needle in our compass points towards magnetic north, but in a plane horizontal to the Earth's surface where we stand. The key difference in the birds' compass is that they are measuring not where north is on a flat plane, but the angle (in space) that the lines of force make heading towards the magnetic pole. Thus, at the north magnetic pole their 'compass needle' points vertically downwards (Diagram B). Over the Equator, the needle is horizontal, but from the Equator northwards the 'angle of dip' of the needle steadily increases. This pattern of the lines of force is reasonably uniform round the globe, which helps explain why migrants seem able to migrate (almost) any time, anywhere.

Where and when migrants do have problems can be explained by a breakdown of these uniform magnetic fields, either in areas such as the 'Bermuda Triangle', where human navigation systems also often fail, or when they are disrupted by violent electrical storms or vigorous sunspot activity (flares on the sun producing pulses of electromagnetic energy). Perhaps it is some such disruption of their

B

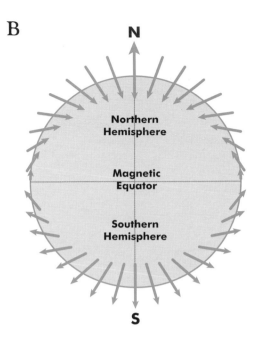

The 'angle of dip' potentially detected by birds

Orca (or Killer Whale): Whales are normally amongst the most competent long-range navigators – Rob Robinson

electromagnetic compass that appears to compel groups of whales to beach themselves, sometimes repeatedly, in the face of all logic. Maybe they are instinctively obeying incorrect 'instructions' from their compass.

The ability to detect the Earth's magnetic field may seem like magic to us, with our impoverished senses, but there must be a mechanism they are using that we ought to be able to discover. How do they do it? Until recently, this was where anatomical knowledge and the understanding obtained from experimental results ceased and theories took over. However work by Gould and Walcott has led to the discovery in pigeons of a minute crystal of a magnetically-active substance, lying between the brain and the skull. If this 'receptor' is confirmed, and similar crystals located in other species, we may begin to understand just how migrants read the lines of the magnetic field so accurately and be one step further on in comprehending how birds navigate so effectively.

This relatively superficial survey may, at the least, have provided some idea of the scope and diversity of abilities, innate and learnt, that provide a migrant bird with its navigational skills. Just how much still remains to be discovered, who can tell? Certainly there will be much fine detail to unravel surrounding what we already know, and it must be very probable that further major discoveries await researchers. Well may we step back in wonder and amazement at the migratory achievements chronicled in this book. No matter that some components of the question 'How?' remain unanswered, the questioner is left with a profound respect for the power of the genes.

Index of species names